Studies in the
Life History
of the Song Sparrow

by

Margaret Morse Nice

in two volumes

VOLUME I

A Population Study of the Song Sparrow

Dover Publications, Inc., New York

This Dover edition, first published in 1964, is an unabridged republication of the work first published by the Linnaean Society. Volume I was first published in 1937 as Volume IV of the *Transactions of the Linnaean Society of New York;* Volume II was first published in 1943 as Volume VI of the *Transactions of the Linnaean Society of New York.*

The illustration on page 7 of Volume I was the frontispice in the previous edition, and was formerly reproduced in color.

Library of Congress Catalog Card Number: A38-691

Manufactured in the United States of America

Dover Publications, Inc.
180 Varick Street
New York 14, N. Y.

TABLE OF CONTENTS

CHAPTER IX

A. The Situation During One Season.
  1. Desertions.
  2. Is There a Reserve Supply of Unmated Birds?
B. The Situation from Year to Year.
C. Bigamy.
D. Sexual Selection.
E. Summary

CHAPTER X

A. Position of the Nests. Plate III. (Facing page 17.)
B. Security.
C. Building Technique.
D. Building of Old and Young Birds.
E. Summary.

CHAPTER XI

A. What Factors Influence the Start of Laying?
B. The Start of Laying in Relation to Temperature. Table VII. Charts XI, XII, XIII, XIV.
C. The Start of Laying and Other Factors.
D. The Start of Laying of Other Species.
E. Dates of Laying of Individual Females.
F. Summary.

CHAPTER XII

A. The Number of Eggs in a Set.
B. Time of Replacement of a Destroyed Set.
C. The Color of the Eggs.
D. The Size of the Eggs. Table VIII.
  1. Average Size of Eggs in Relation to Various Factors.
  2. Weights of Sets.
E. Inheritance of Color, Size and Shape.
F. Summary.

CHAPTER XIII

A. Role of the Female.
  1. Length of Incubation.
  2. The Rhythm of Incubation. Table IX.
B. Role of the Male. Table X.
C. Summary.

CHAPTER XVIII

CHAPTER XIX

CHAPTER XX

APPENDIX I

APPENDIX II

APPENDIX III

APPENDIX IV

APPENDIX V

INTRODUCTION

For the past eight years the writer has concentrated on the study of the life history of one species of bird. The technique was based on recognition of the individual in the field by means of colored bands, and on repeated censuses over Interpont to check the status of the community. The opportunity to examine at intervals the birds in the hand was an important feature of the work.

The method has been almost entirely that of observation with a minimum of experimentation and no collecting, the hope being to find out what actually happens in a population of wild birds. The first year was devoted to intensive study of two pairs, an indispensable foundation for the later work, which at one time included observation of 75 banded males.

Through trapping, banding, and continued search, individuals were traced throughout their lives, and family histories established, the place of residence of relatives determined, and the inheritance of migratory behavior, song characteristics, egg color, etc., investigated.

The present volume is concerned with the population aspects of the study, leaving more detailed treatment for a second volume. Volume I deals with the Song Sparrow and its environment, its ecology, migration, territory, and reproduction, all from a somewhat statistical point of view, and finally with survival problems. Volume II will deal with the behavior of the Song Sparrow, including detailed observations on the technique of territory establishment, "courtship," song, and so on.

Eight years' concentration on one species has brought results of undoubted value. Yet no one can be more aware of the deficiencies of the study than is the author—the meagerness of data on various points, the failure to find certain important nests, the uncertainty as to the exact course of events with particular pairs, and many other unfortunate gaps. The explanation lies in the difficulty and complexity of the problem and in the fact that it was undertaken by one person alone.

Grateful acknowledgements are due to Mr. Edward S. Thomas for the loan of three photographs, and to Dr. Selig Hecht for plotting the curves of the temperature thresholds for the start of singing and laying. I am much indebted to Dr. Erwin Stresemann for asking me to write a report of my study in the winter of 1932-33 for the *Journal für Ornithologie;* the preparation of this paper brought many problems to light and enabled me to work more intelligently during the last three years. Thanks are especially due to Dr. Lawrence E. Hicks and Dr. Paul L. Errington, and most of all, to Dr. Ernst Mayr and Mr. William Vogt, for their kindness in reading the present manuscript and for their helpful criticisms.

The attempt has been made—by division into headings, by full summaries after each chapter, and by indices—to present the material in as clear and orderly a manner as possible. But a word of warning to the reader may not be amiss. As the study proved to be a complicated one, so some of the tables may seem inconsistent, involving as they often do somewhat different sets of birds, for instance, the breeders on Central or Upper Interpont are not entirely the same as the total *banded* breeders on and near Interpont. I have tried to explain each table adequately, and in case of apparent contradictions, I hope the reader will study the captions and text carefully before concluding that there are errors. In the summaries after each chapter, it must be remembered that their application is narrow, referring to the Song Sparrows that I studied and not to birds in general. Finally it must be kept in mind that "Upper Interpont" is merely a shorter way of saying "Central and North Interpont," not a third area.

It is my earnest hope that this work on the Song Sparrow will stimulate others to study intensively the biology of our common birds.

To my Friend
Ernst Mayr

CHAPTER I

The Song Sparrow as a Subject for Study

Melospiza melodia "is a bird of very extensive geographic range, breeding throughout the temperate parts of the North American continent including the plateau of Mexico. No other bird of the Nearctic Region has proven so sensitive to influences of physical environment, and as a result of this plasticity of organization it has become divided into a large number of geographic forms, some of extensive, others of very circumscribed range, the area of distribution in every case coinciding strictly with uniformity or continuity of physical conditions" (Ridgway, *160*). Some of the races are migratory, while others are resident. The Mississippi Song Sparrow (*Melospiza melodia beata**) is the subspecies that nests throughout Ohio.

A. SUITABILITY AS AN OBJECT FOR STUDY

Although the Song Sparrow is an abundant, widely distributed, friendly and attractive bird, yet it has been almost wholly neglected as a subject for life history studies. Nevertheless, it has proved eminently suited for such investigations.

Here on Interpont, there is a large population right at my door; no time is wasted in going to and from the field of study and I am able to keep track of my subjects all the time except when I am absent from Columbus during a portion of each summer. This population shows much stability, little tendency to scatter, and a high proportion of returns of the young. The birds are much attached to their homes, so the pair can always be found on its territory during the breeding season, and resident birds remain in the near vicinity throughout the year. As a rule the birds can be trapped without too much trouble and are not disturbed by the experience. The bands can be seen fairly easily, except in the coldest weather when the feathers are so fluffed out that the legs are concealed. The parent birds will endure visits to their nests daily or even oftener without desertion. And finally, a point that makes the Song Sparrow of unique interest and value, the male shows great individuality in his songs.

---

*Dr. A. Wetmore has renamed this subspecies *euphonia* (A New Race of the Song Sparrow from the Appalachian Region. 1936. Smithsonian Misc. Coll. 95 (17) :1-3).

As to disadvantages, the first is the uncertainty of locating nests unless a great deal of time is spent with each pair. Persons studying hole-nesting birds, such as Tree Swallows, Starlings, and Titmice in Europe, have a great advantage here. The other difficulty is that both sexes and all ages after the post-juvenal molt are alike in plumage. Male and female can usually be distinguished by measurement of the wing. In the breeding season, the sexes can be distinguished by their behavior, but this is not true in fall or winter. The juvenal males, when residents, can be known in January or early February by the character of their songs, but with juvenal summer residents this can be done but rarely. When I was in Berlin in July, 1932, Dr. Stresemann told me that juvenals of some species have pointed tail feathers and adult birds rounded tail feathers. After that I noted this character, finding in the fall that most of the males were easily classifiable into one category or the other, but in winter the difference is less pronounced, and in spring little reliance can be placed on it. All birds classified as juvenals by this method, in the fall, and later heard singing, corroborated my judgment by the warbling character of the song. As to the males considered adult, I made only one wrong diagnosis of those birds whose age could be checked by their manner of singing. Unfortunately the shape of the tail feathers is of no help in estimating the age of the females as birds of all ages have more or less pointed rectrices.

During the nesting season the presence of the incubation patch in the female and its absence in the male is a sure criterion of sex with a captured bird.

B. Resumé of the Life History

The Song Sparrow on Interpont is a strongly territorial bird from the time of taking up territory in the late winter or early spring to the end of nesting, but territory is not held during the molt, very little in fall, and not at all in winter. About half the nesting males are permanent residents; the rest migrate south in October and return from late February through March, but only about one-fifth of the females are residents.

The resident males start to sing in late January or in February according to the weather; they sing almost constantly until joined by a mate, when singing abruptly drops to almost zero. Territory is defended and acquired by a special ceremony that includes song, posture and fighting. The male "courts" or, better, dominates his mate by "pouncing" on her—i.e., suddenly flying down, hitting her, and flying away with a loud song. Although the male carries nesting material during preliminary nest-hunting stages, all the work on the real nest is done by the female. The male at this time starts to sing again, singing to quite an extent while his mate incubates. The female incubates for approximately 20-30 minutes at a time, staying away from the nest for about 8 minutes. The eggs hatch in 12 to 13 days as a rule, and the young usually stay in the nest 10 days. The role of the male is that of guardian of his territory, mate, eggs and young; he feeds the last from the time they hatch, and takes the major responsibility for them soon after they have left the nest, when his mate is normally busy with a new nest. The young become independent at the age of 28 to 31 days. Song Sparrows in this region regularly make three to four attempts at nesting, some of them raising three broods.

The food of the Song Sparrow consists largely of weed seeds and insects, 66 per cent of the contents of 401 stomachs examined by Judd, *91,* being vegetable matter, 34 per cent animal matter. Berries are eaten to some extent, as are spiders, snails and millipeds. From May to August insects "compose more than half the food."

C. The Technique of the Investigation

An account of the course of the study, of methods of trapping and banding the birds, an explanation of the nomenclature used, and a description of the system of record keeping, are given in Appendix I.

The most essential points for the understanding of the text will be given here.

The spring and summer of 1929 were spent on intensive observation of two pairs of birds—1M and K2, 4M and K7. The next year the study extended over most of Central Interpont, while beginning in 1931 North Interpont was also included. During the breeding season of 1932, all the males on Upper Interpont—69 in number—and most of the females were banded; while during the next two years all but two of the males were banded. During 1935 this was true of only 14 of the 25 males present, and in 1936 of 9 out of 18.

Most of the birds had to be trapped on their territories. All the adults were given colored celluloid bands, the aluminum band always being placed on the left leg, while with nestlings it was put on the right leg.

Individual "field numbers," having no relation to the band numbers, were given to all the nesting adults, 1M, 2M, etc., for the males, K1, K2, etc., for the females.

The plan of the work consisted in repeated censuses over Interpont (and on occasion over surrounding territory), in order to keep a careful check on the personnel of the population.

D. SUMMARY

1. The Song Sparrow offered a favorable object of study because of its availability and abundance, and the individuality in song of the males; the chief disadvantage proved to be the difficulty of locating nests.

2. Sex can usually be distinguished by wing measurement, and in the breeding season by the presence or absence of the incubation patch.

3. Whether males are adult or young can be told in the fall from the shape of the tail feathers, and young resident males by the character of their singing.

4. Male Song Sparrows are strongly territorial during the breeding season.

5. Part of the breeding population is permanently resident, the rest migratory.

6. Although both sexes are alike in plumage, the male takes no part in building the nest, incubating the eggs, or brooding the young.

7. The male defends his territory, mate, nest and young, and often does the major part in feeding the last.

8. The food of the Song Sparrow consists of two-thirds vegetable matter and one-third animal matter.

9. The main features of the technique of the study consisted in trapping the subjects on their territories, in banding them with colored as well as aluminum bands, and in keeping track of them by repeated censuses. The first season was spent in intensive study of two pairs, the six subsequent years in extensive work.

Courtesy Bird-Lore Magazine

PLATE 1—SONG SPARROW (*Melospiza melodia*)

CHAPTER II

The Song Sparrow and Its Environment

Certain fundamental environmental factors that affect the Song Sparrow in this region will be discussed in the present chapter: temperature, precipitation, and sunshine, and also the flora and fauna of the habitat.

A. THE CLIMATE

Columbus is situated near the center of Ohio, latitude 40 degrees north, and longitude 83 degrees west. The elevation of Interpont is about 220 m.

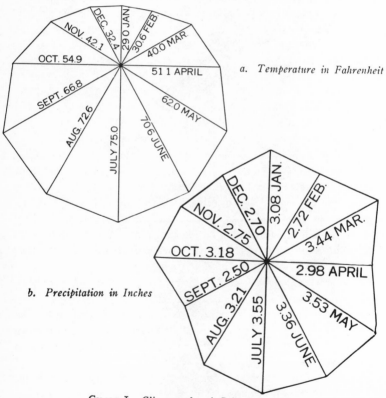

a. Temperature in Fahrenheit

b. Precipitation in Inches

CHART I. *Climographs of Columbus, Ohio*

The average monthly temperature and precipitation are shown in the climograph in Chart I.

According to records of the United States Weather Bureau at Columbus, the annual mean temperature during the last 55 years has ranged from 9.4° C. (49° F.) in 1917 to 13° C. (55.4° F.) in 1931, averaging 11.2° C. (52.3°F.) The average mean temperature by months follows: January —1.6° C. (29° F.); February —0.8° C. (30.6° F.); March 4.4° C. (40° F.); April 10.6° C. (51.1° F.); May 16.6° C. (62° F.); June 21.5° C. (70.6° F.); July 23.9° C. (75° F.); August 22.6° C. (72.6° F.); September 19.3° C. (66.8°F.); October 12.7° C. (54.9° F.); November 5.6° C. (42.1° F.); December 0.2° C. (32.4° F.). The absolute highest temperature reached has been 41° C. (106° F.) in 1934 and the absolute lowest —28.9° C. (—20° F.) in 1884 and 1889.

During the period covered by my study, every year but 1929 and 1935 was warmer than the average, 1931 having the highest temperature of any year of record, largely because of unusually mild weather from September through December. The absolute highest temperatures ranged from 33.3° C. (92° F.) in July 1929 to 41° C. (106° F.) in July 1934. The absolute lowest ranged from —9.4° C. (13° F.) in January 1931 to —26.7° C. (—16° F.) in January 1936.

Annual precipitation has ranged from 548 mm. (21.6 inches) in 1930 to 1,301 mm. (51.3 inches) in 1882, the average being 919 mm. (36.19 inches). During the period of study only one year—1929— surpassed the average, with a total of 1,074 mm. (42.27 inches). Precipitation in 1931 and 1935 almost reached the average, in 1933 it was 10 cm. short, in 1932 15 cm. short, while in 1934 there were only 560 mm., and 1930 was the driest year of record. The average of the seven years was 794 mm. (31.26 inches).

The average amount of snowfall per year is 609 mm. (24 inches).

The number of hours of daylight ranges from 9 hours 19 minutes in December to 15 hours 1 minute in June. During January the days lengthen about 1½ minutes per day, but for the next three months about 2½ minutes per day, slowing down in May to less than a minute a day.

The amount of sunshine averages 54 per cent of the possible total. It ranges from a minimum of 33 per cent in December, increasing each month and reaching a maximum of 70 per cent in July.

Further details as to the temperature, precipitation, and amount of sunshine in Columbus will be found in Appendix V.

B. The Habitat

The eastern flood plain of the Olentangy River between Dodridge Street and Lane Avenue Bridges I have named Interpont. Central Interpont, about 30 acres (12 ha.) in extent, has been the main field of my studies, but North Interpont, about 10 acres (4 ha.) has also been of much importance. *These two tracts taken together I call Upper Interpont.*

South Interpont, being mostly occupied by a city playground, has less to offer the Song Sparrows; only about 10 acres of land are suitable for their purposes and I have done little work there. Across the Olentangy above and below Interpont the river was bordered by country suitable for Song Sparrows; in some places there was only a narrow strip of such land, but in others it amounted to a width of some 300 m.

Upper Interpont for the most part was waste land flooded periodically and little used for purposes of cultivation. But in the late summer of 1932 a squad of unemployed laborers "cleaned-up" all the cover but the trees along the river bank, while in the following spring the bulk of the land was converted into gardens, the destruction extending even to most of the dikes in the following year. In 1935 the dikes and river banks were left undisturbed.

When I started the study, Interpont was largely covered with a rank growth of bottom land weed association, blue grass (*Poa pratensis*) being present in some places. There were large patches of elderberry (*Sambucus canadensis*) and, near the river and along the bluff to the east, a number of trees. The most important weeds were: wild rye (*Elymus canadensis*), sweet clover (*Melilotus alba*), smartweed (*Persicaria*), tick-tre-foil (*Meibomia*), Indian-cup (*Silphium perfoliatum*), cow-parsnip (*Heraclium lanatum*), giant ragweed (*Ambrosia trifida*), burdock (*Arctium minus*), beggar-ticks (*Bidens*), teasel (*Dipsacus*), dandelion (*Leontodon taraxacum*), thistle (*Cirsium*), sunflowers (*Helianthus*), golden rod (*Solidago*) and asters (*Aster*).

The most abundant trees are the cottonwood (*Populus deltoides*), American elm (*Ulmus americanus*), buckeye (*Aesculus glabra*), hackberry (*Celtis occi-*

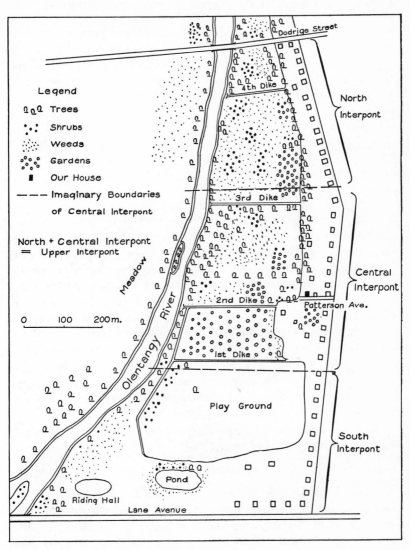

MAP I. *Interpont in the Spring of 1932*

dentalis), silver maple (*Acer saccharinum*), red maple (*Acer rubrum*), box elder (*Acer negundo*), sycamore (*Platanus occidentalis*), and willows (*Salix*). Poison ivy (*Toxicodendron radicans*) and Virginia creeper (*Parthenocissus quinquefolia*) are common.

The trees offer singing posts and look-outs for the male Song Sparrows, while the same is true of shrubs and large weeds. The shrubs, grasses and weeds provide the birds with food, protection and nesting sites.

Interpont is not typical Song Sparrow country in that there is no permanent water supply except the river, the majority of the territories offering no water whatsoever. The birds must leave their territories several times a day to procure water for drinking and bathing purposes.

C. Relations to Other Animal Species

From 1930 to 1932 the Song Sparrow was the most abundant avian species on Interpont, but now first place goes to the Robin (*Turdus m. migratorius*). Yet among the birds nesting in the weeds and shrubbery *Melospiza* still holds first place. Interpont used to support a rich and varied bird life. In 1931 30 species and about 220 pairs, an average of 5.5 pairs per acre (14 per ha.), nested on the 40 acres, but in 1935 there were only 25 species and about 150 pairs, or 3.75 pairs per acre (9 per ha.). Nesting censuses for Interpont for four years are given in Appendix III.

According to the censuses taken for the U. S. Biological Survey the number of nesting birds on farm land in northeastern United States averages 1.1 pairs per acre (2.8 per hectare), *41, 44*.

The relation of the Song Sparrow with the other animals on Interpont will be briefly touched upon.

1. *Invertebrates*

The role of the Song Sparrow in relation to insects and various other invertebrates is largely that of predator (see Judd, *90, 91*). As for invertebrates that prey upon the Song Sparrow, this species in this region appears to be comparatively free from parasites, the only one that I was able to procure being a Hippoboscid fly—*Ornithomyia anchineuria*.

Peters, *146*, reports the following external parasites as taken from Song Sparrows: 6 species of lice (*Mallophaga*)—*Degeeriella vulgata, Machærilæmus mæstum, Menacanthus chrysophæum, Myrsidea incerta, Philopterus subflavescens, Ricinus melospizæ*; 2 bird-flies (*Hippoboscidæ*)—*Ornithoica confluenta, Ornithomyia anchineuria;* 4 mites (*Analgesidæ*)—*Analgopsis* sp., *Liponyssus sylviarum, Trombicula bisignata, Trombicula cavicola;* and 3 ticks (*Ixodoidea*)—*Hæmaphysalis leporis-palustris, Ixodes brunneus, Ixodes* sp.

During the spring of 1935 I collected all the Song Sparrow nests after the young had left and gave them to Mr. E. S. Thomas of the Ohio State Museum for examination for Protocalliphora. Negative results were obtained from all but one nest (Thomas, *188*). This nest had had five young that I had weighed daily till the age of 7 days, four leaving the nest when ten days old; during the first four days their weights were less than average, but after that they compared well with other nestlings of like age.

In 1936, out of seven nests that raised young, two were found to be infested. Each of these nests had about the same number of pupae—9 to 10—yet all the birds left the nest at the average age.

Manwell and Herman, *119, 119a,* found by blood smears and inoculations that 22 out of 62 Song Sparrows at Syracuse, New York, were affected by one or more species of malaria parasite.

2. *Reptiles*

There are many garter snakes (*Thamnophis s. sirtalis*) on Interpont and they may take toll of the eggs and young of the Song Sparrows.

Dr. H. K. Gloyd has called my attention to the fact that this species is supposed to feed entirely on cold-blooded prey. Yet one instance (*22a*) has been reported from Iowa where a nestling Yellow Warbler (*Dendroica a. æstiva*) was taken by a 12 inch garter snake identified by A. G. Ruthven as *T. parietalis*.

Gabrielson, *62,* reports this species as swallowing the eggs of a Bobolink (*Dolichonyx oryzivorus*), and Ruthven, *163a,* states that it has been observed eating fledgling birds.

3. *Other Birds*

Other birds, as they affect an individual Song Sparrow on Interpont, might be divided into four categories; its own species; more or less neutral species; predatory species; and the brood parasite.

The Song Sparrow, by intra-specific hostility in spring and summer, ensures a spacing of pairs, thus eliminating competition for food, and interference in family affairs. In the fall and winter hostility is much diminished, but there never is pronounced gregariousness with my birds.

As to the largest category of birds, all those species not predatory nor parasitic on the Song Sparrow, I believe there is little competition between them and *Melospiza* either for food or nesting sites, because there always appears to be an abundance of both, and also because the habitat niches of the different species are somewhat different. It is true the Song Sparrows during the nesting season are somewhat hostile to most other species not too large or indifferent (see Chapter VII under Defense of Territory), but I believe that this comes from an hypertrophy of the territorial instinct. It does not prevent the other species from nesting side by side with the Song Sparrows. I do not believe the abundance of *Melospiza* on Interpont has been prejudicial to the abundance of any other species.

Many of these birds, on the other hand, may be an aid to the Song Sparrow by attracting some of the attentions of the Cowbird to themselves. This seems to be especially true of the Northern Yellow-throat (*Geothlypis trichas brachidactyla*) and probably also of the Indigo Bunting (*Passerina cyanea*).

As to predators, one pair of Sparrow Hawks (*Falco s. sparverius*) nested until 1933 on North Interpont and another just across the river from Central Interpont, but they appear not to hunt in this region. In fall and winter Sparrow Hawks sometimes try to catch Song Sparrows, but I have never seen one succeed. The Song Sparrows have almost no fear of these Falcons. The Sharp-shinned and Cooper's Hawks (*Accipiter v. velox* and *A. cooperi*), on the contrary, are greatly dreaded by all the small birds; they undoubtedly get some of the Song Sparrows on their occasional visits in fall and winter. The Screech Owl (*Otus asio naevius*) is a resident in the region and may well be responsible for the disappearance of some of the nesting adults, especially recently when cover was inadequate for protection.

Blue Jays (*Cyanocitta c. cristata*) and Bronzed Grackles (*Quiscalus quiscula aeneus*) may take some of the eggs and young. I once surprised a Ring-necked Pheasant (*Phasianus colchicus torquatus*) just after she had emptied a nest of two-day old nestlings, and I suspected it was she that threw three four-day-old nestlings out of another nest.

4. Mammals

The relations of the Song Sparrow to some of its mammalian neighbors are neutral—notably the cottontail rabbit (*Sylvilagus floridanus mearnsi*), but it is a far different matter with others. We will consider the native predators, the introduced predators, and man.

Unfortunately I have seldom been able to get good evidence of the destruction of nests by any particular predator.

The list of native mammals that might prey on the Song Sparrows is not long, and there are few representatives of each: the opossum (*Didelphis v. virginiana*), weasel (*Mustela n. noveboracensis*), skunk (*Mephitis nigra*), red squirrel (*Sciurus hudsonicus loquax*), and chipmunk (*Tamias striatus fisheri*).

The three introduced predators are far more abundant and all, I believe, are much more inimical to the Song Sparrows than the native mammals; these are self-hunting dogs, the Norway rats that frequent the dumps at each end of Interpont, and most destructive of all, cats.

The influence of man has many ramifications: the clearing of the land, at first beneficial to the species, later disastrous; the ploughing of occupied territories; the introduction of new enemies—cat, rat, dog and Pheasant; the activities of boys; and finally, for this study, myself.

Interpont was undoubtedly a much better habitat for *Melospiza melodia* in 1932 than it had been when covered with forest. But the cultivation of the land since then and the entirely unnecessary destruction of cover on the dikes, in the ditches and along the river bank have wrought havoc with the area as a home for ground-nesting birds. Many of the Song Sparrows that come into Interpont during the nesting season—both males taking up territories and females joining males that have lost mates—have probably lost their homes in neighboring regions as a result of the activities of man. *Melospiza melodia* is an adaptable bird and will utilize, as its home, sites on the bluff in South Interpont and further down the river that are nothing but masses of tin cans and weeds.

The introduction of the House Sparrow (*Passer domesticus*) into this country has been a calamity to our native birds in many ways, not the least of which has been the prejudice it has cast on our native sparrows, in consequence of which boys think it a meritorious deed to shoot any small brownish bird. Since Interpont is within the city limits, it is illegal to use any rifle or shot gun here; yet, in spite of all my efforts to educate the boys, telling them of the laws, and trying to interest them in the birds, they continued shooting the Song Sparrows. Finally in desperation, I procured a commission as Special Game Protector of the State of Ohio and then I found that my words of warning, backed up by the shining badge, were listened to with respect, and the shooting largely stopped, at least while I was in Columbus.

As for myself, I have tried not to interfere with the course of events, not removing Cowbird eggs (except in 1934), nor killing natural enemies—i.e., native animals. I fear that dogs followed my tracks to at least two nests and destroyed them, but on the other hand, I saved various nests from destruction and moved threatened young to other nests when Interpont was plowed in June 1933. The nests found by me suffer fewer disasters on the average than those nests I do not find, as judged by the re-nesting of the birds. On the whole I feel that my activities are somewhat beneficial to the Song Sparrows.

D. SUMMARY

1. The annual mean temperature at Columbus, Ohio, averages 11.2° C.; the annual precipitation averages 919 mm. (Chart I).

2. The period covered by the study showed a small excess of temperature and marked deficit in precipitation.

3. From 1928 till the spring of 1933 Upper Interpont was largely waste land supporting a rank growth of weeds, many shrubs and some trees.

4. Fifteen species of external parasites of the Song Sparrow have been reported.

5. The Song Sparrow's relation to most of the birds about its size and smaller is one of hostility during the nesting season, although

PLATE II.

PHOTO BY E. S. THOMAS

SONG SPARROW NEAR COLUMBUS.

PHOTO BY M. M. NICE

TYPICAL HABITAT ON INTERPONT

PLATE III.

PHOTO BY E. S. THOMAS

TYPICAL GROUND NEST OF SONG SPARROW NOT FAR FROM COLUMBUS;
ONE COWBIRD EGG AND FIVE EGGS OF THE OWNER.

PHOTO BY E. S. THOMAS

TYPICAL NEST OFF THE GROUND.
K132'S SECOND SET OF UNMARKED EGGS; NORTH INTERPONT.

these birds probably do not compete seriously with it for food, and some of them relieve it of part of the burden of Cowbird parasitism.

6. Seven avian predators are mentioned, besides five native mammalian predators, and three that have been introduced. The cat and Norway rat are considered the worst enemies of the Song Sparrows.

7. The influence of man on the Song Sparrow is a complicated matter, some of it being beneficial, but much deleterious.

CHAPTER III

Weights and Measurements

The measurement of birds has been one of the foundation stones of systematic ornithology, but the matter of weights of birds has been much neglected. Yet the biological significance of the latter subject far surpasses that of the former. The taking of measurements is particularly suited to bird skins, but for most of the problems connected with weight it is essential to deal with live birds.

A. MEASUREMENTS

Ridgway's method, *160*, was followed for the wing measurement with one point of the divider "resting against the anterior side of the bend, the other touching the extremity of the longest primary." Tail

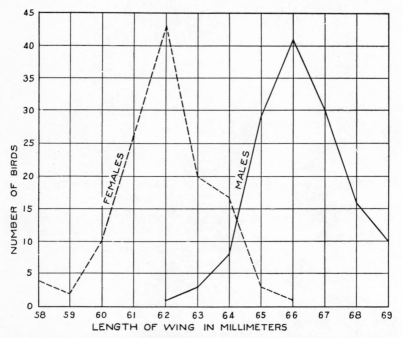

CHART II. *Wing Measurements of Breeding Song Sparrows.*
137 Males; 123 Females

measurements proved so variable that little attention was paid to them, but the wing measurement became an important index of sex.

The wing measurements of 90 resident and 47 summer resident males ranged between 62 and 69 mm., averaging 66.3, the residents averaging 66.3, the others 66.2. Tail measurements ranged between 62 and 72 mm., the median being 68. The wing measurements of 32 resident females and 91 summer residents ranged between 58 and 66 mm., the average of both classes being 62.1. The tails ranged between 56 and 65 mm. with a median of 62.

It will be seen in Chart II that the majority of the males had larger wings than the females, but that there was a certain overlap. Any bird with a measurement of 63 mm. or under is almost certainly a female; any bird with a wing measurement of 65 mm. or over is almost certainly a male, but the birds with wings of 64 mm. were fairly evenly divided as to sex. There were 8 males among the breeding birds with wings of 64 mm., 3 of 63 and one of 62. Among the breeding females, there were 17 with wings measuring 64 mm., 3 measuring 65 and one 66—the last four being quite exceptional, just as were the four smallest males.

131M—the male with a wing of 62 mm. in 1932, but 63 mm. in 1935—I considered the female of the pair until I observed him singing after being banded. K155—the giant with the wing of 66 mm.—I could not believe was a female until I had watched her in the field. But as a rule there was no difficulty in assigning the bird to the proper sex.

The measurements of the transients did not appear to be different from those of the breeding birds; at least none was larger or smaller. I called all birds with wings 63 mm. or under females; all those with wings 65 mm. or over males, while of the 10 birds with wings of 64 mm., the three with tails 66 and 67 mm. were called males, and those with shorter tails females.

I never attempted to take the total length, but Wetherbee, *197*, reports an average of 150.7 mm. for adult summer resident males and 144.8 mm. for females of *Melospiza m. melodia* (the Eastern Song Sparrow) in New England; the wing and tail measurements of her birds agree well with those of mine except that some of her breeding males reached a wing length of 70.75 mm. and some transients 72 mm.

B. WEIGHTS

Beginning with September 1931 each bird captured was brought into the house, and after being banded and measured was placed in a small cloth bag and weighed on scales sensitive to one-tenth of a gram. The weight of the bag fluctuated with atmospheric conditions and had to be determined each day. Seven hundred and forty-six weights of some 455 individuals were taken.

Almost no difference was found in the weights of residents, summer residents, transients, and winter residents taken at the same time of year. The noon weights of 126 males in March and April gave the following averages: 52 residents 22.8 g., 52 summer residents 22.6 g., and 22 transients 22.4 g.

The weights of Wetherbee's, *197*, 39 spring transients of the Eastern Song Sparrow were higher than those of any other category—24 g.—but these were all weighed in March. The 34 breeding males taken from April 15 to August 30 averaged 21.8 g., the 21 breeding females 19.8 g., 121 immature birds from June 24 to September 5 averaged 19.7 g. and 81 fall transients 21.9 g. The weights of 18 male Song Sparrows collected by Dr. L. E. Hicks in various localities in Ohio from March 19 to July 8, 1935, ranged from 19.7 g. to 24.3 g., averaging 22.1 g., which compares closely with what I consider standard weight for my males—22.4 g.

TABLE I

Song Sparrow Weights According to Time of Day

Sex	Month	Total No.	6-8 A. M. No. Birds	Av. Wt.	9 A.M.-2 P.M. No. Birds	Av. Wt.	3-6 P. M. No. Birds	Av. Wt.	Per cent Increase	Av. of all Wghts.
Male	February	82	18	23.5	49	24.2	15	24.6	4.7	24.1
Male	March	148	23	22.6	90	22.9	35	23.7	4.9	23.0
Female	April	78	19	21.0	48	21.4	11	22.0	4.8	21.4
Male	11 Mos.	463	105	22.3	263	23.1	95	23.4	4.9	23.0
Female	10 Mos.	267	75	20.8	140	21.5	52	21.7	4.3	21.3

1. *Weights Throughout the Day*

An increase in weight takes place towards noon and especially late afternoon. This is shown in Table I where samples are given of three months where sufficient numbers of birds were weighed at the three different periods to give trustworthy results, and also the total weights of all the males and all the females (except for 16 that were laying eggs).

The percentage of daily increase is somewhat less than 5 per cent. Partin, *145*, with some 740 weighings of adult House Finches (*Carpodacus mexicanus frontalis*) reported an average daily fluctuation of 3.5 per cent. Linsdale and Sumner, *108*, weighed four captive *Zonotrichia coronata* three times a day for 35 days and found a daily fluctuation of "less than 4 per cent."

2. Weights Throughout the Year

The 746 weights of the Song Sparrows are shown distributed by sex and months in Table II and also in Chart III. Immatures are included in September and October, but juvenals less than a month old are omitted.

TABLE II

Weights in Grams of Adult Song Sparrows Throughout the Year Including Breeding Birds, Winter Residents and Transients

Month	Number of Birds	Males Range	Average	Number of Birds	Females Range	Average	Total Number
September -	16	19.2-25.0	21.1	17	17.0-23.0	20.1	33
October - -	45	18.8-24.4	22.0	25	18.9-24.3	20.8	70
November -	27	20.0-24.3	21.8	14	19.4-23.2	20.8	41
December -	24	20.7-26.8	23.8	18	18.9-24.4	22.2	42
January - -	30	21.2-30.0	24.9	6	21.7-25.8	22.9	36
February -	82	20.1-29.0	24.1	22	20.0-24.4	22.7	104
March - -	148	19.2-27.9	23.0	64	18.1-24.2	21.2	212
April - - -	63	19.6-25.8	22.4	87 (78)[1]	17.1-26.0 (17.1-25.7)	21.7 (21.4)	150
May - - -	20	19.6-23.4	21.2	23 (17)[1]	18.2-25.1 (18.2-22.7)	21.8 (20.7)	43
June - - -	6	19.9-23.6	21.7	7 (6)[1]	17.6-23.4 (17.6-21.7)	20.5 (19.9)	13
August - -	2	19.7-21.4	20.6				2
Total -	463	18.8-30.0	23.0	283 (267)	17.0-25.8	21.4 (21.3)	746

[1]Figures in parentheses represent values without the 16 laying females.

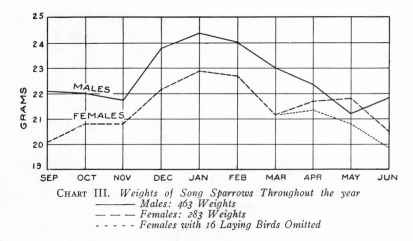

CHART III. *Weights of Song Sparrows Throughout the year*
———— *Males: 463 Weights*
— — — *Females: 283 Weights*
- - - - - *Females with 16 Laying Birds Omitted*

The weights are somewhat low in fall, reach their maximum in late December, January and early February, gradually decrease to what we might call a "standard weight" in April and from then on (except for laying females) decrease to a lower point than in fall. The January figure is 11 per cent higher than the April one for the males, and 7.5 per cent higher for the females. It is unfortunate that July and August are practically unrepresented in my data. My birds normally molt in August and September and their weights are undoubtedly lowest at this period.

The fall weights are slightly lower than the late spring weights. If we compare the two main migration months—October and March —we find the average of the spring birds some 3 per cent heavier than the fall birds in both sexes.

The males are heavier than the females in every month but May— when 6 out of a total of 43 birds of both sexes happened to be laying females. The average of the 463 males is 23.0 g., that of the 283 females is 21.4 g., or 93.0 per cent the weight of the male. Linsdale, *106,* found female Fox Sparrows (*Passerella iliaca*) 98 per cent as heavy as the male, and Partin the female House Finch 99 per cent as heavy as the male.

If we omit the 16 laying females, as shown in the figures in parentheses in Table II, we find that the males average consistently heavier than the females, the differences ranging from 0.5 to 2 g. per month, and averaging 1.6 g.

a. *Weights in Winter*

The height of the curve for both sexes from December through February is striking, as are also many of the weights of individual birds, some gaining as much as 25 to 44 per cent of their lowest weights. The weight increase was not a matter of the birds growing fat on food provided by me, for the highest weights came from birds that seldom benefited from my bounty. The supply of weed seeds on Interpont is apparently ample for the needs of all the Song Sparrows.

A few individual weights will be given; the bird's year of birth being given in parantheses:

50M (1930)—1932: Jan. 7, 27 g.; Mar. 7, 24.2 g.; May 20, 23.5 g.; Dec. 16, 25.8 g.; 1933: Apr. 21, 23.1 g.

4M (1926?-1927?)—1931: Sept. 7, 21 g.; 1932: Jan. 11, 30 g.; Mar. 11, 27.9 g.; Mar. 22, 25.1 g.; April 25, 24.2 g.; May 3, 23.1 g.; May 18, 22.3 g.; Dec. 14, 26.6 g.; 1933: Apr. 29, 23.7 g.; 1934: Mar. 31, 24.1 g.; Apr. 23, 24.2 g.; 1935: Mar. 29, 23.6 g.; Apr. 2, 23.6 g.; May 30, 23.4 g.

187M (1933)—1933: Dec. 3, 24.5 g.; Dec. 26, 26.3 g.; 1934: Mar. 16, 23.6 g.

83M (1931)—1931: Sept. 7, 23 g.; 1932: Feb. 5, 26.4 g.; Mar. 8, 23.3 g.; Apr. 12, 23.9 g.; June 6, 21 g.

86M (1931)—1931: Nov. 6, 20.8 g.; 1932: Jan. 6, 25.3 g.; Mar. 7, 20.8 g.

221M (1934)—1934: Nov. 24, 22.3 g.; 1935: Jan. 25, 25.5 g.; Mar. 29, 21.9 g.; Apr. 23, 21 g.; May 17, 20.6 g.

The curve for Partin's House Finches in California is fairly similar to that of my Song Sparrows, especially in the marked increase from December to February. Other birds for which increased weight in winter has been recorded are Golden-crowned Sparrows (*Zonotrichia coronata*); Fox Sparrows (*Passerella iliaca*), *109*; Bramblings (*Fringilla montifringilla*); Yellow Hammers (*Emberiza citrinella*); and Fieldfares (*Turdus pilaris*) (Zedlitz, *216*); House Sparrows (*Passer domesticus*), *94*; Starlings (*Sturnus vulgaris*), *78*; Slate-colored Juncos (*Junco h. hyemalis*) about 6% on Interpont, and Cardinals (*Richmondena c. cardinalis*) about 3% on Interpont. Kendeigh speaks of having data that indicate "that this same weight relation between summer and winter may be generally true for passerine species," *94*: p. 333. Zedlitz says, however, that Magpies (*Pica pica*) lose in winter, and that he found no gain in the Northern Willow Titmouse (*Parus atricapillus borealis*) and the Marsh Titmouse (*Parus p. palustris*) ; I found practically none in Tufted Titmice (*Baeolophus bicolor*) and Carolina Chickadees (*Penthestes c. carolinensis*).

On the basis of 287 specimens of the Chinese Tree Sparrow (*Passer montanus saturatus*) taken throughout the year Shaw reports that the "seasonal variation is very slight," *176*. Dr. Ernst Mayr suggests that the lack of gain may be correlated with the habit of sleeping in holes.

Linsdale's and Sumner's captive *Zonotrichia coronata* "tended to gain weight during cool weather," *108*, but there seems to have been no question here of really cold weather. Hicks weighed nearly 3,000 Starlings between December 6 and March 28, finding the following average in grams: males—December 81.46, January 84.65, February 87.42, March 85.15; females—December 77.15, January 80.73, February 82.24, March 79.46.

"Starlings commonly gain weight in cold weather if the ground is bare or the snowfall light. . . . Starlings at Columbus (winter of 1933-1934) did not lose weight during the near-zero weather of December 26th-29th and actually gained weight during the near-zero weather of January 28th-31st. However, the sub-zero weather of February 8th-10th, followed by the long near-zero cold wave and snows of February 20th-28th, resulted in an average loss of 9.1 grams weight per bird. Many are known to have perished from starvation," *78*.

I do not have much data on the relationship between weight and changes in winter temperature, but there is evidence of an initial loss of weight in some cases during a cold spell. In January 1935 four Song Sparrows caught from the 19th to 22nd, during a week in which the mean temperatures averaged 4.4° C. (8° F.) *above* normal, averaged 24.4 g. in weight, but the same birds on recapture from the 25th to 28th, during a week with temperatures averaging 6° C. (11° F.) *below* normal, averaged only 22.9 g. However, in the very severe weather of the following winter, when from January 19 to 31 the mean temperature averaged 11° C. (20° F.) below normal and from February 1 to 21 6° C. (11° F.) below normal, 8 weights of male Song Sparrows from January 19 to 25 averaged 24.6 g., and 12 weights of males from February 1 to 18 25.5 g. And these were not all birds that fed at my feeding shelf; four males that were captured February 10 by the river, where they had been baited to only a small extent, averaged 25.4 g. So even though the ground was covered with snow and the nights were long (about 14 hours), these birds adjusted to the abnormally low temperatures by increased weight.

The decreased temperature in winter with consequent increased appetite in the birds (see Kleiber and Dougherty, 96), the absence of territorial and reproductive activities, and the sedentary habits of the Song Sparrow all favor an increase in weight. "Another factor that may be involved in giving birds a resistance to extremely low temperatures in the winter," writes Kendeigh, 94, p. 336, "is a potentially more active endocrine system and the ability, when necessary, to increase greatly the rate of metabolism or heat production in the body. The regulation of heat production in the body is an involuntary function, controlled in large part through endocrine action (Baldwin and Kendeigh, 1932). The necessity for a rapid metabolism and consequently more rapid utilization of reserve food supplies is generally avoided at medium winter air temperatures by the substitution of a better insulating coat of feathers and fat. A greatly increased rate of metabolism in order to maintain the body temperature would be advantageous and necessary only during periods of unusually low temperature." Kendeigh gives a table (p. 335) showing that plumages are appreciably heavier in fall and winter than in spring and summer, that of *Passer domesticus* averaging 1.7 g. in fall, 1.5 g. in winter and 1.2 g. in summer (without rectrices and remiges). He found that "Heavier birds live longer than do lighter birds at low air temperatures" 94, p. 341.

Riddle, 155, 156, and Haecker, 69, reported that the thyroids in birds are heavier in fall and winter than in spring and summer, while Küchler, 98a, found that winter was a period of storing up of material in these glands.

Wetmore, 198a, established by actual count the greater number of feathers on birds in winter than in summer. Six Song Sparrows taken in March had from 2,093 to 2,335 feathers, while a bird on July 2 had only 1,304.

b. *Weights in Spring*

It will be noted in Chart III that the males, after reaching their peak in January decline almost consistently till May, showing a slight upward peak in June which is of no significance because of the small number of birds involved. The figures by half months are: February 24.4 g., 23.2 g.; March 23.4 g., 22.7 g.; April 22.6 g., 22.2 g.,—a steady loss of the excess weight of winter.

This loss undoubtedly results in part from activities connected with territory matters, involving singing for perhaps half the day-light hours, but that is not the whole story. For W6—the male that wintered on Interpont for four seasons—also showed a spring loss, weighing 27.3 g. on February 5, 1932, 27.6 g. on January 29, 1933, and only 24.6 g. on March 27, 1933.

In April the male has reached his "standard weight"—22.4 g.

A few males in 1933 reached it as early as February 9; perhaps this is not surprising when we realize that they had been proclaiming territory for nearly three weeks by this date.

Linsdale and Sumner, *109*, found from 1,422 weights of the Golden-crowned Sparrow a peak in weight in January and a much higher one in May, while 711 weights on the Fox Sparrow showed similar peaks in December and May. "Supplementary records . . . indicate that high weight is maintained until arrival on breeding grounds." Heydweiller, *77a*, reports that the Tree Sparrow (*Spizella a. arborea*) attains its maximum weight "just preceding the spring departure during the first two weeks in March." Kendeigh, *94*, reports higher weights in spring than fall with White-crowned (*Zonotrichia leucophrys*) and White-throated Sparrows (*Zonotrichia albicollis*). My own figures on the latter on Interpont show an average fall weight of 25 g. (124 birds) and an average spring weight of 29.9 g. (35 birds), a 20 per cent increase. The Slate-colored Junco (*Junco h. hyemalis*) averaged somewhat heavier in winter and spring than in fall: 19.5 g. in fall (75 birds), 21.2 g. in winter (81 birds), 20.6 g. in spring (12 birds). The weight curves of Golden-crowned and Fox Sparrows are very different in spring from that of my Song Sparrows that do *not* gain then, but lose steadily.

The average weight in May was low, because over half the males were feeding young at the time of capture. These 11 birds averaged only 20.3 g., while 9 more care-free males averaged 22.3 g. In June the four fathers averaged 20.9 g., the other two 23.2 g. It is interesting how these hard working individuals lost some 9 per cent of their normal weight, an average loss of 2 g.

The females show a similar decline from January to April, but after that the course of their weight depends on the stage of the nesting cycle. The 38 birds weighed in the second half of March averaged 21 g., while the 75 females (not within 4 days of laying) weighed in April averaged 21.3 g. The female at this stage spends a great deal of her time eating. Five birds, three to four days before starting to lay, averaged 22.8 g.; 16 birds, one to two days before laying and during laying, averaged 24.1 g. (ranging from 23 to 26 g.); 9 birds, during incubation, averaged 21.5 g., while 11 birds feeding young averaged 19.3 g.

In the first two categories we see reflected the growth of the eggs, profoundly affecting the female's weight when she is in the midst of laying a set. (See Chapter XII under The Size of the Eggs.)

As to the matter of incubation, a slight gain is evident here. In three birds near the end of incubation there was an average increase of 4.5 per cent in comparison to their pre-nesting weight. Riddle and Braucher, *158,* found that Doves gained some 8 per cent during the 15 or 18 days spent in incubation and attributed this to the relative inactivity of the birds. Perhaps incubation is a time of rest and recuperation for the Song Sparrow; certainly it is not the "arduous duty" that some would have us think.

Feeding the young, on the other hand, is a strenuous period as is shown by the drop in weight. Just as in the 15 males, the 11 females showed a 9 per cent loss from the 21.3 g. average weight with which they started the nesting season. Heydweiller, *77a,* found an even greater loss with the Tree Sparrow (*Spizella a. arborea*) in Manitoba while feeding young—"almost 20 per cent for the males and 10 per cent for the females."

3. *Weight and Age*

Does weight increase with age? Whittle, *203,* and Wetherbee, *197,* found the weights of immature Song Sparrows in summer slightly less than those of adults, the average of 23 weighed by the former coming to 21.37 g., and 121 weighed by the latter 19.68 g. I could not find any consistent difference in the fall between immature and adult birds. The heaviest weight in the three fall months of any bird was that of a young male, (99M), nearly through the post-juvenal molt on September 13, at which time he weighed 25 g.

As to older birds, 4M was heavy, but other long-lived males have not weighed more than average. Two birds at least four years old weighed as follows: 23M, 22.7 g. on April 5, and 131M, 19 g. on May 17 while feeding young. When nearly five years old, 10M weighed 22 g. on April 30; 57M, when nearly six years old, weighed 24 g. on February 10, 1936, but only 21.7 g. on February 18.

Two of my old females were heavy birds with large wing measurements: K11, when at least three years old, showed a wing measurement of 65 mm. and a weight of 23.3 g. on March 28; K24 at the same age, had a wing measurement of 64 mm. and weight of 24.2 g.

on April 11. The other females I was not able to capture late in their careers.

Young birds in fall and winter have been reported as weighing less than adult birds by Hicks for Starlings, *78*, and Crows (*Corvus brachyrhynchos, 81*), Zedlitz for Hooded Crows (*Corvus cornix, 216*), Haigh for Pink-footed Geese (*Anser brachyrhynchos, 70*), and Sumner for California Quail (*Lophortyx californica, 184a*).

In conclusion, let me emphasize the fact that my data on weights are almost entirely a by-product of capturing Song Sparrows for banding, not a deliberate attempt to investigate problems connected with weights. Nevertheless, much valuable information has accumulated and light has been thrown on various aspects of the biology of this bird. The possibilities of investigations along this line are great, especially with species that enter traps more readily than does *Melospiza* with me.

C. Summary

1. Measurement of the wing has been used as an aid in determining sex, the great majority of males having wings 65 to 69 mm. in length, the majority of females 59 to 63 mm. (Chart II.)

2. Seven hundred and forty-six weights of adult Song Sparrows were recorded. Weight increases as a rule during the day, the increase reaching 4.3 to 4.9 per cent as shown in Table I.

3. Weight is at a minimum in late summer and fall starting to increase in December, reaching a maximum in January and decreasing again to a "standard" weight in April. (Table II, Chart III.)

4. Some of the Song Sparrows increased as much as 25 to 44 per cent in winter. The average January weight was 11 per cent above standard for the males, 7.5 per cent for the females.

5. Increased weight in winter has been noted in a number of other birds, but in a few species there appears to be little or none.

6. Males. while feeding young averaged 9 per cent less than standard weight.

7. The weight of females increases markedly just before and during the deposition of eggs; it appears to increase slightly during incubation, but decreases again (as much as 9 per cent), while young are being fed.

8. Some old birds were heavy, others not.

CHAPTER IV

Migratory Status of the Song Sparrows on Interpont

The Song Sparrows on Interpont have proved particularly interesting in the matter of migration, because part of the breeding population is resident and part migratory. By means of banding it has been possible to find out something about the behavior of brothers and sisters, parents and children, grandparents and grandchildren, in respect to migration and permanent residency. It has also been possible to observe the stability of the migrating character in the individual.

The Song Sparrow population on Interpont is made up of four categories: residents, summer residents, winter residents and transients. Of the 533 adults banded, 306 (158 males, 148 females) belonged to the first two categories; 80 were assigned to the third and 147 to the fourth, or approximately 57, 15 and 28 per cent respectively. There is some uncertainty in regard to these figures for a potential resident, captured in the winter, that died before spring, would be counted a winter resident; a potential summer resident captured in March and never seen again would be called a transient. Of 353 nestlings banded from May 1929 to June 1935, 26 males and 14 females have joined the ranks of nesting birds, thus bringing the totals of banded breeding birds to 184 males and 162 females, or 346 in all. (See Appendix II for data on the birds banded through 1935.)

Of the 886 birds banded not a single one has been reported away from Columbus. Hence, we do not know where the last two groups breed, nor do we know where our summer residents or transients spend the winter. (A Song Sparrow banded in May at Gates Mills, Ohio, was taken in December in Georgia; see Appendix II.) It is not possible to distinguish any of these classes by weights or measurements. But in the spring there is a difference in appearance, as the birds that arrive from the south are much cleaner and lighter in color than those that have been subjected to the soot of the city of Columbus.

As to the sex ratio of the trapped adults, if we count each individual only once each month (some birds were captured several times), males made up the following percentage: September 52; October and November 70; December through February 74; March 67 and

April, May and June 45. This last figure does not represent the population present, which actually shows a small preponderance of males; it merely means that most of my capturing of nesting females was in April and May while a large proportion of the males were caught earlier. The figures show that the wintering population consists largely of males.

The preponderance of males in the migration months may be due to the fact that in the fall I get the late transients (having trapped in September only in 1931), and in spring the early transients, for the spring transients have seldom entered the traps except in the cold and snowy weather of March 18 to 20, 1934, when I caught 26 unbanded Song Sparrows, 15 of which I judged to be males and 11 females.

A. The Transients

The transients arrive in March, the bulk of them from the middle to about the 25th of the month, a few still being recorded during the first week in April. On their return journey the first birds arrive the last of September, but October is the chief month of both arrival and departure. Transients do not differ in appearance from summer residents, except that a few appear especially light in coloring; their behavior is different, for they are quiet and inconspicuous, the adult males being silent, although the young birds warble. No transient has ever been taken in a later season.

B. The Winter Residents

These birds come in October and possibly early November; banded individuals have been recorded until February 18, 1930; February 12, 17, 22, March 27, 1931; March 3, 5, 18, 1932; March 27, 1933; March 7, 1935; March 11, 1936.

Although I have banded over 70 winter residents, only two birds have returned to Interpont—W1 and W6.

The former, wearing an aluminum and faded celluloid band, was seen in the fall and early winter of 1931 and again in 1932; I was not able to capture it, but it must have been a bird banded in 1930. (I had considerable trouble with the fading of the first bands, which I made out of celluloid toys.)

W6 is a most exceptional character, since he settled four winters in the same spot on North Interpont. I first captured him Feb. 26, 1931, and heard him warbling from Feb. 28 to Mar. 27. In the fall I found him (November 2) in the same region, noting him at intervals each month until his capture, Feb. 5, 1932, but never hearing him sing, except a little on Feb. 8. The next winter I did not locate him until Jan. 4, trapping him the 29th, and giving him the fine new colored bands of the Biological Survey. Interestingly enough, this year he sang quite a little from Feb. 18 to Mar. 1, at first rather softly and from only half way up a weed, but later loudly.

Immediately after this all the cover was destroyed on W6's wintering home and I saw nothing more of him until I happened to trap him on Mar. 27, 135 meters directly to the east along the bluff. In the fall I was delighted to see him on his old stamping ground on Oct. 17, 1933, and hear him sing his queer, distinctive song. He sang again the next day, but that was the last I ever saw of him. The cover on Interpont had been so destroyed that his former winter home was no longer suitable; either he was captured by some enemy, or he moved elsewhere. It is curious how two wintering birds should be so faithful while not one of the 70 others was recorded in a season after it was banded. Wharton, *200,* records the return of two Song Sparrows to their winter quarters at Summerville, South Carolina.

Winter residents are sometimes more numerous than the residents and sometimes present in about equal numbers. (Hicks and Chapman, *82,* found the Song Sparrow ranking as the fifth most abundant winter bird in Ohio on the 392 Christmas censuses taken in the state for Bird-Lore from 1900 to 1932.) The proportion of females appears to be very small indeed, 14 out of 36 different birds of this sex captured December to February having been assumed to have been winter residents, but a number of these were probably residents. Adult males seldom sing, but the juvenals warble a considerable amount.

In Oklahoma Song Sparrows were present only as transients and winter residents; I recorded adult songs occasionally, but curiously enough, I never heard warbling. Ridgway, *159,* says that in southern Illinois this species "is a winter sojourner, abundant, but very retiring, inhabiting almost solely the bushy swamps in the bottom-lands, *and unknown as a song bird."* Howell, *87,* in writing of this bird in Florida, says it "is practically silent during its stay in the south."

C. RESIDENTS AND SUMMER RESIDENTS

When I started this study, I shared the common opinion that the breeding birds were summer residents and that all the birds present in winter had nested to the north. Therefore it was a great surprise to me in the winter of 1929-1930 to find 4M continuously present.

(Later I came upon four published instances where 8 banded Eastern Song Sparrows (*Melospiza m. melodia*) had been found to be resident, two in Pennsylvania (Gillespie, *63,* and Middleton, *124*), one in New York State (Baasch, *8*), and one at Martha's Vineyard (Eustis, *56*)).

The next season I discovered that half of my banded nesting males spent the entire year on Interpont, while the other half went south for the winter. At first I believed that all the females migrated, but in the spring of 1931 I began to suspect that the few dark colored females that joined their mates from the second to the fourth week in February might be resident and the next winter I found this to be true.

1. *"Individual Migration"*

The situation with these Song Sparrows is that called "individual migration" by Thomson, *190, 191,* where "individual birds belonging to the same species and native to the same area may behave differently as regards migration." He cites Lapwings (*Vanellus vanellus*) nesting in Aberdeenshire and asks: "If the racial custom is similarly inherited by all the birds, what is it that stimulates it to greater activity, or to different activity, as between one individual and another? . . . Are there various *gentes* not morphologically distinguishable but differing in constitution and temperament in ways not at present definable, as, for instance, a resident *gens,* an Ireland-seeking *gens,* and a Portugal-seeking *gens?*" He also remarks that "evidence is lacking as to whether, in cases like this, any given individual behaves in the same way in successive years," *190,* p. 301.

With my Song Sparrows I have been able to trace the "inheritance" of migratory behavior in many families, and I also have evidence on the status of a considerable number of individuals in successive years. Is the difference in migratory behavior a matter of the young wandering and the old remaining on their territories? Is it a matter of different *gentes* or strains? Or is it a matter of the migratory impulse being present in all the birds, and stimulated or inhibited by weather conditions and individual temperament?

The logical way to treat the subject would be first to examine the numbers of residents and summer residents present each year; and next the inheritance of migratory behavior, but the fact that this behavior has not been entirely stable in all individuals necessitates a different approach, and proves that we cannot consider migrating or non-migrating as a definitely fixed character in any one bird.

2. *Stability of Migrating and Non-Migrating Behavior*

The majority of my birds have been definitely migratory or definitely sedentary, but a few have changed their status. Twenty-four males have remained consistently resident—18 during 2 winters, 4 during 3 winters, one for 6 winters and one for at least eight. Thirty-one males have been consistently migratory—15 for 2 years, 11 for 3 years, 4 for 4 years, and one for 5 years. But 6 other males and one female changed their status. A total of 55 males have thus retained their status, in contrast to the six that changed it.

As for the females 5 remained consistently resident—2 for 2 years, 2 for 3 years, and one for 4 years, while 37 were consistently migratory—28 for 2 years, 7 for 3 years, and 2 for 4 years. One changed status in contrast to 42 that retained it.

I have only one certain record of a summer resident turning resident—19M—although I thought this was the case also with 121M, that was noted as a light colored bird when first seen February 26, 1932, but remained the following winter. 19M migrated two winters, but remained the third—1931-1932.

The fact of a summer resident spending the winter is not so strange as that of residents migrating. I can find no instance of this in the literature. Nevertheless it has happened with 5 of my males and one female.

9M was a juvenal resident, banded Jan. 26, 1930. He settled near us and remained through the next winter, starting to sing Jan. 24. But in the fall of 1931 he disappeared, so I concluded he had been killed. On Mar. 2, I was greatly astonished to have him reappear on his territory in light, clean plumage. 54M, banded in the nest May 11, 1930, son of a summer resident—12M— and brother of a resident—52M—remained on his territory continuously until late Oct., 1932; he returned, bright and shining, Feb. 26, 1933. 96M was an adult resident when captured Feb. 8, 1932, but migrated in the fall, returning on the same day as 54M. 100M and 107M were juvenals banded in the fall of 1931; they were recorded throughout the winter, with occasional captures, and nested in 1932, but both migrated the second winter, 107M returning Mar. 19, 100M not until April.

In previous publications I recorded 131M as supposedly a resident when first recorded on Mar. 17, 1932, because of his sooty appearance; he has migrated and returned three times since then, so it may well be he was migratory from the first. I thought he had moved onto Interpont from across the river; perhaps he had arrived early and acquired a coat of soot.

The one female that changed status was a resident with only one foot—K75; I captured her Feb. 15, 1932, and followed her history until June 14; I did not see her again until Mar. 18, 1933, the day she arrived from the south with no soot on her plumage.

Unfortunately, every one of these birds that surely changed status, and 121M also, disappeared the summer following the change, so that I was not able to follow their histories further.

3. *Inheritance of Migratory Behavior*

When I first found the difference in the migratory status of my Song Sparrows, I believed there must be two strains, with sons doing as their fathers had done. Therefore it was an exciting time in February and March 1931, capturing my 7 resident males that had been banded the previous summer, and reading their bands. And my fine theory was soon exploded!

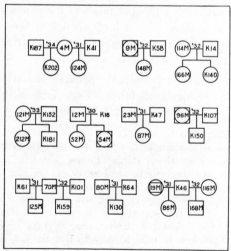

CHART IV. *Genealogies Showing Inheritance of Migratory Behavior in the Song Sparrows. Circles indicate residents; rectangles summer residents. Where birds have changed status, the first status is indicated inside second. Numbers of birds not enclosed are of unknown status.*

The accompanying charts show most of the data obtained on the migratory status of relatives among my Song Sparrows.

Chart IV gives a number of examples of resident sons of resident fathers, and of migratory sons of migratory fathers, but it also shows many exceptions. 87M, banded in the nest May 15, 1931, and captured the following December, but never seen again, was a resident son of two migratory parents, 23M having migrated four winters. The two sons of the summer resident 12M were both resident for two years, but 54M as already mentioned migrated his third winter. 70M and all his known relatives—two mates and a son and daughter— were all migratory. The case of K46 is contradictory: with a migratory husband that later turned resident she had a resident son, but the next year with a resident husband, she had a migratory son. The children of 121M, nest mates, behaved in opposite ways—the brother remaining stationary, like his father, the sister migrating, like her mother. But a similar parental situation with 114M and K14 gave two resident children—brother and sister. The two resident females both had resident fathers but migratory mothers, while three other females on this chart and the next, with the same parental situation, were migratory.

Three other genealogies, not shown on the charts, were as follows: a resident father (14M) and mother of unknown status (K34) had a resident son (56M); a migratory pair (119M and K116) had a migratory son (169M); while a resident father (225M) and migratory mother (K211) had a migratory son (265M).

The genealogies shown on Chart V are of especial interest. There is one straight summer resident line for three generations—22M and his descendants—all five birds involved being known to have been migratory.

The mates of K2 were both summer residents, as she was herself, yet she had one resident son (55M) and two resident grandsons.

The history of the descendants of 25M and K28 is noteworthy because of the remarkable fact of three young from one brood surviving. Unfortunately, the status of 145M is not known: he was caught some 50 meters to the south of our grounds, October 4, 1932, but never seen

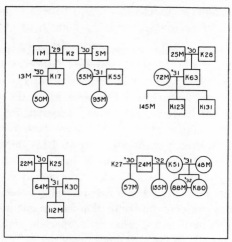

CHART V. *Additional Genealogies of Song Sparrows*

again. Possibly he had nested in town and had left his territory because it no longer offered food and shelter. The two sisters nested here in 1932 (one ¹35 meters from her birthplace, the other 450) and the grandmother also; on May 25 I banded K28's children in the nest, and on May 28 and 31 two broods of her great grand-children.

The family histories of 24M and K51 are also of great interest. In 1930, 24M, a summer resident, and a mate of unknown status, had a resident son 57M, who lived to be almost 6 years old—my second oldest Song Sparrow so far as known. In 1932, 24M and K51, a resident female, had a resident son, 155M. But the year before, K51 and a resident male, 48M, had had a son and daughter from the same nest that wintered along the fourth dike and mated in the spring. So far as I can find out, there is only one other instance of known brother and sister, in the wild, mating—Downy Woodpeckers (*Dryobates pubescens medianus*) in New Hampshire—as reported by Shelley, *178*. All three eggs of the first nesting of 88M and K80 hatched. 88M disappeared that summer, but K80 lived in the same locality until the spring of 1934, reaching an age of nearly three years.

To sum up, we find that seven resident fathers had seven resident sons, and that four migratory fathers had four migratory sons. But two resident fathers had two migratory sons and five migratory fathers had seven resident sons.

As to the daughters, four migratory pairs had migratory daughters; two resident males and migratory females had three migratory daughters, while two other pairs with the same combination had two resident daughters; a resident pair had a resident daughter, while 96M that changed status had a migratory daughter.

In five cases nest mates were known to have survived: two migratory sisters and a brother of unknown status, two resident brothers, two instances of resident brother and sister, and one of a resident brother and migratory sister.

It has been suggested that perhaps the migratory impulse was a recessive character in these birds, but theorizing as to the inheritance or non-inheritance of this character seems to me futile, when we have seen that the very same bird may migrate one year and remain the next, or more commonly, remain one winter (and in two cases two winters) and migrate the next. The instinct would appear to be present in all the birds, but for some reason is inactive in many of the birds most of the time.

4. *Numbers of Residents and Summer Residents*

In 1930 the banded males on Central Interpont were equally divided as to migratory status. The proportion of residents among the breeding males on Upper Interpont rose from 50 per cent in 1931 to 59 in 1932, dropped to 40 in 1933, and to 35 in 1934, reached 40 in 1935 and increased to 61 in 1936. (The numbers were as follows, the residents being given first: 1931, 24 and 24; 1932, 41 and 28; 1933, 18 and 26; 1934, 10 and 19; 1935, 10 and 15; 1936, 11 and 7.)

The increase of residents in 1932 was due to the large number of young birds that remained through the winter in 1931-'32. Among the summer resident males nesting on Interpont approximately a third were first-year birds, but this was true of more than half of the banded resident males—23 out of 43. The decrease of residents the next year is partly accounted for by the change from resident to summer resident of five individuals, while only one bird made the contrary change. But by 1933 it became evident that the survival rate of the resident males was becoming much worse than that of the summer residents.

This was not due to the severity of the winters at Columbus; in the years from 1927 to 1936 I have not known of a single Song Sparrow coming to its end through cold and starvation here. I believe the explanation lies in increased ease of predation on Interpont during recent years, making this area a more dangerous place to winter on, than the wintering quarters in the South. But during the past winter—1935-36—the summer residents must have suffered heavy losses from the severe weather, for their percentage of the breeding population is the lowest in seven years.

As to the females, the proportion of residents has fluctuated between 11 and 33 per cent, averaging 19 per cent. In 1931, 5 of 46 breeding birds were residents (10.8%); in 1932, 14 of 65 (21.5%); in 1933, 11 of 41 (26.8%); in 1934, 3 of 25 (12%); in 1935, 4 of 25 (16%); and in 1936, 4 of 12 (33.3%).

5. *Differences Between the Residents and Summer Residents*

It might be expected that the migratory Song Sparrow would have longer wings than his sedentary neighbor, and that the resident would be heavier than the summer resident. However, I have been able to find no significant difference between these two sets of birds in length of wing or tail, and only a very slight one in weights taken at the same time of year. As to coloring, there is no difference in the fall, but an artificial one in spring, the result of Columbus soot. In the matter of zeal in singing, there is considerable variation between males in this respect, some of the most enthusiastic being residents, and also some of the least so.

Among the females, the two really energetic singers have been residents. (Females sometimes give harsh, unmusical songs early in the season before nesting begins, *137, 198*). Resident females occasionally start to nest earlier than some of the late-arriving migratory females, but on the whole there is little difference. Resident females do not differ from the others in the number of eggs laid.

6. *Comparison With Other Species*

"Individual migration" has been found to occur in a number of species: the Cormorant (*Phalacrocorax carbo sinensis*), *73,* the Lapwing (*Vanellus vanellus*), *190,* the Woodcock (*Scolopax rusticola*),

191, Buzzard (*Buteo buteo*), *22, 186,* Hooded Crow (*Corvus cornix*), *186,* Greenfinch (*Chloris chloris*), *24,* Song Thrush (*Turdus philomelus*), *211,* European Blackbird (*T. merula*), *48,* Starling (*Sturnus vulgaris*), *98, 187,* and California Shrike (*Lanius ludovicianus gambeli*), *125.*

Details as to the correlation of sex and age with migrating and non-migrating are largely lacking, except for the general rule that females often winter further south than males, and that the young, in some species, wander while the adults are sedentary.

With Robin Redbreasts (*Erithacus rubecula*), *29,* Cabanis's Woodpeckers (*Dryobates villosus hyloscopus*), *111,* Prairie Chickens (*Tympanuchus cupido americanus*), *42,* Chaffinches (*Fringilla coelebs*), *49,* European Blackbirds (*Turdus merula*), *49,* and Eastern Mockingbirds (*Mimus p. polyglottos*), *100, 100a,* the males are sometimes permanent residents and the females migratory.

According to Thienemann, *186,* and von Lucanus, *115,* the young of Titmice and Woodpeckers are much more migratory than are the old, and Wachs, *195,* reports the same of the Blackbird (*T. merula*), the Buzzard (*Buteo buteo*) and the Sparrow Hawk (*Accipiter nisus*). Eaton, *51,* found that first-year Herring Gulls (*Larus argentatus*) on the Atlantic Coast make very long migrations, second-year birds shorter ones, while older birds do not appear to migrate at all. Thomas' data from 7,000 banded Starlings show that the birds of the year are responsible for the spread to new territory, *187.*

With the Buzzard and the Blackbird, young from the same nest were found to behave in opposite ways in the matter of migration, but the sex of these birds is unknown.

The only case I can find of banded birds migrating one year and failing to do so the next, besides my Song Sparrows, is that of the Starlings banded by Thomas, *187,* in winter in Columbus, a number of which were taken in subsequent winters considerable distances to the northeast. Of 21 December and January returns, 14 or exactly two-thirds, were recovered to the northeast of Columbus, while 7 were taken to the southwest. "It would thus seem unquestionable that a large number of Starlings, after once having migrated at least as far south as Columbus, fail to do so in some subsequent year, remaining as permanent residents in the north." Dr. Hicks informs me that he has similar records with the Starlings banded by him.

The Blackbird (*Turdus merula*) is reported as becoming resident in Holland during the last 60 years (Wolda, *212*), in Hungary during the last 40 years (Csörgey, *45*), and recently in Sweden according to Dr. E. Lönnberg in a paper at the Eighth International Ornithological Congress at Oxford in 1934.

7. Discussion of "Individual Migration" in the Song Sparrows

It is clear that the difference between migrating and non-migrating, with my birds, has nothing to do with age and also is not a matter of inheritance. The fact that seven birds changed their status shows that the character is not a hard and fast one.

If we examine the years in which the birds changed status we find in the exceptionally mild fall of 1931, 19M remained, as well as 54M, 96M, 100M, 107M and K75, but that in the bleak fall of 1932 the last five birds migrated. 9M is an exception, for he migrated for the first time in 1931—although probably not until quite late. But the behavior of the other five lends support to the theory that the weather had a good deal to do with the migrating or non-migrating of these birds. Rowan, *163*, in telling of the Mallards (*Anas p. platyrhynchos*) some of which fail to migrate each fall from Alberta, says, "In years in which the fall is late and open, a far larger number stay behind." Mute Swans (*Cygnus olor*) sometimes fail to migrate in mild falls (v. Sanden, *167*), sometimes starving to death later in the season in such cases (Heinroth, *76*, II, p. 147).

In those Song Sparrows that change status the migratory urge cannot be very strong; perhaps the warm weather of October, 1931, nullified its promptings, while the bleak temperature of the following year gave sufficient stimulus to start the birds south.

It has been suggested that perhaps the Song Sparrows that leave Interpont in October and return from February to April are not true migrants but "wander about somewhere in the vicinity." It is entirely contrary to Song Sparrow character as I know it to "wander"; this bird settles down wherever it is, the wintering individuals both on Interpont and in Oklahoma remaining within an area of an acre or two for months. My birds may not go for more than a few hundred miles, but I believe that those that leave Interpont are as true migrants as any. The data on the spring migration given in Chapter V points to a true migration and not to an absence somewhere near Columbus.

Perhaps the migratory impulse is latent in all my Song Sparrows; it functions normally in the majority of the individuals, but for some reason lies dormant in others most of the time. Miller, in discussing "individual migration" in California Shrikes, says, "For some reason, certain individuals, adult and first-year birds alike, fail to respond to the changing seasons. It is possible that psychic differences of the individual overcome what must be in Shrikes a relatively weak physiological migration drive, and thus permit certain birds to remain on their breeding territories," *125*.

Relationship between weather and fall migration is reported in the case of the Golden-crested Kinglet in Finland by P. Palmgren, *Ueber den Massenwechsel bei Regulus r. regulus (L.).* 1936. *Ornis Fennica,* 13: 159-164. "The Golden-crested Wren is a typical representative of those birds in which the migratory instinct functions in only a part of the population. . . . At the period when migration may take place, low temperature stimulates the migratory impulse and sets the greater part of the population in motion. If cold weather comes after the waning of the migratory impulse, migration is no longer possible. Those birds that have remained have little prospect of surviving the winter."

D. SUMMARY

1. There are four categories of Song Sparrows on Interpont; spring and fall transients, winter residents, summer residents and permanent residents.

2. The sex ratio of banded Song Sparrows shows a decided preponderance of males from October through March, being highest during the winter.

3. The transients pass through in March and October. There has been no return from approximately 150 transients banded.

4. The winter residents arrive in October and stay until March. There have been only two returns out of some 70 banded birds; one of these being present three winters and the other four.

5. About half the nesting male Song Sparrows are permanent residents on Interpont, the others migrating south in October and returning in February or March.

6. The proportion of residents among the females has ranged from 11 to 33 per cent.

7. The majority of the Song Sparrows have been consistently migratory or sedentary, but six males and one female changed status.

8. One male migrated for two winters and remained the third.

9. Three males and one female remained one winter and migrated the next, returning the following spring; two males remained two winters, migrated the third and returned in the spring.

10. Charts are given showing information obtained on the migratory status of parents and children, and in three cases for three generations.

11. A brother and sister wintered in the same territory and mated in the spring.

12. The supposition of two strains of Song Sparrows on Interpont, one migratory and the other not, is not substantiated.

13. The survival of residents and summer residents was equally good during the first three years of the study, but after that the mortality of the residents increased, due, presumably, to lack of sufficient cover.

14. The percentage of summer residents dropped in 1936 to the lowest point in the seven years, apparently on account of the severity of the winter.

15. No significant differences could be detected between residents and summer residents in length of wing, weight or coloring, except that the plumage of the former becomes darkened through soot.

16. "Individual migration" has been recorded in 10 other species; in at least 6 species besides the Song Sparrow males are sometimes permanent residents and females migratory; while in still other species the young are more migratory than the old.

17. The migratory impulse is believed to be latent in all the Song Sparrows, functioning normally in the majority of the birds, lying dormant in most of the others, but perhaps capable of stimulation or inhibition in a few by weather conditions in October.

CHAPTER V

Spring and Fall Migration

In the following discussion of the migration of the summer residents, it must be remembered that the foundation of the study was recognition of the individual in the field, involving almost daily censuses of Interpont. In this way I was able to know the date on which each male and each female arrived, rather than depending on trapping records which in most cases would fall later than the real arrival. Fall data, naturally, are much less definite. But the arrival of a male on his nesting grounds, unless the weather has happened to turn bleak, is a conspicuous thing, for he himself sings his loudest and his neighbors, in turn, have to settle affairs with him with repeated territory establishment activities. The arrival of a female is the converse of the picture; indeed, I often say to myself on nearing a territory where silence reigns over night, "Such and such a male must be either dead or married," and upon careful search I find either two birds or none.

A. SPRING MIGRATION

The subject of the spring migration is a complicated one, due to the various categories of Song Sparrows that I distinguished, and to the vagaries of the weather, but it has proved a fascinating problem. We will first consider the migration in relation to time of year and temperature and later the data on individual birds.

1. *Migration in Relation to Temperature and Time of Year*

The arrival of the Song Sparrows on Interpont is shown in Chart VI where the mean temperatures at Columbus are given from Feb. 17 to Apr. 5 during five years; male and female summer residents and transients are differentiated, while the arrival of the breeding Cowbirds is also indicated.

The records of 1930 and 1936 are not given because of their incompleteness; during the early spring of 1930 I was watching only a few pairs, while in 1936 I was absent from Interpont the first and last weeks of March. In 1930 there was an early migration of summer resident males in late February in connection with a marked warm wave with mean temperatures of 9°-15.6° C. (48°-60° F.), the first male being recorded Feb. 23 and the first female Mar. 1. The main migration occurred between the 15th and 22nd of March. In 1936 the first *transients* were seen Feb. 28 after a warm spell from the 23rd to 25th with mean

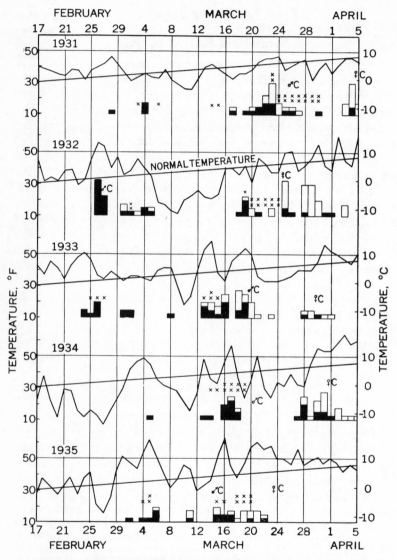

= 1 BREEDING MALE SONG SPARROW.   x = MANY TRANSIENT SONG SPARROWS.
□ = 1 BREEDING FEMALE SONG SPARROW. ♂C = FIRST ARRIVAL OF MALE COWBIRDS.
x = A FEW TRANSIENT SONG SPARROWS. ♀C = FIRST ARRIVAL OF FEMALE COWBIRDS.

CHART VI. *Migration and Daily Mean Temperatures at Columbus* temperatures from 9°-11° C. (48°-52° F.). The first week of March with mean temperatures of 5.6°-7.2° C. (42°-45° F.) brought a few breeding males and one female, while four days from the 8th to 11th with temperatures of 4.4°-12° C. (40°-54° F.) brought more birds.

It will be seen that there are usually two well defined migrations—an early migration and the main migration. Summer resident males have always arrived first with the exception of 1936. (Perhaps their absence this year from the earliest migration was due to the great lack of summer resident Song Sparrows at present—only seven of these males having settled on Upper Interpont by April 6. It may have been that the birds that would have migrated earliest wintered farther north than the others and were killed by the severity of the past winter). Transients are the next to arrive, and the breeding females last. The main migration brings most of the males (except in 1932 when the majority came early), as well as the bulk of the transients and females, some of the latter not appearing until April.

Song Sparrow migration is closely correlated with temperature. The early migration is absolutely dependent on a warm wave the last of February or the first of March, but the main migration is only relatively dependent on a rise in temperature. Severe cold waves stop migration short.

It will be noted on the chart that early migration never took place except in connection with a decided rise in temperature of 9°-16° C. (17°-28° F.) above normal the last of February, or 7°-9° C. (12°-17° F.) in early March. The main migration started a few days before the middle of March with mean temperatures 4°-9° C. (8°-16° F.) above normal, but in the absence of warm waves at this period (1931 and 1932) occurred at normal temperatures the 19th and 20th of the month.

It is not only the migration of the Song Sparrows that depends on warm waves; the other February and March migrants on Interpont behave in a similar manner. Eight species (besides the Song Sparrow) appear here practically without fail either in February or March; they are: Eastern Mourning Dove (*Zenaidura macroura carolinensis*); Killdeer (*Oxyechus v. vociferus*); Bronzed Grackle (*Quiscalus quiscula aeneus*); Eastern Meadowlark (*Sturnella m. magna*); Red-eyed Towhee (*Pipilo e. erythrophthalmus*); Eastern Fox Sparrow (*Passerella i. iliaca*) ; Northern Flicker (*Colaptes auratus luteus*) ; and Eastern Cowbird (*Molothrus a. ater*). Let us take the median date of arrival of these nine birds from 1928 or 1929 to 1935 and see how their migration agreed with one another each year. In 1930 every one was early; in 1931 8 were late and 1 on time; in 1932 8 were early and 1 late; while in 1934 all were late. In 1933 5 were early and 4 late; possibly the wholesale destruction of cover that was started on Interpont the first of March drove away some birds. In 1935 5 were late, 3 early and 1 on time—a record that corresponds well with the course of the temperature that year.

And it is not only the very early arrivals that are influenced by weather. The Brown Thrasher (*Toxostoma rufum*) arrived on Interpont between April 11 and 13 each spring from 1930 through 1934, but after the extraordinarily warm weather in late March and early April, 1929, it came on April 3, and during the cold April of 1935 it did not appear till the 21st, while during the present cold April (1936) the first bird was heard on the 18th. The House Wren (*Troglodytes a. aedon*) came very early in 1929—April 5—and very late in 1935—April 24—its other arrivals falling between the 12th and 21st. (For temperatures in April see Charts XI, XII and XIII.)

In order to study the relationship of migration with temperature and time of year, we will examine the data concerned with the migration of the breeding males, since their arrival is more conspicuous than that of the females or the transients, and the results are more consistent.

TABLE III

First Arrival of the Breeding Male Song Sparrows on Interpont

Year	Average Temperature in February				Early Males				Later Males			
	Month C.° F.°		Last 10 Days C.° F.°		Date	Mean Temp. C.°F.°		Departure from Normal C.° F.°	Date	Mean Temp. C.° F.°		Departure from Normal C.° F.°
1930	4.7	40.4	11.1	52.0	2:23	13.3	56	13.3 24	3:15	5.6	42	1.7 3
1931	1.6	36.8	3.7	38.5	2:28	8.3	47	7.2 13	3:17	0.6	33	—3.4 —6
1932	4.2	39.6	5.1	41.2	2:26	13.3	56	12.8 23	3:18	2.2	36	—2.2 —4
1933	0.2	32.4	5.6	42.0	2:24	10.6	51	10.1 19	3:13	12.2	54	9.0 16
1934	—5.6	22.0	—8.4	16.9	3:5	7.2	45	5.6 10	3:13	8.9	48	5.6 10
1935	0.2	32.4	—1.1	30.1	3:2	10.6	51	9.4 17	3:11	6.6	44	3.9 7
*Avg.	1.0	33.9	2.7	36.8	2:27	10.6	51	10 18	3:15	6.1	43	2.3 4
†Nor'l	—0.6	30.8	0	32.0	2:27	0.6	33		3:15	3.8	39	

*Average temperature for the particular dates during the six years.
†Average temperature for these dates during 57 years.

It is at once apparent in Table III that *the early males migrate at markedly higher temperatures than the later ones*—at an average of 10.6° C. (51°F.) in contrast to 6° C. (43° F.). The difference is even more marked when we note the amount above normal—10° C. (18° F.) for the early individuals and only 2.3° C. (4° F.) for the main migration. *It is evident that the later birds are not waiting for higher temperatures.*

This same relationship is also shown within the two groups. The three earliest dates—Feb. 23 to 26—occurred at mean temperatures of 10°-13° C. (19°-24° F.) above normal, while the three from Feb. 28 to Mar. 5 took place at 5.6°-9.4° C. (10°-17° F.) above normal. Turning now to the later males, we find the four arrivals from Mar. 11 to 15 coinciding with temperatures 1.7°-9° C. (3°-16° F.) above normal, while the two on the 17th and 18th took place despite temperatures 2.2°-3.4° C. (4°-6° F.) below normal.

Correspondence between temperature and early migration is also shown in Table III where the average mean temperatures of the last ten days of February are given. These show consistently that the warmer the weather, the earlier the migration, and the colder the weather, the later the migration. This is graphically shown in Chart VII.

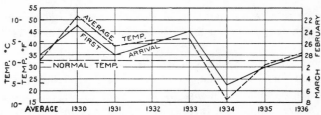

CHART VII. *Average Mean Temperature of Last Ten Days of February and First Date of Arrival of Male Song Sparrows*

Further evidence of the decreasing temperature threshold is given by the average mean temperatures for the *ten days up to and including the day of arrival.* They were as follows: Feb. 23, 6.4° C. (43.4° F.); Feb. 24, 4.8° C. (40.7° F.); Feb. 26, 3.4° C. (38.2° F.); Feb. 28, 3.6° C. (38.5° F.); Mar. 2, —1.3° C. (29.7° F.); Mar. 5, —2.8° C. (27° F.).

It is evident from the charts and Table III that an average temperature during the last ten days of February 5°-11° C. (9°-20° F.) above normal will bring some of the breeding males and transients, but that no migration will take place when these temperatures run below normal. The high temperatures of late February in 1930 and 1932 brought the first of the breeding females on Mar. 1, but in other years the temperatures were not sufficiently high to bring a female before the 6th of March (1935).

The decreasing temperature threshold for the migration of the males is graphically shown in Chart VIII in Chapter VII, where the mean temperatures of the days of arrival of the males as given in Table III are indicated. Disregarding the two values for Mar. 13 which were evidently much higher than necessary, a tentative line has been drawn to indicate the threshold. The formula for such a curve would be: Tm.=53° F. —0.7 d. (or 11.6° C. —0.39d.).

Tm.=the average temperature at which migration took place, d.= day, and 0.7=the constant indicating the slope of the curve. Or in other words, the threshold of migration is set at 53° F. (11.6° C.) on Feb. 23, and decreases about ¾ of a degree Fahrenheit (about 2/5 of a degree Centigrade) each day for a month.

If we return to Chart VI we notice a very large migration in February in 1932 and a medium one in 1933, while only one bird came in February, 1931. These differences correspond with the height and duration of the warm waves in late February, but a further possible explanation for the contrast between 1932 and 1933 lies in the temperatures for the whole month of February. In 1933 this was only slightly above normal, but in 1932 this month was "persistently warm, with two exceptions, the warmest February of record," 2a. It may be that the Song Sparrows had migrated part way north during the warm weather of 1932. As to 1931, the temperatures in late February and throughout March were characterized by an unusual lack of fluctuations; and although February averaged 3.3° C. (6° F.) above the normal and March only 1.4° C. (2.5° F.) below normal, yet the early migration was almost nil, and the main migration was the latest of any year from 1929 through 1936.

It may be objected (see Cooke, *43*), that the temperature at the place of arrival is not what should be studied, but that at the place of departure. But we are in the unfortunate situation of not knowing where these Song Sparrows winter. Since they sometimes arrive on the second of two warm days (they are night migrants) it seems probable that the last stage of their journey was made from a region approximately 160 km. (100 miles) south of here. The mean temperatures at Portsmouth, Ohio, 160 km. south of Columbus, of the days before the arrival of the early males averaged 9.4° C. (49° F.), and before the arrival of the first males of the main migration 7.8° C. (46° F.). (The average mean temperature at Portsmouth for February is 3.4° C. (6.1° F.) above that at Columbus, and the average for March 3.3° C. (5.9° F.) above.)

Warm waves are not local affairs here, but sweep up from the Gulf of Mexico. I believe that the study of the temperature at the place of arrival on the day of arrival has much to teach us in the case of early migrants.

The Song Sparrow is sometimes said to follow the isotherm of spring or 35° F. (1.7° C.) in its spring migration, *161;* in reality, a study of the weather maps shows that in central Ohio its migration typically follows an isotherm about midway between 40° F. and 50° F. (4.4° and 10° C.). This results in getting the first birds here at a time when the "normal" temperature is not far from 35° F. The Song Sparrows can stand much lower temperatures than this in March, *yet a "normal" temperature of 35° F. does not stimulate them to migrate.* In late March they need no stimulus from temperatures higher than average, but a decided drop in temperature inhibits migration.

That time of year is one of the fundamental factors in Song Sparrow migration is shown by the fact that *high temperatures in December, January, and early February,* although lasting one to three weeks with means of 5.6°-10° C. (42°-50° F.) *never bring a migration.*

Migration is conditioned by both lengthening days and temperature. None of the birds is ready to come to its breeding grounds until late February no matter how high the temperature is. A few of the males will respond to marked warm waves in late February and early March, but most stay away until the middle or last third of March, when they will migrate on a moderate rise in temperature.

a. *Discussion of Some Contrary Theories*

Although many observers have mentioned the importance of warm waves in connection with migration, others have failed to realize this relationship, perhaps because they are searching for a rule applicable to *all* migratory birds. Cooke, *43*, stated that "Birds prefer to migrate in spring during a rising temperature," and cited the case of the Robin (*Turdus migratorius*) that arrived at Lanesboro, Minnesota, from 1885-1890 at an average temperature of 41° F. (5° C.) on the average date of Mar. 16, the normal temperature of which is 31° F. (—0.6° C.). But because he also worked with dates of the Baltimore Oriole (*Icterus galbula*) and other late migrants, he could find no consistent relationship between weather and migration as a whole.

Rowan, *162, 163,* largely rules out temperature as a factor in inducing migration, and Lincoln, *104a,* goes so far as to say, "The state of the weather at any point has little if anything to do with the time of arrival of migratory birds."

These authors fail to distinguish between *Wettervögel* and *Instinktvögel* as Weigold calls them, *196,*—the early migrants that are strongly influenced by the weather and the later migrants that are far less affected by temperature. They try to average the whole spring with the whole migration, and the result, naturally, is a failure.

Table III shows that we cannot take even the average for one month and have it correlate with the arrival date of one species; compare 1933 and 1935. If we add the average temperatures of February and March in 1931 and again in 1932 we find their totals are the same, but in the former year all but one of the February and March migrants on Interpont were late, while in the latter all but one were early. Yet if the weather records are studied in detail, excellent correlation is found between temperature and migration.

As Kendeigh, *94,* has pointed out, it is impossible to single out one factor that is responsible for inducing migration. My results with the Song Sparrows support his conclusion that "The regulation of migration as to time is controlled in the spring by rising daily maximum and night temperatures and changing relative proportions daily of light and darkness."

2. *Migration of Individual Males*

The dates of spring arrival of 22 banded males, for which there are records for two to five years, are given in Table IV. These figures (with a few exceptions enclosed in parentheses) are believed to give the actual dates on which the birds arrived, as determined by daily censuses over Interpont.

TABLE IV

Dates of Spring Arrival of 22 Summer Resident Males

Birds	1930	1931	1932	1933	1934	1935
2M	Feb. 26	Mar. 20	Mar. 1	Mar. 8		
10M	Mar. 15*	Apr. 3-5	Mar. 26	Mar. 18	Mar. 16	
23M	————	Apr. 3-5	Mar. 21	Mar. 18		
24M	————	Mar. 23	Feb. 26			
47M	————	Mar. 19	Feb. 26			
62M		Mar. 23	Mar. 19			
64M		Mar. 30*	Feb. 26			
68M		Mar. 26	Feb. 27	Mar. 1		
70M		Feb. 28	Feb. 26	Mar. 2		
111M			Feb. 27*	Mar. 15	Mar. 28	Mar. 17
112M			Feb. 27*	Mar. 13		
115M			Feb. 26	Feb. 24	Mar. 17	
119M			Feb. 26	Mar. 2		
120M			Feb. 26	Feb. 24		
123M			Mar. 5	Mar. 16	Mar. 18	
134M			Apr. 1*	Mar. 13		
131M			(Mar. 16)	Mar. 16	Mar. 31	Mar. 11
141M			(Apr. 19)	Mar. 14	Mar. 16	
176M				(Apr. 4)	Mar. 28	Mar. 17
183M				(Mar. 27)	Mar. 30	Mar. 15
185M					Mar. 16*	Mar. 2
204M					Mar. 27	Mar. 6

( )=first record, but perhaps not the first arrival.
————=present as breeding bird.
*=a first-year bird.

A study of the table will show us that the so-called punctuality to the calendar does not exist with my Song Sparrows, which are strongly influenced by the weather prevailing each spring. The dates of arrival of one bird may range over more than a month (64M and 68M), although usually there is considerably less difference.

How consistently do these birds appear early, late or with the bulk of the migrants? On the whole they fall rather definitely into early and late groups, exceptional behavior in a certain season being usually explainable by variations in the weather. For instance, because of the lack of marked warm waves in 1931, many of the birds that in other years came early did not appear until the height of the migration, and in 1934, because of the exceptionally cold February and meager warm wave in early March there was really no early migration at all. On the other hand, in 1932 the exceptionally warm weather of the month of February brought more than half of the males to Interpont in late February. Thus some males that in other years came early, in 1931 delayed till the 19th or 20th of March, while others that came in February in 1932 waited the following year till the middle of March.

Birds belonging in the early group are 70M, 115M, 119M, and 120M. 2M was moderately early except in 1931. Birds consistently late were 10M (except in 1934 when he came with the majority), 23M, 123M and 131M. 176M and 183M were late arrivals except in 1936 when the former was found on Mar. 8, the latter Mar. 10; apparently the main migration was very early this year.

62M arrived both years at the height of the migration. Other birds that typically belonged here were 111M and 112M, that were brought early their first year by the exceptional weather of 1932. We cannot be sure where 24M and 47M really belonged, whether they were early migrants delayed by the lack of warm waves in 1931 and migrating at their proper time in 1932, or whether they belonged with the bulk of the migrants and were tempted north unduly early in 1932, as 111M and 112M appear to have been. 64M, 134M and 185M came late their first year and much earlier the next. The chief difficulty in deciding upon the status of many of the males comes from the small number of dates available.

It is an interesting problem as to why one Song Sparrow should regularly migrate early and another regularly migrate late. It may be a matter of physiological constitution, and again it may be concerned with the location of the winter home, or perhaps there are other factors.

3. *Migration of Individual Females*

The dates of the arrival of 19 banded females for which there are records for two and three years are given in Table V.

TABLE V

Dates of Spring Arrival of 19 Summer Resident Females

Birds	1929	1930	1931	1932	1933	1934	1935
K2	-	-Mar. 15*	Mar. 15				
K11	- -	———	Apr. 3-5	Mar. 25			
K14	- -	Apr. 8*	Apr. 3-5	Mar 29			
K24	- -		———	Mar 26-28	Mar. 28		
K41	- -		Mar. 24	Mar. 20			
K46	- -		Apr. 3-5	Mar. 25			
K52	- -		Apr. 1	Mar. 1			
K58	- -		Mar. 24	Mar. 3	Mar. 14		
K60	- -		Apr. 3-5	Mar. 28			
K89	- -			Mar. 26-28	Mar. 15		
K90	- -			Mar. 30	Mar. 15	Mar. 18	
K101	- -			Mar. 19	Mar. 18		
K102	- -			Mar. 20	Mar. 16		
K110	- -			Mar. 23	Mar. 13		
K117	- -			Mar. 28	Mar. 16		
K125	- -			Apr. 1-3	Mar. 19		
K131	- -			Apr. 18**	Mar. 23		Apr. 3
K165	- -				Apr. 22	Mar. 17	Mar. 19-20
K181	- -					Apr. 2**	Apr. 2-3

*Believed to be Young from Egg Quota.
**Known to be Young from Bands.
——— Present as a Breeding Bird.

Age appears to make more difference in arrival with females than with males, first year birds sometimes arriving very late the first year and much earlier the next. It is not easy to classify most of these birds into early and late groups. K58 was a consistently early bird, while several (K11, K14, K24, K46, K131, K165) usually came late. The females, as well as the males, show the lateness of the migration in 1931 in comparison with 1932 and 1933.

4. Migration in Relation to Sex and Age

It is evident that most of the males come before most of the females, but it is also true that quite a number of females come before the last of the males. As to age, the individual often comes later the first year than in after years, although here the weather may reverse matters. In the population on Interpont many first-year individuals arrived before some of the adults.

There appears to be no special advantage in early or late arrival. The early Song Sparrows in 1932 experienced the coldest weather during the entire winter, but did not appear to be any the worse for it. The fact that the nights were comparatively short at this time— about 12 hours instead of almost 15 in December—made the severe temperature less of an ordeal than it would have been at mid-winter.

The late bird is usually able on the day of his arrival to wrest his territory from any first-year resident that has settled on it. The late arriving female usually finds her old place pre-empted, but there are almost always other males that still lack mates.

B. Fall Migration

The transients pass through on their return journey from late September to late October.

The breeding females can still be found the last week in September and early in October, always in the vicinity of their nesting territories. The summer resident males usually leave about the middle of October. The exceptionally early molt in 1930, over two weeks earlier than usual (see Chapter XV), did not affect the date of migration. There is some evidence that mild weather during the first half of October tempts the birds to stay longer, while bleak weather hastens their departure.

During October, 1930, the weather was unusually mild till the 17th when a sudden drop in the temperature took place; three males were last recorded on the 15th, one on the 16th and one on the 17th. The next year October was mild throughout the month, the average temperature of the fourth week being 4° C. (7° F.) above normal; one male was last seen on the 15th, five on the 16th (including one juvenal), and two others exceptionally late—October 28 and 31. In 1932, on the contrary, the first half of October was cold and bleak and the birds apparently left early; after the 12th I could locate only one male, and he stayed till the 16th. The first 12 days in October 1935 were cold, but after that there was a marked warm spell for 10 days; I recorded one summer resident until the 20th.

As to October dates for the nesting females: in 1930 four birds were seen from Oct. 2 to 8; in 1931, two birds, Oct. 1 and 2; in 1932, two, Oct. 7 and 9; in 1933, one on Oct. 13, and 1934 three individuals, Oct. 2, 10 and 13. The latest date I have for a migratory female happens to be for a young bird, banded Sept. 11, 1931, as she was finishing her molt and re-trapped Oct. 16; she returned the next spring, Mar. 27 or 28.

2M in 1930 migrated shortly after losing his tail, returning the following spring. I also saw a transient that fall, in the same condition, that disappeared within a day or two.

C. Summary

1. The spring migration normally shows two main flights: an early migration of breeding males in late February or early March, and the main flight of breeding males and females, and also transients the middle of March (Chart VI).

2. The early migration is absolutely dependent on a warm wave the last of February or the first of March, but the main migration is only relatively dependent on a rise in temperature. Severe cold waves stop migration short.

3. The early males migrated at markedly higher temperatures— an average of 10.6° C.—than the later males—average of 6° C. (Table III).

4. The migration of 8 other February and March migrants corresponded well with that of the Song Sparrows.

5. The decreasing temperature threshold is shown by the average mean temperature of the last 10 days in February (Table III and Chart VII) and also by the average mean temperature of the 10 days up to and including the day of arrival.

6. A formula for the temperature threshold for the migration of the males is suggested, viz.: $Tm. = 53°$ F. -0.7 d, as shown in Chart VIII; i.e., migration may occur on Feb. 23 at an average mean temperature of 53° F., its threshold decreasing about ¾ of a degree Fahrenheit each day for a month.

7. The migration of the early males appears to follow an isotherm of some 45° (7° C.).

8. High temperatures in December, January, and early February have never brought a flight.

9. Migration is dependent on both increasing day-length and rising temperature.

10. Some males will migrate in late February if strongly stimulated by a decided rise in temperature, but most of the birds fail to migrate till mid-March, when they will migrate on only a slight rise in temperature.

11. Some authors do not distinguish between *Wettervögel* and *Instinktvögel,* and fail to recognize the important role played by temperature in the case of the early migrants.

12. Fifty-seven migration dates of 22 banded males are given. Five birds came consistently early and six consistently late. Others showed considerable difference in different years depending on the weather and also on age (Table IV).

13. Forty-three dates of arrival of 19 banded females are given (Table V). First-year females sometimes arrive very late.

14. The fall migration of the transients takes place in late September and throughout October.

15. Summer resident females have been recorded as late as Oct. 16, and males as late as Oct. 31, but normally the former are not seen after the 13th and the latter after the 16th.

16. Bleak weather tends to hasten the fall migration, mild weather to delay it.

CHAPTER VI
Territory Establishment

Melospiza melodia, in my experience, is a typically territorial bird, behaving very much as does Howard's classic example—the Reed Bunting (*Emberiza schoeniclus*). Territory is of fundamental importance to the Song Sparrow on Interpont—the basis of its individual and social life for more than half of the year. Special ceremonies are concerned in the establishment of territory; the matter of song is closely bound up with territory, while males show a strong and lasting attachment to their individual territories.

A. The Establishment of Territory

That territorial behavior is deeply ingrained in my birds is evidenced from two things: the elaborate ceremonies that are involved in its maintenance, and the part it plays in the change from juvenal to adult singing.

When a new male Song Sparrow arrives in spring, the neighboring males at once try to drive him off. If he is a transient, he flies, but if a candidate for a territory, he stands his ground—and then the "territory establishment" begins.

The complete procedure consists of five parts: assuming the role; staking out the claim; the chase; the fight; and finally the proclamation of ownership of each bird on his own bit of land.

In the first part the two birds show diametrically opposed behavior. The invader—puffed out into the shape of a ball, and often holding one wing straight up in the air and fluttering it—sings constantly but rather softly, the songs being given in rapid succession and often being incomplete. The defender, silent and with shoulders hunched in menacing attitude, closely follows every move of the other bird.

The newcomer continues to sing flying in this peculiar puffed out shape from bush to bush that he wants to claim. Soon the owner begins to chase the intruder, but the latter, if determined, always returns to the spot he wants to claim. The chasing continues and at last finishes with a fight on the ground. After this the new bird is either routed or both males retire to their respective territories, and sing loud and long, answering each other.

In less serious encounters the chasing and fight are omitted, the first and last parts only being indulged in. When, however, affairs are in deadly earnest, as in the spring when a summer resident returns and finds a resident has adopted his old territory, there is little wing fluttering and puffing, merely the singing, chasing and fight.

With a thickly-settled Song Sparrow population, territory establishment ceremonies of all degrees of seriousness may be seen throughout the year except during the molt; in fall and winter they are not common and occur only on mild days. At these seasons a bird will go some distance to start a "territory establishment" with another male with whom there is no question of real conflict over boundaries. In such cases the roles of despot and underling are freely interchanged. Excluding the very mildest territory establishment manifestations that are indulged in only by a young bird in the fall on some occasions when another Song Sparrow alights on a branch above him, the less serious the encounter, the more prominent is the posturing, bluff taking the place of action. As Howard, *86*, p. *37*, says "violent wing-action and violent contortions of the body are associated with postponed reaction."

When a summer resident returns to find his old territory preempted by another bird, at first the new arrival takes the role of the invader and is pursued by the bird in possession, but it does not take long for an old bird to reverse matters; after a fight or two he becomes the defender and drives his rival. Burkitt, *29*, tells of an old Robin Redbreast (*Erithacus rubecula*) being driven from his territory by a young bird; but this has not happened to my knowledge with the Song Sparrows; with them the old bird usually drives off the interloper, although sometimes he will take a neighboring territory. But as this sometimes happens under no pressure from other males, we cannot be sure that the old male was really intimidated by the young one.

Territory establishment ceremonies have not been worked out in such detail with any other species so far as I know. Howard writes of "butterfly-like" and "moth-like" flights, and of rapidly vibrated

wings, and Pickwell, *147,* describes the boundary quarrels of the
Prairie Horned Lark (*Otocoris alpestris praticola*) which show much
resemblance to those of my Song Sparrows, except that the fight takes
place in the air. But neither of these authors clearly differentiates
between the behavior of the two participants, perhaps because they
worked with unbanded birds. The Micheners describe what they think
may be "a ceremony marking territorial lines" with Mockingbirds
(*Mimus polyglottos leucopterus*), where one of the owners of the
territory "came to the fence and approached the unbanded bird facing
it and bowing and bobbing. One would step forward and the other
back and then they would reverse," *123,* p..126. Closely similar behavior
is reported by Laskey, *100a,* with *Mimus p. polyglottos.*

It is reasonable to expect strongly territorial species to have special
instinctive reactions by which territory questions can be settled. In
order to observe and understand these, however, one must have individuals plainly differentiated; one must study the birds from the
first taking up of territory; one must study two or three pairs intensively at first and finally there must be a sizeable population, so that
territory establishment behavior can be shown. In 1935, for instance,
when there were very few Song Sparrows, I saw almost no activity
of this nature, although I was especially on the look out for it.

B. Territory and the Development of Song

Volumes could be written on the matter of song and territory, but
I will confine myself to a brief treatment of two features.

With *Melospiza melodia* song is the chief means of proclaiming
territory; the taking up of territory in late winter and the beginning
of zealous singing coincide; while the main season of Song Sparrow
song on Interpont is in March before the arrival of the females.

Territory has a powerful influence on the development of the
Song Sparrow's juvenal warble into the short separate songs of maturity. A young bird may be warbling along peacefully by himself,
but the moment a territory rival appears, the singing becomes almost
typically adult. In late February a young bird may warble in low
situations on his territory, but when he sits high in a tree proclaiming
ownership, his songs are adult in form. The young transient males
that pass through in March warble freely, but I have never heard a

young summer resident male warble in the spring on Interpont; upon the arrival at the nesting grounds the bird reacts as an adult. With the young residents the warble is given up in late February and never reappears, all of the late summer and fall warbling coming from young birds.

C. Summary

1. The Song Sparrow has a special ceremony consisting of posture, song and fighting for the procuring and defending of territory.

2. The new bird takes a humble, subservient role, the owner a dominating, threatening attitude.

3. The complete ceremony consists of five parts: assuming the role; staking out the claim; the chase; the fight; the subsequent proclamation of ownership.

4. Song is *Melospiza melodia's* chief means of proclaiming territory.

5. The young male has a continuous song of warbling character; but in territorial situations this is changed to the adult form of song.

CHAPTER VII

Territory Throughout the Year

The actual breeding season of the Song Sparrow lasts from 3½ to 5 months, but the territory is inhabited by the summer resident male from 6½ to 8 months and by the resident throughout the year. It is not, however, defended during the molt, nor the cold of winter, and only to a limited extent in fall.

A. TERRITORY IN THE FALL

The Song Sparrows normally molt in August and September, an occasional bird not finishing till October. Because of my absences from Columbus at this season I do not have much data on the molt of the adults. Wharton, *199*, in Groton, Mass., says the molt of his local Song Sparrows begins during the second 10 days in August and lasts from 40 to 45 days, but from my scattered observations I should expect it to last longer. Magee, *118a*, states that the wing molt of Purple Finches (*Carpodacus p. purpureus*) takes 10 weeks on the average. In 1930, perhaps in some way due to the unprecedented drought, the birds started to molt the middle of July and were through molting more than two weeks before their usual time.

1. *Singing in the Fall*

With the adult males there is a recrudescence in fall, in a lessened degree, of spring behavior so far as territory is concerned. Young males that have settled unmolested during the molt of the owner, are now driven off with appropriate territory establishment procedure, although other Song Sparrows are tolerated. Singing is heard again from some of the adult residents, while others are practically silent. During normal years the singing from summer residents is of irregular occurrence, but in 1930 there was a wonderful amount from both classes of males.

With many of the birds entirely through the molt the 10th of September instead of the last of the month as usual, with fine weather in September and an extraordinarily mild early October, and with the migration not taking place until its usual time in mid-October, we enjoyed a most unusual treat of Song Sparrow music. The summer resident 1M in 1929 sang Sept. 28, 29 and Oct. 4, but in 1930 from Sept. 17 to Oct. 11. Song was recorded from another summer resident—10M —Sept. 10 to Oct. 11 in 1930; Sept. 28 and Oct. 4, 1931; Oct. 9, 1932, and Sept. 28, 1933.

4M's early morning singing has started on the following dates: Sept. 29, 1929; Sept. 10, 1930; Sept. 28, 1932 (we returned to Columbus the day before); Sept. 28, 1933; Sept. 30, 1934; and Sept. 29, 1935. Considerable warbling is heard from juvenals in the fall—from residents, summer residents, transients and winter residents.

2. *Taking Up of Territories*

Many young residents take up their territories in their first fall and keep them for the rest of their lives; others try to do the same but are driven out by the owner when he completes his molt; still others do not settle down until February. I do not know whether this difference depends on age or other factors.

Some young summer residents also choose their territories in their first fall and return to them the following spring.

185M was caught in our garden Aug. 3, 1933, in juvenal plumage and was noted warbling 50 meters to the south from Oct. 4 to 6; on Mar. 16 he returned to the very same spot. In 1931 a right-banded bird warbled constantly west of our garden on Sept. 28 and Oct. 15, but I was not able to trap him; on Feb. 27 a right-banded bird returned and took up his territory in this same spot (112M). On Oct. 1 I banded 134M and found him Oct. 6 warbling south of the third dike; on Apr. 1 he returned and took up his territory about 100 meters to the south of this place, which at this time was entirely filled by other males.

Burkitt's, *28,* young Redbreasts (*Erithacus rubecula*) took up territories in July and August; Miller, *125,* found that with California Shrikes (*Lanius ludovicianus gambeli*) fall is the main time for taking up of territories; the Micheners report that young Mockingbirds (*Mimus polyglottos leucopterus*) do so in August and September, *123,* while British Stonechats (*Saxicola torquata hibernans*) settle in pairs on their territories in October, *101a.* But all these species defend their territories throughout the year. It is interesting to find the Song Sparrow, which defends his territory only during the breeding season, settling on it so early in life.

B. BEHAVIOR IN WINTER

It may be largely a matter of habit that keeps the adult residents of both sexes in the vicinity of their territories throughout the winter, if sufficient food and cover are present. Similar behavior is shown by the winter residents, in a few cases for a number of years, as with W6, as told in Chapter IV.

At this season the male resident may range over an area approximately 150 by 225 meters, a district six to ten times as large as the breeding territory. In cold spells birds may come unusual distances for brief visits to my feeding station, several from 270 meters, while two traveled more than 500 meters (57M and 58M, see Maps 9 and 13).

In cold, snowy weather Song Sparrows are apt to form into small flocks, the organization of which is very loose. On Jan. 16, 1931, I watched 50M leave his regular flock in our graden and join another below the first dike, the birds here paying no special attention to him. After staying with them for five days, he returned to his former companions. These flocks on Interpont are *not made up of "family parties" nor of "neighborhood groups,"* since they are composed of both residents and winter residents, and family ties are broken with the young when the latter are a month old; while mates, even if both are resident and winter near together, apparently pay no more attention to each other in fall and winter than they do to strangers.

C. Behavior in Spring

In late January or early or mid-February, depending on the weather, the resident Song Sparrows begin to take up their territories —isolating themselves through hostility to other members of their species and making themselves conspicuous by song.

1. *Song and Temperature*

Song gradually comes to an end in November, and no matter what warm and pleasant weather may occur in December, only occasional snatches of song are heard. (There have been three warm spells in December of three days duration and one of six days during the period of this study; mean temperatures ranged from 7.2°-14.4° C. (45°-58° F.), or 7.2°-15° C. (13°-27° F.) above normal, the median temperature being 10° C. (50° F.).) But in January song usually begins again, there having been from 4 to 16 days per month on which a fair amount of song was recorded from 1930 through 1935. Table VI shows the mean temperatures at which the Song Sparrows started singing.

TABLE VI

Lowest Mean Temperatures That Started Singing

Date of Start of Singing	Mean Temperature of Day of Start and Two Previous Days						Normal Temperature of Day of Start	
	Centigrade			Fahrenheit			C.	F.
Jan. 7, 1930 - - -	3.8	9.4	12.2	39	49	54	—1.7	29
Jan. 8, 1935 - - -	8.3	10	12.2	47	50	54	—1.7	29
Jan. 13, 1930 - - -	— 2.2	5.6	8.9	28	42	48	—1.7	29
Jan. 13, 1932 - - -	0	8.9	13.3	32	48	56	—1.7	29
Jan. 19, 1933 - - -	7.2	6.6	8.9	45	44	48	—2.2	28
Jan. 21, 1934 - - -	2.2	4.4	8.3	36	40	47	—2.2	28
Jan. 24, 1931 - - -	— 2.2	1.1	6.1	28	34	43	—2.2.	28
Feb. 2, 1930 - - -	— 3.3	0.6	4.4	26	33	40	—1.7	29
Feb. 2, 1932 - - -	— 6.6	—4.4	2.2	20	24	36	—1.7	29
Feb. 2, 1935 - - -	— 2.8	1.1	0	27	34	32	—1.7	29
Feb. 7, 1934 - - -	— 1.7	—3.3	—2.8	29	26	27	—1.7	29
Feb. 9, 1935 - - -	— 3.3	3.8	2.8	26	39	37	—1.1	30
Feb. 11, 1934 - - -	—16.8	—8.9	—2.2	2	16	28	—1.1	30
Feb. 14, 1936 - - -	— 6.6	1.1	0	20	34	32	—1.1	30
Feb. 24, 1936 - - -	— 5.5	2.2	8.9	22	36	48	0	32

There has been some singing on the 7th and 8th of January following two warm days, and from the 13th to 21st following one warm day. From Jan. 21 singing has started in earnest when the previous day was only 3.3° C. (6° F.) above normal; by Feb. 2 singing has been heard on the first warm day, and by the 7th may reappear after an interval of bleak weather at a temperature slightly below normal. Singing appeared Jan. 7 and 8 at temperatures 14° C. (25° F.) above normal; from the 13th to 21st at 10°-15° C. (19°-27° F.) above normal; on the 24th at 8° C. (15° F.) above; on Feb. 2 from 2°-7° C. (3°-12° F.) above and Feb. 7 and 11 at 1.2° C. (2° F.) *below*. In 1936 when there had been no previous singing, it started on Feb. 14 at 1.1° C. (2° F.) above normal, and restarted on the 24th at 9° C. (16° F.) above.

That singing appears at progressively lower temperatures is clearly shown in Chart VIII, for which Prof. Selig Hecht of Columbia University kindly drew the curve and gave me its formula.

Ts.=54.2° F. —0.7d. (12.3° C. —0.39d.).

Ts.=the temperature at which singing starts, d.=day, 0.7=the constant indicating the slope of the curve. Or in other words the threshold of singing was 54.2° F. (12.3° C.) on Jan. 7 and decreased about ¾ of a degree Fahrenheit (about 2/5 of a degree Centigrade) each day.

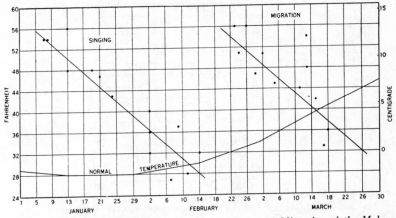

CHART VIII. *Threshold of Singing of the Residents and Migration of the Males. Dates of Start of Singing, 1930 to 1936, as shown in Table VI. Dates of Migration of Breeding Males, 1930 to 1935, as shown in Table III.*

It is of great interest that the curves for the threshold for the start of singing and for migrating should start at approximately the same temperature and have a similar slope, but the dates are a month and a half apart.

Singing and territory activity are well established the fourth week in January at a mean temperature of 6° C. (43° F.). This is also the average temperature at which the main migration of the males took place (Table III). It is of interest to note that 100 years ago De Candolle found that 6° C. or 43° F. was the threshold for growth with wheat and other plants. This "has formed the base used by Merriam (1894) in working out his life zones. This is also the base commonly used by meteorologists" (Shelford, *177*).

Temperatures at which the birds will *start* singing and those at which they *will* sing after once being well started are two very different things. If the Song Sparrows are once well started, they will sing to some extent at surprisingly low temperatures for a day or two. But a sudden drop in temperature, especially if accompanied by a bleak wind may stop singing temporarily, even as late as Mar. 6 (1932). There is also a difference between restarting and making the first start, as was shown in 1936. The birds that have been well

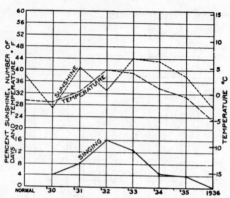

CHART IX. *Average Temperature, Percentage of Sunshine, and Number of Days
on which Song Sparrows Sang in January from 1930 to 1936*

started, and then stopped by a bleak spell, begin more readily than did
those in 1936 that got no chance to sing until Feb. 24, except for one
day—Feb. 14. (During the last half of January, 1936, the highest
mean temperature was 3.8° C. (39° F.); after that there was nothing
but cold weather till Feb. 13 and 14, after which there was another
cold spell lasting till the 23rd.)

Singing in January is not an automatic response to a certain temperature; it is influenced by the temperature of the previous days, and
also by other weather conditions, being inhibited by strong wind, and

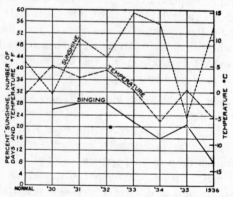

CHART X. *Average Temperature, Percentage of Sunshine, and Number of Days
on which Song Sparrows Sang in February from 1930 to 1936*

sometimes apparently by cloudiness. It also depends on the individuality of the bird—some males starting to sing much earlier than others—, and upon whether or not he has already been singing.

The influence of light upon the breeding cycle has been much emphasized by Bissonnette, *22b,* Cole, *40b,* Rowan, *163,* and Witschi, *211a.* Let us see whether the percentage of sunshine appears to affect the singing of the Song Sparrows. In Chart IX the percentage of sunshine in Columbus in January from 1930 through 1936 is given, as well as the average temperature of these months and also the number of days on which singing occurred, while corresponding data for February are given in Chart X.

The amount of singing correlates very well with the average temperature of these two months throughout the seven years, but does *not* correlate with the percentage of sunshine.

An interesting case that bears on this point of the effect of temperature versus lengthening days is given by Laskey, *100a:* a certain banded Mockingbird (*Mimus polyglottos*) in Nashville, Tenn., began to sing on Feb. 26 in 1933 and on Mar. 4 in 1934, but on *Jan. 10* in 1935. "The temperature during January was unusually high and the excess for the month up to the 12th was 99 and reached 162 by the 19th." For 12 days he sang and courted his last year's mate, and then the temperature "dropped in one day from 59 to 14, followed by snow. Each bird retired to its own territory and they took no further interest in one another until Mar. 3." Excessive temperature had started courting activity at a time when the days had barely begun to lengthen.

2. Defense of the Territory

Hostile behavior towards territorial rivals begins at the time that singing is well established. Other Song Sparrows, that is, juvenal residents that have not yet started to sing, and winter residents, are tolerated. Perhaps this is a matter of personal acquaintance. 4M showed no hostility to two different young winter residents that stayed on his territory through February and one until Mar. 7. Warbling, being as it is, an expression of youth and of entire lack of intention to establish a territory, does not antagonize an adult male.

By March, however, all Song Sparrows are driven off, as are most other birds unless they are too large or too indifferent. House Sparrows (*Passer domesticus*) and Goldfinches (*Spinus tristis*) ignore the threats of the Song Sparrows that learn in turn to ignore these species. Field Sparrows (*Spizella pusilla*) are driven off with special vigor; nevertheless, two pairs used regularly to nest on Interpont in the midst of the Song Sparrows.

The Song Sparrow pair dominates most of the species that come into the territory; transients usually fly away, while the nesting birds merely avoid the threatened attack. The species driven off by both male and female Song Sparrows include: Juncos (*Junco hyemalis*), Tree Sparrows (*Spizella arborea*), Field Sparrows (*Spizella pusilla*), White-throated Sparrows (*Zonotrichia albicollis*), White-crowned Sparrows (*Zonotrichia leucophrys*), Fox Sparrows (*Passerella i. iliaca*), female Cardinal (*Richmondena c. cardinalis*), Red-eyed Towhee (*Pipilo e. erythrophthalmus*), Indigo Bunting (*Passerina cyanea*). Grey-cheeked Thrush (*Hylocichla minima aliciae*), Olive-backed Thrush (*Hylocichla ustulata swainsoni*), Hermit Thrush (*Hylocichla guttata faxoni*), Northern Yellow-throat (*Geothlypis trichas brachidactyla*), House Wren (*Troglodytes a. aedon*), Alder Flycatcher (*Empidonax t. trailli*), and Ruby-crowned Kinglet (*Corthylio c. calendula*). The approach of a Cowbird (*Molothrus a. ater*) is greeted with the anxiety note; if the enemy comes near the nest site it may be attacked by both of the Song Sparrows.

Territorial zeal is stated by Meise, *121,* to show a recrudescence at the beginning of each new nesting cycle, but this has not been my experience with the Song Sparrow. Territorial zeal typically diminishes as the season advances, unless a new territorial situation arises, such as the arrival of a new male, or as in the case when K2 nested outside of her mate's—1M—territory in the territory of her neighbor 4M.

D. SUMMARY

1. Some of the male Song Sparrows sing regularly in the fall.

2. In 1930 there was an exceptional amount of autumn singing, with all the birds through the molt two weeks or more early, and unusually warm weather in October.

3. 4M has shown a remarkable regularity in the beginning of his singing each fall from 1929 to 1935 with the exception of 1930.

4. Some young males, both residents and summer residents, take up their territories in their first fall.

5. Song Sparrows flock to a certain extent in cold, snowy weather. These flocks are not made up of family parties nor exclusively of neighborhood groups.

6. The resident males start their singing and take up their territories during warm weather in late January or early February.

7. Mean temperatures of 10° C. (50° F.) on Jan. 7 and 8, and of 9° C. (48° F.) on Jan. 13 will bring some singing, while singing will be well established in late January at temperatures from 8°-6° C. (47°-43° F.), and on Feb. 2 at 2° C. (36° F.), as shown in Table VI.

8. The threshold of singing was 54.2° F. on Jan. 7 and decreased 0.7 of a degree Fahrenheit each day, as will be seen in Chart VIII. This is similar to the threshold for migration, but occurs a month and a half earlier.

9. The number of days on which singing was recorded in January and February from 1930 through 1936 correlates well with the average temperature of these months, but not with the percentage of sunshine (Charts IX and X).

10. Song Sparrows try to drive from their territories most other species except those decidedly larger.

CHAPTER VIII

The Territories from Year to Year

The question of the return of birds to their homes is one of perennial interest. How faithfully do adult birds—males and females—return to their territories? How far from their birth place do young birds settle? Over how much ground does one family scatter? Answers to these questions can be given in regard to the Song Sparrows on Interpont.

A. THE TERRITORIES OF THE ADULT MALES

On Maps 2, 3, 4, 5, 6, and 7 we see the territories of the male Song Sparrows on Central Interpont during 6 seasons. The last five give the status at the beginning of the nesting season Apr. 6, but

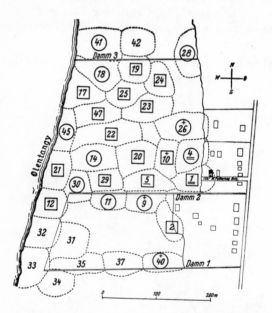

MAP 2. *Territories on Central Interpont, June, 1930. 33 males*
A circle means a resident, a square a summer resident, a cross a first-year bird.
A bird present the previous year is underlined, a line being added for each
subsequent year. (Map 2-5 by courtesy of the Journ. f. Ornithologie.)

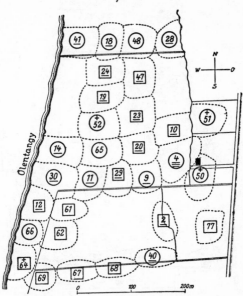

MAP 3. *Territories on Central Interpont, April 6, 1931. 31 males*

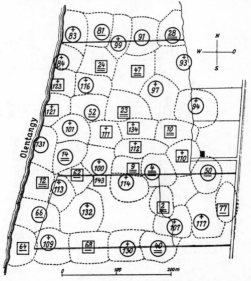

MAP 4. *Territories on Central Interpont, April 6, 1932. 44 males*

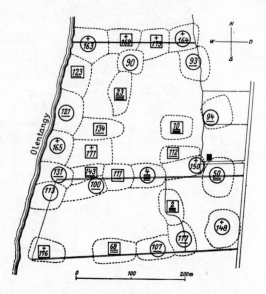

MAP 5. *Territories on Central Interpont, April 6, 1933. 29 males*

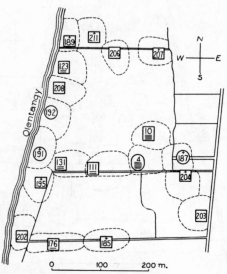

MAP 6. *Territories on Central Interpont, April 6, 1934. 19 males*

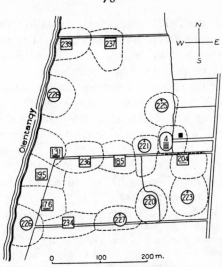

MAP 7. *Territories on Central Interpont, April 6, 1935. 17 males*

Map 2 represents conditions in June of 1930. The reason for this is that the June map shows two males that were not present in April, while the four that had disappeared between April and June of course could not be present the following years.

In the first map there are 33 males (35 in April), in the second 31, in the third 44, in the fourth 29, in the fifth 19, in the sixth 17. Unfortunately a number of the 1930 birds were never banded, hence I do not know how many of the 6 numbered from 31 to 37 are included among those numbered 61, 62, and 66-69. I believe that 42M was the same bird as 48M, but cannot be sure.

The map of 1931, when there was a scarcity of Song Sparrows and yet no destruction of cover, is of interest in showing that the birds did not spread out any more than usual. I have often noticed that a new arrival in spring—a first year bird—will try and try to establish a territory among a group of Song Sparrows, at the same time ignoring equally favorable land at a little distance, that is entirely unclaimed.

Do the males have exactly the same territories year after year? This has been true of many birds, notably 2M, 12M, 20M, 23M, 28M,

40M, 41M, 50M, 52M, 54M, 58M, 131M, and others, for periods ranging from two to four years. But some change of territory has been a
common occurrence; often the new and old partly coincide, but at
other times they do not. In some cases this may perhaps be due to
the exigencies of the situation a summer resident finds on his arrival;
occasionally an old bird apparently adopts a slightly different territory
rather than driving out the birds already established; this was true
of 24M and 47M, in 1931. But a resident or an early summer resident may shift his territory with no pressure from other birds; this
was the case with 4M, 18M, 19M, and 111M; while 185M moved from
the first to the second dike, on his second return, although only one
male was in residence along Dike I.

4M I believe to have nested in much the same territory shown in Map 3 as
early as 1928, although I did not band him until 1929. He has had a somewhat
different territory each year, and in the winter of 1931-32 he moved 30 meters
to the west, although there was no question of any Song Sparrow driving him.
In his early years he was a pugnacious bird, the tyrant of the neighborhood, and
kept 1M continually stirred up defending his boundaries. In 1932, however, 4M
spent much less energy in picking quarrels and allowed 110M—a summer resident juvenal—to settle down in 1M's former land with hardly a protest. The
next winter he moved even further west over into 9M's former territory, and
there he nested for three years, but in 1935 he came back into our garden.

As to changes of territory following destruction of cover, in
March, 1933, four banded males were driven from Upper Interpont;
two first-year birds left the region and were never seen again; but
two adults made short moves: 96M settled across the river and later
in the season returned to his old territory, while 90M moved 180 meters
to the south, settling just south of Dike 3.

Territories may range in size from 2,000 square meters to nearly
6,000 (half an acre to one and a half acres), depending partly on the
pugnacity of the owner and partly on the amount of space available.

B. The Returns of the Females

The female that has nested before tries to return to her former
home, but this is often impossible because another bird may have pre-
ëmpted her place. In that case she often settles next door, but sometimes joins a male at a distance from 200 to even 700 meters, even
though there may be unmated males near her old territory.

In 54 instances involving 41 birds I know the territories of females two years in succession; 20 of these were the same, 16 were neighboring territories, in 9 cases the birds moved about 100 meters, in 7 from 150 to 250 meters, in two 400 meters, and one 700.

On Map 8 territories are shown of 14 females: two for four years in succession, three for three years, and nine for two years. Maps 11-14 show the locations of four females two years in succession, four for three years and one for four years. There are 20 other females whose residences two years in succession are known, but these five maps present all kinds of situations from those females

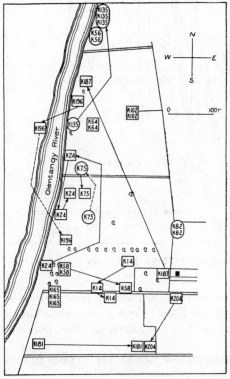

MAP 8. *Territories of 14 Females, two, three and four years in succession. A broken line indicates a change of residence during one season. K24 and K135 were present four years, K14, K58 and K165 three seasons, 9 others two seasons. K75 changed status from resident to summer resident.*

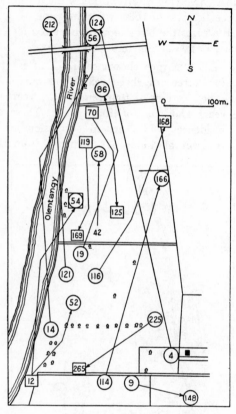

MAP 9. *Territories of 13 Males in Relation to Birth Place. 9 residents, 4 summer residents.*

that stayed on or returned to the very same territories for two or in two cases (K135 and K165) three years, to the birds that moved the longest distances, with a fair sample of short distance moves besides.

C. TERRITORIES OF THE MALES BANDED IN THE NEST

The territories of 13 young males banded in the nest are shown in Map 9 with arrows connecting these territories with their birth places. Territories of eight other young males in relation to birth place are shown on Maps 11-14. 106M was hatched just below Dike 1 in 1931 and found in 1933 nesting 1,400 meters south of his birth place.

Three right-banded males that established territory (two across the river and one below Lane Avenue) were not captured despite repeated efforts on my part; although all three were present in April only one survived till June and he disappeared later that summer. The parentage of these birds is not known. In one case—145M—the parentage is known, but not the bird's territory (Map 14).

The distances that the 22 young males settled from their birth places ranged from 100 to 1,400 meters, the median being 280 meters.

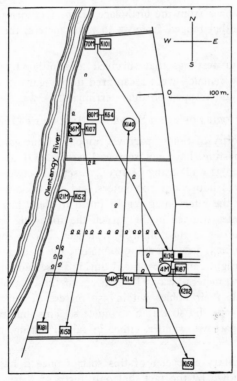

MAP 10. *Territories of 6 Females in Relation to Birth Place, 2 residents, 4 summer residents*

The 15 residents settled from 100 to 660 meters from their birth places, the median being 330 meters; the 7 summer residents settled from 155 to 1,400 meters from their birth places, the median being 270 meters.

D. Territories of the Females Banded in the Nest

Fourteen females banded as nestlings survived to start the following breeding season, but two right-banded birds disappeared before they could be captured. K66 banded in 1930 just south of Dike I was found in 1933 almost one mile south. Territories of five of these birds in relation to birth place are shown on Maps 11, 13 and 14. The territories of the other six are given on Map 10.

The distances from the birthplace of the territories on which the 12 females settled ranged from 45 to 1,300 meters, the median being 270 meters.

Of the 40 nestlings that survived to adulthood only five—four males and one female—were recaptured in our garden; all the others were located and trapped on their territories.

E. Territories of Song Sparrows Banded in Our Garden

The majority of Song Sparrows trapped in our garden, that were later found nesting, have not scattered widely. Of 20 males caught in the fall of 1931 and spring of 1932, 18 settled between 120 and 550 meters from our house, one 700 meters, and one 1,600 meters. Careful censuses over the intervening region failed to show any other banded birds. Six males trapped in the garden the following fall and winter took up territories at the following distances: one in the garden, and the others, 90, 225, 300, 450 and 900 meters, the median distance being 260 meters. Eight females captured during these same periods settled from 90 to 550 meters away. To sum up, of these 34 birds, 31, or 91 per cent, made their homes within 550 meters of our garden, while 26, or 77 per cent, did so within 360 meters. This illustrates how little these Song Sparrows wander, either in fall or spring, before settling down.

The sedentary character of this species once it has taken up its territory is shown by the fact that only three of these 34 birds were later recaptured in our garden; the others were located by repeated searches and recognized by their colored bands. Probably most of them were young when banded. *It is not possible to judge of the survival of a territorial bird like the Song Sparrow—either adult or young—by the birds retrapped at a central point.*

F. Some Family Histories

Genealogical trees of several families have been given in Chart V in Chapter IV.

Let us see where these different relatives settled on Interpont. Maps 11 to 14 show the direct descendants in each of the lines, and the mates of these descendants if any offspring are known to have survived to breed, or if anything is known of the previous or subsequent history of these mates, in which case the earlier or later territories are shown. The territories are given of eight young males and five young females, in relation to birth place; and the territories of

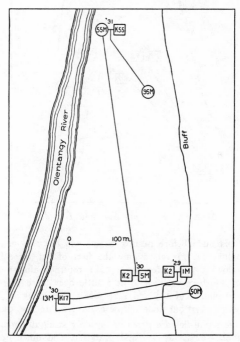

Map 11. *K2 and her Descendants. The date gives the year of nesting*

four males two years in succession, of four for three years in succession, and one for four years.

Map 11 shows the descendants of K2, a summer resident female that had two summer resident mates, a summer resident daughter, resident son, and two resident grandsons. The son (55M) died during his second summer. His son (95M) in his first winter sustained a broken leg that never healed properly; he

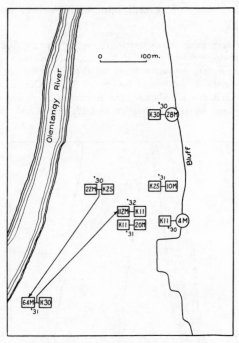

MAP 12. *22M, his Son and Grandson*

was deserted by his mate before nesting began and did not survive his second winter. The daughter (K17) raised only the first of her three broods and did not return the following year. Her son (50M) returned almost to the territory of his grandfather and here he lived to be a little over three years old. Twice I banded great-grandchildren of 1M and K2; 50M's five young in June, 1931, and three young May 17, 1933, but none of these survived, to my knowledge.

On Map 12 the territories are given of my only straight summer resident line for three generations—22M, his son and grandson, and other nesting places of the mates of each of the males. Both 64M and his son 112M nested two sea-

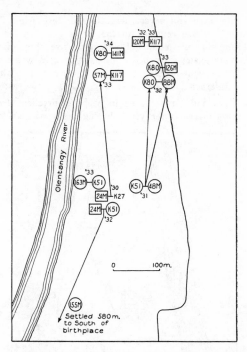

MAP 13. *K51's and 24M's Descendants. See Map 14 for 24M's and 126M's mates in 1932. K117 rejoined 120M in 1933, but after his death joined 57M*

sons, but only one brood of young was raised by either bird in the three years before we left Columbus in June.

On Map 13 there is no third generation, but a number of half brothers and one case of full brother and sister. A summer resident (24M) has had two resident sons that settled in opposite directions from home. 57M is a particularly interesting bird, because he has always been retiring, almost never singing, yet he survived to be almost six years old, obtaining mates during each of the five seasons, and raising young at least once (1932) and probably several times. (In 1934 his mate laid five eggs; two were taken by Cowbirds and the other three were sterile.) His mate in 1933 (K117) had remated with her former mate (120M), but upon his death joined 57 M. K51 was the mother of 88M and K80— the brother and sister that mated; none of the young from their first nest survived.

The descendants and different residences of K28 are given on Map 14. For two years this bird lived in a pretty, tangled spot on Central Interpont, but the third year I found her 700 meters to the south nesting on a dump below Lane

Avenue. And there were still several bachelors in the vicinity of her former home. The fourth year she returned to the dump, but disappeared soon after. Her daughter (K63) was the mother of a brood of five, three of which survived to adulthood, my only example of such a happening. 145M was caught 50 meters to the south of our grounds on Oct. 4, 1932, and never seen again; he certainly had not nested on Interpont, nor in the vicinity, unless to the east in town.

The sisters K123 and K131 settled in opposite directions from their birth place; the latter was present three years, having the same mate during the last

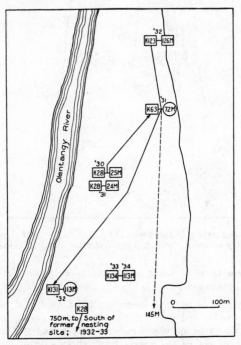

MAP 14. *K28: her Descendants and Residences during four Seasons. Nesting place of 145M unknown; trapped in place indicated, Oct. 4, 1932*

two years. In May, 1932, I banded K28's children and also two broods of her great-grandchildren, but none, unfortunately, were found in subsequent seasons.

If all the young of all the birds shown on the maps could have been banded each year, the genealogical tables undoubtedly could have been continued for some of the lines. But that was not possible and the known history of all these families has come to an end. Of all the birds shown on the four maps, not a single one is alive at the date of writing—April, 1936.

G. Summary

1. Some male Song Sparrows keep the same territory year after year, while others make slight changes, as shown in Maps 2-7 where the territories on Central Interpont are shown from 1930 to 1935.

2. Females have returned to their former nesting territories in 20 of 54 cases, have settled next door almost as often and in the other instances, have settled at distances from 100 to 700 meters (Map 8).

3. Twenty-two males banded in the nest have taken up territories from 100 to 1,400 meters from their birth places, the median distance being 280 meters (Map 9).

4. Twelve females banded in the nest have settled from 45 to 1,300 meters from their birth places, the median distance being 270 meters (Map 10).

5. Of the 40 nestlings known to have survived to adulthood, only five were captured in our garden.

6. Thirty-four Song Sparrows trapped in our garden have settled from 0 to 1,600 meters away, 77 per cent of the birds within a distance of 360 meters. Only three of these individuals have been recaptured in the garden.

7. The territories of the four families whose genealogical trees are shown in Chart V in Chapter IV are shown in Maps 11 to 14 with other territories of the mates of the birds involved.

CHAPTER IX
The Relations Between the Sexes

The mating-pattern of the Song Sparrow follows the second type as described by Lorenz, *112*, p. *327*, where the male dominates his partner and yet there is for the time being a strong bond between the pair. The role of the male is that of guardian of his territory, mate, nest and young. By his singing he evokes a negative reaction in other males and a positive one in the female. He dominates his mate by "pouncing"; that is, he suddenly darts down at her, collides with her, and flies away with a loud song. Pouncing is evidently analagous to "sexual flight" in the Reed Bunting and Yellow Bunting as described by Howard, *85, 86,* where the male pursues the female which attempts to escape. The Song Sparrow female, on the contrary, stands her ground and gives either her mating note, or a gruff note, which might be called a "threat-sound" (see Schjelderup-Ebbe, *171a*).

Pouncing occurs from the first arrival of the mate till the start of egg-laying; it is not seen again, as a rule, till the start of a new cycle. Copulation is a different matter; it appears later—not until shortly before the start of nest building, and it continues until incubation begins. No note is given by the male after the act, although the female emits a nasal *ee-ee-ee*.

Song Sparrows cannot tell the sex of one of their kind except by its behavior and notes, unless personally acquainted with each other, as was proved by my experiences in trapping with decoys as told in Appendix I. They know perfectly well which is male and which female in the case of their neighbors.

The chief interest of the female lies in her nest. She joins a male in February or early March if a resident, and upon her arrival if a summer resident, announcing her sex by two different notes—a nasal *ee-ee-ee* and a kind of chatter. She is dominated by her mate's pouncing and his care and interest in protecting her, but she tyrannizes over him in various little ways. The pair are in close rapport during the whole of the nesting cycle, he guarding her, the nest and young, and both usually feeding together. From the start of building the female is strongly attached to her mate, so long as she is closely associated with him; and, moreover, she is entirely faithful to him.

A. The Situation During One Season

Faithfulness during a whole season is the rule between Song Sparrow mates, partly, I believe, because they are so attached to their territories, and partly because broods usually overlap, so that there is seldom any occasion for a break in the close association of the birds. Birds that leave their territories between broods as House Wrens (*Troglodytes aedon*), *12,* and Bluebirds (*Sialia s. sialis*), *128, 113a, 196a,* often change mates. From a study of the literature dealing with banded birds in this country and abroad, I am inclined to the opinion that constancy within one season is more common than is the opposite behavior, *128.*

1. *Desertions*

Howard, *86,* states that he never found a female that deserted her mate after once joining him, but I have observed a number of such cases on Interpont. There were five cases of deserting during Howard's "second stage" or "betrothal period," the time after a female has joined a male and before copulation begins. Two females deserted just at the start of nesting, and four between broods.

In at least two of the five cases a disturbing factor had intervened. One female, trapped the day after her arrival, deserted and joined a male 200 meters to the south; fortunately other females caught equally early have not done likewise. The other had joined a young resident that was forced into an adjoining territory by the adult summer resident owner of the territory; the female stayed with the victor. Usually territory affairs are fairly well settled before mating begins.

Three others appeared to be of fickle disposition and changed partners, after from several days to more than a month's stay with the first bird. One stayed from February 22 to March 22 with three different males, after which she returned to her first choice and nested with him. Another changed mates two years in succession.

One female left a mate with a broken leg (95M) at the beginning of nesting.

Four females followed young into the territories of unmated neighbors and remained to nest there, instead of returning to their former mates.

I have had but one case of a male deserting territory, mate and young; he could not have been much attached to the site, having been driven out of his rightful territory by cultivation just before the start of nesting, and, moreover, he was evidently greatly disturbed by my placing a trap over his nest containing two six-day old Cowbirds. He moved 200 meters to the west, succeeded in making a place for himself between the old residents, and later in getting a mate. The following spring he returned to this spot.

Two pairs driven out of North Interpont March 1, 1933, by the destruction of cover, did not seek homes together, but separated. One male disappeared entirely, while his mate joined a bird on Central Interpont some 150 meters from her former home.

As to the other pair, 90M moved south into Central Interpont, his mate—K135—going north above Dodridge Street Bridge where I found her on May 1, as the mate of 124M, who previously had had an unbanded mate.

2. Is There a Reserve Supply of Unmated Birds?

Each year a large number of my nesting adults disappear—(See Chapter XVII). In the case of the males, unless radical changes have been made on the territory, I am sure that disappearance practically always means death. In the case of the females, I do not believe this is always the case; so many disappear, and so fair a proportion of new females appear, that I believe sometimes a female, after the shock of losing her nest, deserts. As I have never found such an individual, if my surmise is correct, the bird must go to some distance before joining a new mate. A Wheatear (*Oenanthe oenanthe*) caught for banding as she was incubating, deserted and was recaptured on a new nest two miles away (Thomas, *189a*).

Only once has a new male appeared and joined a female that was trying to raise a young family alone (79M).

Early in the season, before nesting begins, a male that has lost his mate can usually get a new one before many days, but the situation is entirely different after nesting is under way. Males often have to wait weeks before a new mate appears, and the majority of them never get new mates at all. Every single season by June there have been from two to ten mateless males singing on Upper Interpont, an average of 15 per cent of the total number of males in the six years (See Table XXIV).

Moffat, *126,* believes there is a large reserve of unmated birds of both sexes ready to replace losses of birds on territories, but I find very little evidence of this with my Song Sparrows. In two cases, however, banded males have served as a reserve supply for females in need of mates.

176M was driven from his territory by a late comer the first of May, 1933 (a most unusual occurrence); I did not see him again until June, when he turned up 50 meters away as the second mate of a bird whose first mate had been killed. He has returned to this locality in 1934, 1935 and 1936. A second male came late in the spring (March 30) and chose a poor territory, although there were plenty of good ones unoccupied; after a while he was no longer seen, but in early May was found 225 meters to the north with a bird whose mate had disappeared. Two other males have taken up territory in a half-hearted way, almost never singing, and their presence not being particularly resented by their neighbors; one was not seen after March, while the other was recorded until May 20. The next year, however, this second bird returned to the same spot early, proclaimed territory normally, and quickly got a mate.

All these birds, which probably were young, did not have sufficient drive to defend territory normally in their first year, but two of them responded to the stimulus from females much in need of mates, and thus served as a reserve supply. See Zimmermann's account of replacement of mates in the Red-backed Shrike (*Lanius collurio*), *217*.

In 1936 there was a marked shortage of females, for only 10 of 18 males on Upper Interpont had mates by April 6. Two other females arrived by the 21st, leaving one-third of the males without mates. By the 10th of May only one of the six was still singing. Two I believe were killed, but two or possibly three others may have given up their territories. This has not happened in my experience if a male has once had a mate even for a short time, such birds singing on their territories well into June or early July. It would seem that the presence of a mate for even a portion of the nesting cycle reinforces the male Song Sparrow's attachment to his territory.

B. The Situation from Year to Year

Other banders with only a few pairs of Song Sparrows in their vicinity often report the presence of the same pair two years in succession (Baasch, *8*, Burtch, *30a*, Haldeman, *71*, Hamill, *71a*, and Higgins, *82b*), although I do not know of any case of remating for three years.

On Interpont there have been only 8 cases of remating in something over two hundred possible cases. I believe it is a comparatively rare occurrence with my birds because of the many chances a male has to get a mate before his former mate returns, the presence of the resident females being a complicating factor. I do not have any certain case of a female joining a new mate when the old one was available; either the former mate was dead or was already mated, or, in one or two cases, returned later than she did.

Female Song Sparrows do not fight each other over mates. They often exhibit a defensive attitude towards neighbors of like sex, dogging each others' footsteps in a hunched up or puffed out attitude, in the meantime busily eating. In 1929 two pairs often met at the feeding station on the boundary line, whereupon the males would threaten each other and the females do the same; once the latter had a rough and tumble fight.

C. Bigamy

The male Song Sparrow's impulse is to dominate the female—not only his mate, but the female next door. So long as the latter's mate is around, this impulse is effectively inhibited, but let him disappear—temporarily at the other end of his territory, or permanently through death—then this impulse has free play, and the male pounces on the unprotected female much more roughly than on his own mate. He is always angrily repulsed, so long as the rightful male is living, but if the latter has been killed and the female is occupied with a nest with eggs, she heartily encourages the neighbor's advances, and thus one male may acquire two mates at the same time.

Four cases of bigamy have come to my notice, one each in 1931, 1932, 1933 and 1935. In two cases I know positively the extra bird lost her mate while she was incubating eggs; in the other two I assume this was the case.

The two nests of which 48M was taking charge were 45 meters apart along the third dike; the young in the nest with his first mate, K51, left on May 12; those in the other nest hatched May 13 and 14. On the latter date I watched for an hour and a half, seeing the male feed the older young and guard K76's nest; unfortunately the latter was killed on her nest that night by a dog.

I know very little about the circumstances of 94M's doing double duty; he lived on the bluff to the north of us, outside of my daily round of visits. He had three mates that season: first, his last year's mate that disappeared in April; second, K168 with whom he raised a brood that left the nest June 1; and in the meantime, K122 that must have attached him when her mate 93M was killed and she had eggs in the nest.

113M was a young resident who was retiring and seldom sang; he did not get a mate until April 18, 1932—K131. On April 24 the next-door male 12M had disappeared and his mate K89, instead of joining one of the mateless males in the vicinity remained as another mate of 113M. She must have had a nest at this time, that was broken up about May 6, for she built another in which she laid May 11 to 15. K131 laid her set from May 8 to 11. Each female stayed in her respective ditch most of the time; once I saw them meet on the dike, but neither showed hostility. 113M shared his time between his mates, calling both off their nests and helping feed both broods. Both nests held Cowbird eggs; some enemy must have carried off all the Song Sparrow young from K89's nest, so only the Cowbird was raised. Three of K131's eggs hatched, the fourth being sterile, but only one bird was raised besides the Cowbird; a severe drought was causing losses in most of the Song Sparrow nests at this time and K131 had but inefficient help from her preoccupied husband. It was a curious situation that such a self-effacing bird should have two mates, while eight or ten other males on Interpont were mateless, including a next-door neighbor.

Unfortunately I do not know whether the same situation continued during the rest of the nesting season. Interestingly enough all three birds survived till the following spring; 113M got a resident mate in February while his two former mates, upon their arrival, joined other males in the vicinity.

K181 in 1935 started nesting very early along the first dike with 227M as her mate; sometime while she was incubating he disappeared and she mated with her neighbor, 234M, who had a nest with his mate K209 some 155 meters to the west. A steam shovel was working very near K181's nest and probably disturbed her in her incubating and feeding of the two young that finally hatched May 11 and 12 after a phenomenally long period—14 days for the Cowbird and 15 for the Song Sparrow. On May 12 when I visited the nest, both 234M and K209 showed concern, all three birds scolding and the two females apparently entirely friendly to each other. K209 in the meantime had suffered disasters with both her first and second nests; on the 16th she was carrying material near K181's nest, but her third nest in which she started to lay the following day was situated even further west than her first—fully 180 meters from K181's nest. 234M showed a mild interest in K181 and her nest, but I did not see him feed the Cowbird, the Song Sparrow having perished after two days. I was greatly hoping to see whether K181 would continue as 234M's extra mate for her second nesting, but on May 20 the Cowbird was dead in the nest and its foster mother had evidently come to her end.

With the Nuttall White-crowned Sparrow (*Zonotrichia leucophrys nuttalli*) there appears to be a true *personal* attachment between mates, the pair associating closely throughout the year, as determined by Blanchard (*22c*) who used colored bands on her birds. The "second mate of a polygamous male remained with him throughout the winter and bred with him again, disregarding a young male . . . with adjacent territory." These females were jealous of each other; each "created for herself a sub-division of the main territory which she defended *against the other female* by loud singing and fighting, and in which she finally chose her nest-site . . . Had they not been banded, I should have thought I was watching a boundary dispute between two males."

D. Sexual Selection

In this study there has been an opportunity to watch for evidence of female choice each year among the twenty-five to seventy males all singing for mates. The males differ slightly in size, and notably in belligerency, in zeal of singing, in beauty of song (from a human standpoint) and in brightness or sootiness of plumage. I have no evidence that the female pays the slightest attention to the appearance, character, or singing ability of her mate, nor even to the number of legs he possesses. And it is not that her judgment is prejudiced by the attractions of a superior territory, for she is equally uncritical in this matter also. Old females try to come back to their former homes; otherwise their "choice" of mates appears to be perfectly haphazard.

E. Summary

1. The role of the male Song Sparrow is that of guardian of his territory, mate, nest and young.

2. He dominates the female by a species of attack, which I have called "pouncing."

3. The chief interest of the female lies in her nest.

4. Song Sparrow mates are normally faithful to each other throughout one nesting season.

5. Eleven females have deserted their mates, five in the "betrothal" stage, two just before nesting started and four in between broods.

6. There seem to be very few unmated male Song Sparrows except those on territories. Four birds did not appear to have sufficient drive to hold territory normally their first spring, but two later joined

females that had lost their mates, and a third returned his second year and proclaimed territory in normal fashion.

7. There have been only 8 known cases of Song Sparrows on Interpont remating a second year, less than 4 per cent of possible matings.

8. There have been four cases of bigamy, apparently arising from the situation where a female with a nest of eggs has lost her mate and rather than desert them, attaches herself to a neighboring male, in spite of the fact that he is already mated.

9. Females do not appear to prefer the larger, handsomer, stronger males, nor do they choose the best equipped territories.

CHAPTER X

The Nests of the Song Sparrow

The Song Sparrow's nest is a rather simple affair built largely of dead grass and weeds, with a few fine roots and pieces of grape-vine bark, and lined with fine grass and in some cases horse hair. The inside diameter ranges from 55 mm. to 60 mm. (2.25 to 2.42 inches), the depth from 35 to 55 mm. (1.75 to 2.25 inches). The outside diameter varies considerably according to whether the nest is placed in a depression in the ground or is built above the ground in weeds and bushes; this does not depend on the bird that constructs the nest, but on the site.

In 1935 I weighed 8 nests after the young had left them: 6 nests which had been built on the ground weighed 12.3, 13.5, 16.4, 16.7, 18 and 20 g. K204's first nest placed in a roll of wire weighed 29.6 g., while her second in a rosebush came to 27 g. In 1936 K204's first nest was built on the ground and weighed 17 g. The other early nests this season were also on the ground; they weighed as follows: 7, 13.5, 15.4, 17, 17.2, 17.3, 23.5, 25, 28, and 28.5 g. The median weight of the 17 nests on the ground was 17 g.

I have found records of the weights of three other species of ground nesting birds. Five nests of the Prairie Horned Lark (*Otocoris alpestris praticola*) at Ithaca, N. Y., ranged from 7.9 to 12 g., averaging 9.88 g., while 8 nests in Illinois ranged from 9.4 to 24.4 g., averaging 15.28, *147.* Twenty nests of the Meadow Pipit (*Anthus pratensis*) in Brittany varied from 4 to 13.5 g., *101,* while three nests of the British Stonechat (*Saxicola torquata hibernans*) weighed 15.3 g., 41 g. and 67 g., *101a.*

A. Position of the Nests

Since the birds begin to nest before vegetation has started to any extent, almost the only place where there is sufficient cover for them is the ground. The first nests are usually hidden under tufts of grass, weed stalks, or thistles, and are often placed on the banks of the ditches. When suitable cover above the ground is available, the birds make use of it for their first nests; four such nests have been in vines on houses, one in a mass of flood debris and one in a roll of wire, ranging from 60 to 90 cm. from the ground. As the vegetation grows, an increasing number of Song Sparrows seek somewhat higher elevations, although some continue to nest on the ground. Nine-tenths of the nests of the first attempt have been on the ground, two-thirds of the second attempt, but only one-third of the third attempt. In my experience if a bird has once nested at an elevation, a later nest will not be placed on the ground during that season.

A later nest is always built at some distance from that just preceding, 44 cases during the course of the study ranging from 9 to 50 meters and averaging about 23 meters.

Three observers have reported pairs of Eastern Song Sparrows as using the same nest twice in one season: Gault, *61a,* tells of a nest in which young left June 25 and three eggs hatched July 15; Mr. Lewis Shelley showed me a nest in New Hampshire that had done double duty, while Mr. C. L. Whittle wrote me of a pair of banded Song Sparrows that raised two broods in the same nest, afterwards building another a foot away in the same juniper.

Mrs. Jos. Schantz informs me of a remarkable happening that took place in Columbus: in 1935 a pair of Song Sparrows *raised four broods in the same nest* in a red cedar on her grounds. The first eggs of each set were laid May 1, June 1, July 2, and Aug. 2.

B. Security

As a rule the Song Sparrow nest is a secure affair, well able to hold its four or five young to the age of fledging. But occasionally the cup has not been well enough reinforced and eggs have slipped into pockets; this has happened in several cases with second nests of the season, and with birds known to be adult. Rarely a nest late in the season is placed insecurely on its foundation of weeds, so that the weight of the young birds makes it tip.

Nests differ a good deal in the excellence of their concealment, ranging all the way from being remarkably well hidden to rather conspicuous objects. Each nest that I find I rank according to its concealment from my point of view as excellent, good, fair, or poor. Interestingly enough, omitting nests destroyed by floods or by plowing, of 135 nests whose concealment I considered excellent, 55 per cent succeeded in raising young, while of the 64 others only 36 per cent succeeded (See Chapter XV).

C. BUILDING TECHNIQUE

Although the male will carry material in preliminary nest-site hunting activities, when building starts in earnest the female takes sole charge, while her mate often sits at an elevation watching her. Building takes place almost entirely in the early morning.

Nests are sometimes started only three days before the laying of the first egg, but four or five days are more usual. Six, seven, nine, and even thirteen days have elapsed between the beginning of building and of laying; the last two cases are exceptional, other reactions connected with the reproductive cycle of the two females involved having been low in intensity.

Periods of attention and inattention are the rule in nest building (See Baldwin and Kendeigh, *13*). In 1929 I watched K2 to some extent as she built three of her four nests. She was very demonstrative while building her first nest, chattering loudly as she carried material, but while constructing her six other nests during this year and the next, she was silent and secretive. Unfortunately for me, her exuberant behavior has proved quite exceptional. Her periods of attention and inattention corresponded well with those of incubation —15, 20, 23 minutes of work, interrupted by 5, 7 and 8 minute absences, presumably to feed. During periods of attention she brought a load about every 2.3 minutes in the early morning of April 6 and 7, but her zeal was considerably less on April 8 (the first egg being laid April 10).

The time spent at the nest in placing material measured by stopwatch averaged 44.6 seconds in 17 cases on April 6, 52.3 seconds in 19 cases on April 7, and 173 seconds in 8 cases on April 8. The shortest times were 14 seconds on April 7 and 29 seconds on April 6. On May 22 nine visits to her third nest on the second day of building averaged 44.1 seconds.

D. BUILDING OF OLD AND YOUNG

K2, to judge from her egg quota and her behavior in feeding her offspring, was a first-year bird in 1929, yet she not only built as quickly and surely at the very first trial as she ever did, but her first nest was the most substantial structure of any she built in the two years I knew her. Her second nest was a flimsy affair, while her third was somewhat better; the fourth, placed in a rosebush, whereas all the others had been on the ground, was well-built. The next year her second and third nests were better structures than her first, the later sites being somewhat off the ground. Other females banded as nestlings have been expert in building when less than a year of age.

As to excellence of concealment, the records of some females show improvement, but more show the opposite. It seems to be a matter of chance, rather than of consistently good or bad judgment on the part of individuals.

Birds that build very elaborate nests as Baltimore Orioles (*Icterus galbula*) as reported by Williams, *207,* and Oropendolas (*Zarhynchus wagleri*) as described by Chapman, *37,* improve their technique as they grow older.

An interesting situation is described by Ali with the Baya (*Ploceus philippinus*) where the males are the nest-builders, but probably do not breed until their second year. Young cocks "take to nest building late in the season and have their own separate colonies. Obviously they work without previous training or experience, and just as to the manner born, but seem to lack the requisite earnestness and purpose. In consequence of this a great many—in my experience certainly *all*—such juvenile nests are never completed, and they are not infrequently of the queerest shapes and 'unprofessional' appearance," *5,* p. 953.

But with the Song Sparrow, in the matter of nest building, the young bird is in every way the equal of the older one in respect to choice of site, skill in building, the quality of the finished structure, and the excellence of its concealment.

E. Summary

1. The Song Sparrow nest is built entirely by the female.

2. Song Sparrow nests that had been built on the ground weighed from 7 to 25.5 g., averaging 17 g., while two built above ground weighed 27 and 29.6 g.

3. Nine-tenths of the first nests have been placed on the ground, two-thirds of the nests of the second attempt and one-third of the third attempt.

4. Later nests have been built from 9 to 50 meters from preceding nests, the average distance being about 23 meters.

5. Nests differ a good deal in the excellence of their concealment, but this seems to be a matter of chance, not depending on the individuality of the builder.

6. A bird will spend from 15 to 23 minutes at nest building and then interrupt her work for 5 to 8 minutes. This rhythm is much the same as in incubation.

7. Time spent at the nest on the first and second days of building averaged 44.52 seconds, and on the third day 173 seconds.

8. The young female Song Sparrow builds her first nest as expertly as she does her last.

CHAPTER XI

The Start of Laying

The time of the start of laying is an important subject to which comparatively little study has been devoted.

A. What Factors Influence the Start of Laying?

Although the time of beginning to lay must be a genetically controlled matter in each species, nevertheless it is influenced by environmental factors. Most of these factors are probably climatic, while others are not.

In discussing the theories of Rowan and Bissonnette in regard to the paramount importance of light, Linsdale, *107*, writes, "If the time of beginning of the breeding cycle were entirely or even largely determined by length of day, we might expect birds in the same latitude to have closely similar calendars of breeding activities." Yet he shows that in two such regions in the western United States—California and Kansas—the height of the breeding season comes in April and May in the first region, and not until June in the second, the differences in season depending on temperature and precipitation. Winterbottom, *209*, finds that in three districts in the same latitude in Northern Rhodesia birds breed at different times, temperature, humidity, and altitude being the determining factors.

Moreau, *126a*, has found a "single breeding season of surprisingly short duration" in the birds of the evergreen forests in East Africa; he discusses as possible stimuli light, temperature, precipitation, and food-supply, deciding against any "single-factor hypothesis," but concluding that the breeding rhythm appears to be timed when conditions are at the optimum for the young birds.

Davis, *46*, in California found "a postive correlation between the availability of food used for young birds and the time of nesting." Tolenaar, *191a*, believes that temperature does not have a direct effect on the initiation of nesting, but that in early springs "the 'laying-threshold' is sooner crossed owing to the earlier appearance of insects," and Wolda, *214a*, seems to hold much the same view.

Kluijver, *97*, found a decided correlation between temperature and the start of nesting in Starlings (*Sturnus vulgaris*), and Pickwell, *147*, established the same thing with the Prairie Horned Lark

(*Otocoris alpestris praticola*). In an interesting article, Pitt (*147a*) describes the stimulating influence of warm weather and inhibiting of cold on the activities of various species in Norway, and particularly of those that were subjected to the wind.

As to precipitation, in some places this has a very great influence on nesting; many species in Africa, *83, 83a,* South America, *62a,* and Australia, *21a,* not breeding at all in prolonged droughts, while the first rain will stimulate intense activity in nest building. In this country California Quail (*Lophortyx californica*), *184a,* and Gambel Quail (*Lophortyx g. gambeli*), *101b,* sometimes fail to breed during drought.

Besides these climatic factors, there are others of more local nature that may affect the start of laying, for instance, the time at which particular nesting grounds become suitable for use in the same region (see Lewis, *102,* and Lack, *99,* who gives a number of examples).

B. The Start of Laying in Relation to Temperature

The dates of the laying of the first egg each season and also of the start of general laying are given in Table VII.

TABLE VII
The Start of Laying of the Song Sparrows on Interpont

Year	Date of First Egg	Start of General Laying	First Young — Hatched	First Young — Fledged	Majority of First Brood Hatched
1929 - - - - - - - -	4:10	4:12	(4:26	5:6)*	
1930 - - - - - - - -	4:17	4:20	5:3	5:13	5:5-12
1931 - - - - - - - -	4:15	4:21	4:30	5:11	5:3-10
1932 - - - - - - - -	4:23	4:25	5:8	5:19	5:11-19
1933 - - - - - - - -	4:18	4:30	5:4	5:17	5:14-24
1934 - - - - - - - -	4:16	4:29	5:1	5:11	5:15-19
1935 - - - - - - - -	4:19	4:25	5:3	5:13	5:11-19
1936 - - - - - - - -	4:19	4:26	5:11†	5:21	5:11-18
Average - - - - -	4:17	4:25	5:3	5:13	5:11-18

*Estimated dates at which K2's eggs should have hatched, and the young been fledged, if the nest had not been destroyed. Fully grown young found elsewhere on Interpont May 20 must have been hatched and fledged as early as these dates.
†The earliest set was destroyed.

In six of the eight years the first egg appeared between the 16th and 19th of April; in 1932 none was found until the 23rd, although it is possible that one might have been laid the 21st or 22nd, that I missed; in 1929 the first was found on the 10th. (During the last

three years the same female—K135 banded as an adult in 1933—
has been responsible for the earliest dates.)

The start of general laying sometimes follows closely upon the
first egg (1930 and 1932), but in other years there has been a long
interval (1933 and 1934).

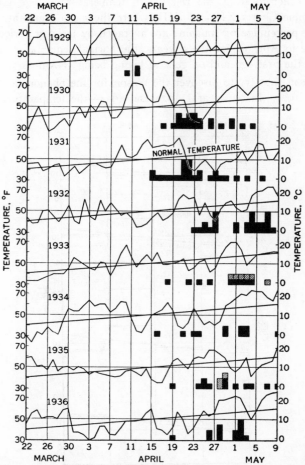

CHART XI. *Daily Mean Temperatures and the Start of Laying. Each square
represents the start of a set. Solid squares are certain dates, cross-barred
squares estimated dates.*

The detailed course of events giving the number of sets started each day in relation to the daily mean temperature is shown in Chart XI.

It will be noticed that laying follows warm waves, much as migration and the start of singing do.

In order to study the relation of temperature to egg laying let us examine Charts XII and XIII, where the mean temperatures and also the percentage of sunshine are averaged by ten day periods from Mar. 22 to Apr. 30 for the 8 years, the normal temperature and the date of the first egg and of general laying being shown as well.

Let us first try to discover the reason for the phenomenally early start in 1929. In two years—1929 and 1934—the temperature of the

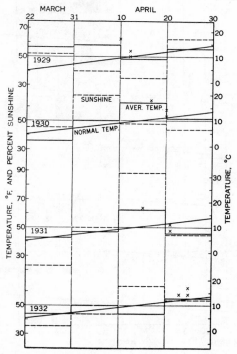

CHART XII. *Average Mean Temperature and Per Cent Sunshine by Ten Day Periods from 1929 to 1932. X=date of first egg, X over X=date of start of general laying.*

first third of April was very high, averaging 6°-7° C. (11°-12° F.) above normal. But *the last third of March* was cold in 1934, while in 1929 it averaged 8° C. (14° F.) above normal, the weather being characterized by "persistent and summer-like warmth" according to the Weather Report. Moreover Chart XI shows that early April in 1929 experienced *much higher daily temperatures* than in 1934—three days having maxima above 27° C. (80° F.). It seems to have been a combination of all the excess temperature—a total excess of 85° C. (153° F.) from Mar. 22 to Apr. 10—and the high daily maxima in early April that brought the Song Sparrows into nesting so extraordinarily early.

The start of general laying shows a close relationship with temperature. In 1930 and 1931 it started markedly earlier than it has

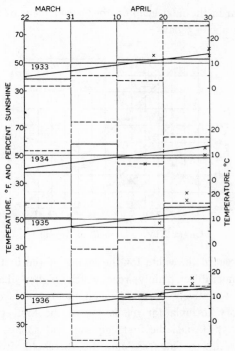

CHART XIII. *Average Mean Temperature and Per Cent Sunshine by Ten Day Periods from 1933 to 1936.*

since then. These two years were the only ones that showed a decided excess of temperature—over 6° C. (11° F.)—from the 10th to the 20th, and this brought the majority of the birds into laying early.

In the five seasons since then, general laying has not started till the last week in April. During the three years in which the temperature of the last third of April averaged normal or above, general laying started on the 25th or 26th, but during 1933 and 1934 when the temperature averaged below normal, general laying did not start until the 29th and 30th.

The lowering of the temperature threshold for laying is shown in Chart XIV. *Here the dates are not those when the eggs were laid, but the average mean temperature of the 5th, 6th and 7th days before.* As will be seen in the next chapter, the development of a Song Sparrow egg takes about 5 days.

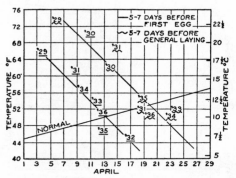

CHART XIV. *Threshold of Laying.*

If we disregard the value for the laying of the first egg in 1930, when the temperature plainly rose much higher than necessary, curves can be tentatively drawn through the two sets of data. The most satisfactory formula for the laying of the first egg appears to be 64.7° F.—1.57 d., i.e., the first egg was laid 5 days after 3 days (Apr. 3-5) averaging 64.7° F. and the threshold decreased about 1½ degrees Fahrenheit each day thereafter for two weeks.

As for the start of general laying, perhaps the best formula is 73.2° F.—1.57 d., i.e., general laying started 5 days after 3 days (Apr. 5-7) averaging 73.2° F. and decreased 1.57 degrees Fahrenheit each day for 2½ weeks.

On the Centigrade scale the formula for the laying of the first egg would be: 18.2° C.—0.87 d.; and for the start of general laying: 22.9° C.—0.87 d.

General laying needs higher temperatures than does the first egg. It is more closely dependent on temperature than is the laying of the first egg, which in 1934 and 1935 appeared at the average time *despite* low temperatures. General laying will not start at lower temperatures than normal until the last days of April.

Both of these curves are more than twice as steep as those found for migration and the start of singing in Chart VIII, where the threshold decreased 0.7° F. a day. Migration of the males extends over nearly a month and the start of singing over considerably more than a month, but the dates of the first eggs have varied only 13 days, and those of general laying only 18, a much smaller spread than with the other phenomena.

It will be noted the curves showing the thresholds intersect the line of normal temperature at April 13 for the laying of the first egg, and at April 20 for general laying. This would mean that the first egg appears with average temperatures on April 18, and the start of general laying on the 25th, just as shown in the averages in Table VII.

To sum up then. The normal time for the first egg of the Song Sparrows on Interpont is between the 15th and 19th of April. Only under extraordinary circumstances of very high temperatures in late March and early April will it be accelerated to the 10th of April. Decidedly low temperatures during the second 10 days of April, 3.9° C. (7° F.) below normal, may delay it, yet in 1935 it appeared on the 19th despite average temperatures during this period averaging 3.6° C. (6.4° F.) below normal.

The normal time for the start of general laying seems to be about April 25. In 1929 it was probably accelerated nearly two weeks. In 1930 and 1931 it was accelerated 4 to 5 days by high temperatures during the second 10 days of April; in 1932, 1935, and 1936, it was "normal" with temperatures normal or above the last third of the month, but in 1933 and 1934 it was delayed 4 to 5 days by average temperatures below normal during this period.

C. The Start of Laying and Other Factors

The amount of sunshine has varied a great deal during late March and early April during the 8 years. How does it correlate with the dates of laying?

In Charts XII and XIII the percentage of sunshine is shown for each ten day period. The average percentage of sunshine for Columbus is 47 in March and 56 in April (see Appendix V).

Only once has an excess of sunshine been followed by early laying, namely in 1931. All the other cases appear to be negative. Laying started early with a low percentage of sunshine during the first two-thirds of April in 1929 and the last two-thirds of April in 1930. Percentage of sunshine was high from April 10 to 20 in 1932, yet no laying resulted, and it was high during the last third of 1933 and 1934, yet general laying began late. The only conclusion I can draw is that the amount of sunshine has no influence on the beginning of laying.

During the period of study, precipitation has had no noticeable effect on the start of laying.

The start of nesting does not depend on the state of the vegetation; the Song Sparrows utilize nesting sites under dead stalks and grass tufts, when the new growth is delayed.

Occasionally laying has started late on a territory that has been largely burned over, just at the time most of the birds were beginning to lay.

D. The Start of Laying of Other Species

A number of species on Interpont begin to nest earlier than the Song Sparrows—Robins (*Turdus migratorius*), Mourning Doves (*Zenaidura macroura carolinensis*), and House Sparrows (*Passer domesticus*) regularly, and Cardinals (*Richmondena c. cardinalis*) and Blue Jays (*Cyanocitta c. cristata*) at times. Other early nesters in the county are Killdeer (*Oxyechus v. vociferus*), Phoebe (*Sayornis phoebe*), Prairie Horned Larks (*Otocoris alpestris praticola*) and Bluebirds

(*Sialia sialis sialis*). It would be of great interest to study the factors that condition the start of laying of these birds, as well, of course, as of later nesters.

The start of laying with the Starlings at Wageningen, Holland, was found to correlate well with the average temperature of April—the normal being 9.4° C. (Kluijver, *97*). During the four springs when the temperature was about normal (8.2° C. to 9.7° C.) the median date of the start of laying came from the 27th to 29th of April; in 1930 with an average temperature of 10.2° C. laying started on April 25; in 1926 with a temperature of 11.5° C., on April 21; and in 1929 with an average of 6.8° C., not until May 5.

With the Prairie Horned Lark, Pickwell discovered that nests were not begun in March and April in Ithaca, N. Y., and Evanston, Ill., "until the mean temperature rose above 40 degrees Fahrenheit for two or more days in succession," *147*: p. 136. A study of his graphs shows the following facts. In March, 1927 the first egg appeared in Ithaca on the 15th after average mean temperatures of 43° F. 7 and 8 days previously, and in Evanston the previous year on the 24th of March after average temperatures of 45° F. 5 and 6 days previously. In April, 1927, the first egg was laid in Ithaca April 8, after 2 days averaging 34° F. 5 and 6 days previously, and on April 11, 1926, at Evanston after temperatures of 33°F. 5 and 6 days before. Here we find a lowered temperature threshold, as with the Song Sparrows, but starting much earlier and at much lower temperatures. (The latitude of Evanston is 42°, that of Ithaca about 42.5° and of Columbus 40°.)

Some birds appear to be unaffected by temperature in the matter of nesting. This is true of European Cranes (*Megalornis g. grus*) according to Heinroth, *76, I*: p. 94, and Pitt, *147a*, and also of ducks, various marsh birds and Hooded Crows (*Corvus c. cornix*), *147a*.

The earliness or lateness of a season has an effect on the number of broods attempted by some species. In an early season Starlings, *97*, *191a*, and European Titmice, *213, 214*, attempt more second broods than in a normal or late season. There appear to be no observations on this matter with birds in America.

E. DATES OF LAYING OF INDIVIDUAL FEMALES

I have a few records of the dates of the first eggs of individual females in succeeding years. Two show a much later date the first year, with a young bird, than a later year: K14 May 2, 1930, April 21, 1931; K131 May 8, 1932, April 21, 1934. But K181 laid her first egg on April 24 both in 1934 and 1935. Other records show the difference between the seasons of 1931 and 1932: K41 April 24, 1931, May 1, 1932; K46 April 21, 1931, May 1, 1932; K60 April 22, 1931, April 27, 1932. The exceptional earliness of 1929 is shown by K2's dates of first eggs that year and the next—April 10, 1929; April 20, 1930. K204 laid her first egg on April 25 in 1935, and on April 28 in 1936. I have three first dates for only one bird—K135, a resident banded February 23, 1933: April 16, 1934; April 19, 1935; April 19, 1936.

The earliest sets are probably laid by adult females, while young females probably lay a little late, as a rule. This has been found true of Starlings, *97, 98, 172,* and also the Grey Heron (*Ardea cinerea*), *193.* With seven Song Sparrows the dates of birth and of the first egg laid are known: K17 June 18, 1929, and April 30, 1930; K80 May 1, 1931, and May 8, 1932; K123 June 9, 1931, and May 6, 1932; K131 June 9, 1931, and May 8, 1932; K150 May 30, 1932, and May 1, 1933; K181 May 31, 1933, and April 24, 1934; K202 May 14, 1934, and May 1, 1935. These birds laid when 10½ to 12¼ months old—or 316 days (K17) to 372 days (K80) of age. It is probable that some late hatched birds lay at even earlier ages.

Females do not start with nest building immediately after having joined a male on their arrival in the spring, although they will do so later in the season, when joining a new mate after having been broken up in their first nesting. With two known first-year females, the periods between joining a mate and the first egg were 20 and 22 days. K14 joined 10M April 8, 1930, yet did not start laying until May 2, a period of 24 days. In 1931 there was an opportunity to check this matter as migration was very late, many of the adult females not arriving until April, yet the consistently warm weather from the 8th on offered most favorable conditions for early nesting. The intervals between arrival and the first egg of seven females ranged between 16 and 22 days, two of the birds with the longest intervals being at least two years old.

F. SUMMARY

1. Temperature, precipitation, availability of food, state of nesting grounds—all are shown to influence the start of nesting in various localities.

2. The start of laying with the Song Sparrows on Interpont is closely correlated with the temperature in April, in one year—1929—being also affected by the temperature of the last third of March. (Table VII and Chart XI.)

3. In six years the first egg was found between April 15 and 19, but in 1929 it was found on April 10, and in 1932 none before the 23rd.

4. The start of general laying is closely correlated with temperature. The normal date is April 25, but this was accelerated nearly two weeks in 1929 and 4 or 5 days in 1930 and 1931, but delayed 4 or 5 days in 1933 and 1934. (Charts XII and XIII.)

5. A formula for the temperature threshold for the laying of the first egg is suggested: $Tl.=64.7°$ F.—1.57 d. (Chart XIV.)

6. A formula for the temperature threshold for the start of general laying is suggested: $Tgl.=73.2°$ F.—1.57 d.

7. Other factors, such as amount of sunshine, precipitation, and advancement of the vegetation have not been found to affect the beginning of laying in these Song Sparrows.

8. The start of nesting of the Starling and Prairie Horned Lark has been found to be closely correlated with temperature, but with some other species it appears to be unaffected by temperature.

9. Although the average temperature of the month of April was found by Kluijver to correlate well with the start of laying in Starlings, it did not prove to be significant in my study of the Song Sparrows. But the *average temperature of ten day periods* showed excellent correlation with the start of laying.

10. Dates of laying of 9 females in successive years are given.

11. The ages at which 7 females laid their first eggs ranged from 316 to 372 days.

12. There is an almost untouched field in the study of the factors that condition the start of laying in different species.

CHAPTER XII

The Eggs of the Song Sparrow

There are a great many fascinating problems of biological significance in connection with the eggs of birds. Although vast multitudes of eggs have been collected, I feel that we have barely begun to study the biologically significant questions related to them.

Let us consider certain problems concerned with the eggs of the Song Sparrows on Interpont: the number in a set as influenced by various factors; the time of replacement of a destroyed set; the color of the eggs; their size in relation to a variety of factors; the weights of sets; and the inheritance of color, size and shape.

A. THE NUMBER OF EGGS IN A SET

On Interpont Song Sparrow nests contain four eggs in about 50 per cent of the cases, five eggs in about 30-35 per cent, and three eggs in about 15-20 per cent (Table XIII). Sometimes there are only one or two eggs when Cowbird eggs are present. Once I found six eggs.

Does the number in a set depend on the age of the bird, on the number of eggs already laid in the season, on the weather, or, perhaps, on the individuality of the female? Also do Cowbird activities have any influence on *the numbers of eggs laid* by the Song Sparrows?

As to egg quota and age, young Starlings (*Sturnus vulgaris*), *97, 98, 172,* and young Pheasants, *209a,* lay smaller sets than adult birds, and this is also true of Canada Geese (*Branta c. canadensis*), in captivity as Dr. A. A. Allen informs me. Some birds are known to lay fewer eggs as they grow old—the Sparrow Hawk (*Accipiter nisus*), *144,* Raven (*Corvus corax*) and Buzzard (*Buteo buteo*), *184,* while this is axiomatic with the domestic fowl.

Kluijver, *98,* gives considerable data on numbers of eggs laid by banded Starlings for several years; in 8 cases the set was smaller the first year than the second or third; in three cases it was equal, but in no case was it larger. Out of 13 sets of first-year females there was no instance of 7 eggs, but in 60 sets of older females there were 7 such sets and one of 8 (laid by a five year old female). The average size of 15 sets of first-year females was 4.9 ± 0.3, and of 57 sets of older females 5.9 ± 0.09.

Several factors have hampered me in my study of these problems, especially during the later years—the poor survival of females, our absences during the summers, and the disconcertingly large amount of parasitism by the Cowbird. When Cowbird eggs are present one cannot be sure that the quota of Song Sparrow eggs is full, unless they number five or have been marked as laid. Also it was unfortunate that the one season when I carried observations to the end of the nesting season should have been 1930 with its shortened breeding season. With eight females banded as nestlings I know the size of the first set laid: in four cases it was four, in two cases three, and in two cases five. Five females believed to be young laid four-egg sets the first year and five-egg sets the second year (and in one case the third). Two females laid four-egg sets two years in succession, and three did the same for three years. K135, banded as an adult in 1933, laid five eggs in her first sets in 1934, 1935 and 1936. With one female I found only three-egg sets—two one year, and one the next, but neither season did I locate her first nest.

One first-year female laid three eggs in her first set and five in her second. K2 laid two sets of five eggs and one of three in her second year, after having laid four four-egg sets during her first year.

The two first-year females that started out with three eggs laid during spells of cold weather. It is well known that sets in cold weather are apt to be smaller than in warm, *72, 147, 175, 194.* Or a sudden drop in temperature may bring laying temporarily to a standstill (Wolda, *213, 214*). Riddle, *154,* has found that cold weather decreases the blood sugar and also the rate of ovulation, for "ovulation in birds is normally associated with the capacity of the organism to effect a temporary increase of the blood sugar above its normal concentration," and "conditions which oppose this capacity tend to suppress ovulation."

As to the six egg set, I believe this was in the nature of a combination of the second and third set, somewhat as with a young bird the fourth egg that normally goes with the first set sometimes appears in the second.

K94 in 1933 was at least three years old. Her first set of 5 eggs, complete April 30, was destroyed between May 6 and 8; the second nest built to the north of the first was destroyed without my finding it, but on June 2 I discovered the third nest to the south and in it were six eggs that all hatched into Song Sparrows on June 4 and 5. My interpretation of the course of events is as follows: if her first nest was destroyed the evening of May 7 or 8 she would have laid the first egg of the second set May 12 or 13; this must have come to grief after she had laid only one or two eggs, and the first egg of the third set must have been laid May 18 or 19, the last May 23 or 24. *I believe that this phenomenally large set had some eggs in it that should have been laid in the second set.*

From my experience I believe a young bird typically lays four sets of four eggs each, and that adult birds may do likewise, but more often lay two sets of five eggs and two sets of three eggs, in both cases totalling 16 eggs in a season. I do not know whether a Song Sparrow ever lays five sets in one season, nor whether she ever lays three sets of five eggs in one season. Only once have I known of a pair *raising four broods* in one season. (See Chapter X.) Occasionally Song Sparrows nest very late, eggs having been found in Connecticut as late as September 1, and in Massachusetts September 2, the young leaving the nest September 13 (May, *120*). The only very late record I have for Interpont was a brood that left the nest the first week in September in 1931.

K52 laid her first set April 24-27; this was destroyed; she laid her second May 13-17 and the young left the nest about June 5. She was feeding young out of the nest September 7 to 15, and scolding on the 19th to 20th. There is such a long interval between June 5 and the first few days of September that I believe she must have laid five sets. She was almost through the molt on September 7. Her mate (50M) did not assist her in the care of this belated brood.

It has been suggested that when Cowbird eggs are present, the Song Sparrow may lay fewer eggs of her own, but this has not proved to be the case. In one instance in which the Cowbird egg was laid the day before the Song Sparrow started her set, the latter laid five eggs. In another nest Cowbird eggs appeared on the first and second days that the Song Sparrow herself laid, yet she laid her full quota of five. Experiments with adding eggs to and subtracting them from nests of the European Tree Sparrow (*Passer montanus*) resulted in no change in the number of eggs laid, *51a*.

We now have partial answers to our questions. Cowbird activities have no influence on the number of eggs laid by the Song Sparrows. The number in a set depends somewhat on the age of the bird, five-egg sets being characteristic of adult females, and four-egg sets of most young birds, and it may well be that three eggs are often laid by really old females. Cold weather occasionally has an influence in reducing the size of the set of a young bird. Small sets of three are laid at the end of the season by birds that have already laid two sets of five each. There seems to be a difference in birds, some adult females laying five-egg sets and other consistently four-egg sets.

B. Time of Replacement of a Destroyed Set

With some birds, according to Stresemann, *184*: p. 377, sets that are destroyed when half incubated or near to hatching are replaced much later than those that come to their ends immediately after having been laid. This is doubtless true of many species (various grouse, for instance) but does not hold with the Song Sparrow; in every case (but one) the first egg of the next set has been laid five days after the loss of the first, no matter whether the eggs of the previous set had just been laid, were half incubated or ready to hatch, nor whether there were young in the nest.

The one exception was with K2 in 1929; she started her first set at the very early date of April 10; this was destroyed the morning of the 12th, and the first egg of the second set was not laid till April 20, a period of bleak weather intervening, as may be seen in Chart XI.

It has been found that the ovum grows very slowly most of the time, but that each ovum "jumps in a *day* from its accustomed rate of increase, to a rate that is probably from eight to twenty times higher." . . . "The time interval between the beginning of rapid growth of the 6 mm. egg (in the fowl) and the breaking of the egg from the ovarian follicle (ovulation) is normally between five and eight days" (Riddle, *150*). This rapid growth is graphically shown by Stieve, *181*, with the Jackdaw (*Coloeus monedula*) and reproduced in Stresemann's *Handbuch, 184*.

C. The Color of the Eggs

Song Sparrow eggs differ markedly in appearance from one bird to another, but are usually fairly uniform in the same bird during one season and to a lesser extent—at least in some cases—from year to year. Often one egg and occasionally two in a set are much lighter in color than the others, appearing blue instead of brown, this condition appearing in perhaps a third of the sets; these eggs are the last to be laid, the explanation apparently being that the brown pigment has been exhausted.

Lack of pigment does not account for all the differences in Song Sparrow eggs in some sets; for instance, the first two eggs of K196 I noted as "grey, smudgy, spotted all over"; the third as having "less outside color than ever"; the fourth as "prettiest yet, green-grey ground color, big crushed-strawberry splotches"; and the last as "queerest yet, pale blue, a few black and blue spotches at far end." As to K194 her first three eggs were noted as "olive brown with a few red-brown spotches and lines, very queer"; the fourth a typically heavily pigmented egg, green-grey ground color, "heavy red markings"; and the last "blue, fairly heavily spotched with brown; resembles Cowbird eggs more than Song Sparrow." Two of these eggs disappeared and the rest were sterile.

The ground color of the Song Sparrow eggs ranges typically from blue through blue-green to grey-green. The spots are brown to red-brown and rarely lilac, and are arranged in an endless variety from small speckles nearly uniformly distributed over the whole egg to a few large splotches irregularly placed, usually the larger part of the pigment being around the larger end, sometimes in quite a regular ring. One female—K132—laid two sets of eggs that were almost a clear blue; some having a few small faint spots, but the others immaculate. (See Plate III.) Only one egg that I have found on Interpont had the wreath of pigment at the pointed end.

D. The Size of the Eggs

It was not until 1932 that it occurred to me to measure the eggs; this I did in the field with dividers and a millimeter rule. Comparatively few of the eggs were weighed, however, as this could not be done satisfactorily in the field.

Measurements of 503 eggs ranged from 17.5 to 22.5 mm. in length and from 14 to 17 mm. in width, the median being 19.9 x 15.5. Most of the measurements for length came between 18.8 and 20.5 mm.; most for width between 14.8 and 16 mm. The longest egg measured 22.5 x 15 mm.; the widest 21 x 17 mm., the smallest 17.8 x 14 mm. The variation in length amounted to 5 mm. or 25 per cent of the median, while the variation in width amounted to 3 mm. or 19.3 per cent of the median.

As to weight, 44 fresh eggs varied from 1.8 to 2.85 g., the median being 2.23 and the average 2.28. This gives a difference of 1.05 g. or

47 per cent of the median. I believe these figures are too low to be representative, being unduly influenced by two sets of small eggs in 1935. The median of the 25 eggs weighed in 1932 and 1933 is 2.3 g.

Schönwetter, *173*, gives a simple formula by which the weight of the fresh egg may be calculated from its measurements and the weight of the egg shell: if G equals the weight of the fresh egg, A the long axis, B the short axis and g the weight of the egg shell, then $G = \frac{1}{2}(AB^2+g)$. He found the weight of the egg shell in small Passerines equalled 5 to 6 per cent of the weight of the whole egg. Calculating g as 5 per cent of G, I found Schönwetter's formula approximated very closely to the actual weights of my eggs; with five typically shaped eggs the real weight averaged 2.35 g. and the Schönwetter weight 2.34 g. But with one elongated egg—22 x 15.2 mm.—the Schönwetter weight ran 10 per cent too high—2.61 g. instead of 2.35.

From Schönwetter's formula (calculating 5 per cent as the weight of the egg shell), the weight of the median egg (19.9 x 15.5 mm.) would be 2.46 g.; of the smallest egg (17.8 x 14 mm.) 1.78 g. and the largest (21 x 17 mm.) 3.11 g.

With domestic fowls the first egg of a cycle—that is, a number of eggs laid on succeeding days—is usually the largest, each one decreasing a little in weight, the last being the smallest, *7a*. Groebbels, Möbert and Timmermann, *66*, in a study of 30 eggs of the Chiffchaff (*Phylloscopus collybita*) and a set of the Willow Warbler (*Phylloscopus trochilus*) found that the weight of the eggs decreased and then increased again at the end of the set.

With my Song Sparrows there appears to be no rule: of 17 sets where each egg was measured as laid, in five cases the first egg was largest, in five cases one of the middle eggs, and in seven cases the last egg.

1. *Average Size of Eggs in Relation to Various Factors*

Does the average size of the Song Sparrow eggs vary in respect to the number of eggs in the set, the parity of the set, the age of the birds, the size of the birds? Data on these questions are given in Table VIII.

TABLE VIII

Average Size of Song Sparrow Eggs in Relation to Various Factors

NUMBER IN SET

		No. Sets	Length	Width	Schön-wetter Weights	Per Cent Increase	Ratio L:W
All Cases April through May }	5 eggs	37	19.7 x 15.40		2.389		1.28
	4 eggs	49	20.1 x 15.50		2.486	4.1	1.30
Known Adults April through May }	5 eggs	12	19.9 x 15.51		2.465		1.28
	4 eggs	12	20.4 x 15.53		2.534	2.8	1.31
Known Adults Early Sets }	5 eggs	8	19.9 x 15.43		2.440		1.29
	4 eggs	8	20.6 x 15.45		2.532	3.8	1.33

AVERAGE SIZE IN SUCCEEDING SETS OF SAME BIRD IN ONE SEASON

	No. Sets	Length	Width	Schön-wetter Weights	Per Cent Increase	Ratio L:W
First Sets - - - - - - - -	17	19.4 x 15.29		2.326		1.28
Next Sets - - - - - - - -	17	20.9 x 15.67		2.643	13.0	1.33

AVERAGE SIZE IN EARLY SETS ACCORDING TO AGE

	No. Sets	Length	Width	Schön-wetter Weights	Per Cent Increase	Ratio L:W
Young Birds - - - - - -	6	19.8 x 14.95		2.284		1.33
Adult Birds - - - - - - -	20	20.1 x 15.40		2.454	7.4	1.30

AVERAGE SIZE IN EARLY SETS IN SUCCEEDING YEARS

	No. Sets	Length	Width	Schön-wetter Weights	Per Cent Increase	Ratio L:W
1st Year - - - - - - - -	10	20.2 x 15.04		2.350		1.34
2nd Year - - - - - - - -	12	20.2 x 15.14		2.378	1.2	1.33
3rd Year - - - - - - - -	5	19.8 x 15.42		2.425	2.0	1.28

AVERAGE SIZE IN EARLY SETS IN RELATION TO SIZE OF BIRD

	No. Sets	Length	Width	Schön-wetter Weights	Per Cent Increase	Ratio L:W
Small Birds - - - - - - -	4	18.5 x 14.25		1.915		1.30
Large Birds - - - - - -	16	20.8 x 15.88		2.696	40.8	1.31
Largest Birds - - - - - -	4	20.6 x 16.20		2.771	44.7	1.27
Median Egg of 452 Eggs - - - - -		19.9 x 15.50		2.400		1.28

If all the cases of five-egg sets and true four-egg sets (a number of instances had to be omitted because of the presence of Cowbird eggs) are averaged, a total of 86 instances, we find that the egg in the four-egg set is larger than that in the five-egg. The same thing is true when we examine the sets of those females known to be adult from having been banded the previous year, and also when we average only the early sets of these same females complete from late April to the middle of May. The average egg of the 49 four-egg sets is 2 per cent longer and 0.6 per cent wider than the average egg of the 37 five-egg sets.

In 17 cases I have measurements of two sets of the same bird in one season. In one case the measurements were the same, in two they decreased, but in 14 they increased. The later sets average decidedly larger than the first sets, 2.5 per cent wider and 8 per cent longer. *This increase in size during the season makes it important to compare first sets with first sets and second sets with second sets.* It is a pity that I have no data on the third and fourth sets, as I was not measuring eggs in 1930.

Several investigators have found a consistent increase in size in one season: Chance with the Cuckoo (*Cuculus canorus*), *36,* Stoddard with the Bobwhite (*Colinus virginianus*), *182,* Allen with the Red-winged Blackbird (*Agelaius phoeniceus*), *4,* Riddle and Spohn with the common pigeon (*Columba livia*), *153,* and many others.

The third division in Table VIII gives the averages of 6 early sets of birds banded in the nest the previous year and 20 early sets of adults banded as breeding birds the previous year. Among the first group there were two sets of five eggs, two of four and two of three; among the second there were eight of five, eight of four, two of three, and two of two. It will be seen that the eggs of the adults average longer (2 per cent) and decidedly wider (3 per cent). A similar table involving 9 adult females and 4 young females in 1932 gave averages of 20.0 x 15.7 mm. for the former and 20.75 x 15.05 for the latter, the eggs of the young birds being 3 per cent longer and 4 per cent narrower than those of the adults, *137*: p. 51. So we see that with old and young birds differences in length appear to be matters of chance, but the increase in width with older birds is significant. Four-year old Bobwhites (*Colinus virginianus*) in captivity lay heavier eggs than do young birds, *182,* while eggs from White Leghorns reach their maximum in the hen's third laying season, *6.*

In the averages concerning size in succeeding years 13 females are involved; with 12 there are records for two years, but for one (K131) for three years. Among the ten "first year" birds there are only three positively known to be young from having been banded as nestlings, the other seven having been banded as breeding birds. Among the 12 second year birds there are three that were banded as adults the previous year but their eggs not measured; they figure also in the third year as well as K131, and also K165 whose eggs were measured the first and third year but not found the second year. So these three groups are not one-year, two-year and three-year old birds; none can be younger, but some must be older. The table shows a decrease in length and consistent increase in width (over 2.5 per cent).

Considering these two divisions of the table, the young and adults and the data on sets in successive years, it is clear that Song Sparrows as a rule lay wider eggs as they grow older, but that length is a variable character.

Some of the old females laid large eggs, but a few did not, as for instance K14 whose first set when at least 3 years old averaged 19.2 x 15; unfortunately she was trap-shy and I could not capture here in 1932 to measure her. K135's set of five eggs laid April 19 to 23, 1936, when she was at least four years old, averaged 19.8 x 15 mm.; she was a medium-sized bird with a wing measurement of 62 mm.

Is there a correlation between size of eggs and size of the bird that lays it? In working over my data I found that sets with the smallest average eggs came from four small females, K125, K181, K111 and K201 with wings measuring 57.5, 59, 60 and 60 mm. respectively, and averaging 19.8 g. in weight. I then averaged the measurements of all the early sets of the 16 females with large wing measurements 63-66 mm., the average weight of these birds being 22.3 g. The great difference in the size of the eggs of these two categories of birds is shown in Table VIII. It must be remembered that "small females" included the two smallest birds whose eggs I was able to measure and also two with wings of 60 mm., but that many others with wings of 60 mm. are not included, most of such birds laying eggs of average size and one (K202) of much larger size. But "large females" includes all the birds with wings over 63 mm.

The table shows a great difference between the eggs of these small and large females, the latter being 12.3 per cent longer and 11.5 per cent wider. The average width of the eggs in early sets of the *four largest females* with wings measuring 65 to 66 mm. was even greater.

Some females with wings of 61 and 62 mm. have laid large eggs, while many with 60 mm. wings lay average eggs and one laid large eggs. But no really large female has laid small eggs. We may conclude that large females usually lay eggs somewhat over the average in size, while some small females lay small eggs.

The last column in Table VIII gives the ratios between the length and breadth of the eggs, the higher figures denoting relatively longer eggs, the lower relatively wider eggs. It will be noted that the eggs in the four-egg sets are both relatively and absolutely longer than those in the five-egg sets, and that the same thing is true in greater degree in the matter of second sets in relation to first sets. On the other hand, the eggs of adult birds are absolutely and relatively wider than those of young birds, while the latter are relatively more elongated than the former.

The width of an egg depends on the diameter of the oviduct and does not vary much except with the age of the bird. If more material is available for each egg, then the increase in size of the egg in one season is shown chiefly in the length.

In the next to the last column in Table VIII the Schönwetter weights are given for the different groups. Eggs in four-egg sets averaged 3 to 4 per cent more than those in five-egg sets. Later sets weighed 13 per cent more than earlier sets of the same birds in the same season. The eggs of 20 adults averaged 7 per cent more than those of six young birds, while the average weight in succeeding years increased slightly. The eggs of the 16 largest females weighed 40 per cent more than those of four of the smallest females, and those of the four very largest birds weighed 45 per cent more.

When I first found when working up my data for the *Journal für Ornithologie* in the winter of 1932 to 1933 that young Song Sparrows lay narrower eggs than older birds, I believed this discovery was going to be a help to me in telling the age of unbanded females, both the actual measurements and this width-length ratio, for from my results in 1932 I found the adult ratio was 1.27, the juvenal 1.31, *137*: p. 51. I did not realize that the number of eggs in a set had anything to do with the matter, so was much puzzled in 1933 to find a five-egg set of a young bird (K150) giving the ratio of 1.26 and the four-egg set of a two-year old (K80) 1.43. But the bird that gave the greatest surprise of all was K202, 4M's daughter that settled within 50 meters of home. She was my only known young bird in 1935; and her four eggs were the largest on Interpont that season, ranging from 19 x 15 mm. to 20.3 x 16.2 mm. and averaging 20 x 15.9 mm. They weighed from 2.4 g. to 2.8 g., and she was a comparatively small bird with a wing measurement of 60 mm.

It is true that the eggs of young birds *average* narrower than those of old birds, but individual differences make it impossible to use egg measurements as a criterion of age for any particular bird. Older birds as a rule lay somewhat wider and hence heavier eggs than first year birds, but since the matter is influenced by the number of eggs in the set, by the parity of the set, by the size of the female, and her idiosyncracies, the whole subject is a complicated and intricate affair.

2. *Weights of Sets*

How much does a whole set weigh? In only three cases have I weighed every egg in a set. K125's set of five eggs complete May 10 weighed 10.6 g.; a set of five brought me by Dr. L. E. Hicks from Buckeye Lake, 40 miles east of Columbus, on May 27, weighed 12.9 g.; K141's second set of four eggs complete May 20 weighed 10.3 g. In other cases I weighed all but one egg; the weights of these sets (including the estimated weight of the unweighed egg), were as follows: five-egg sets—K93 April 29, 12.2 g.; K201 May 1, 10 g. and June 7 10.5 g. Three sets of four gave the following results: K141's first set May 3, 9.7 g., K204 April 26, 9.6 g., K202 May 5, 10.5 g. Thus the five-egg sets weighed 10, 10.5, 10.6, 12.2, 12.9 g.; the four-egg sets 9.6, 9.7, 10.3 and 10.5 g. The average weight of the former is 11.2 g., and the average of the latter is 10 g.

It is evident if five-egg sets outweigh four-egg sets by only the weight of half an egg, that the eggs of four-egg sets are larger on the average than those of five egg sets. Thus the average egg of these five five-egg sets weighed 2.24 g. and the average of the four four-egg sets averaged 2.5 g. The difference in reality is not so marked, as will be seen in Table VIII where a far larger number of eggs is involved. The average weight of the 37 five-egg sets (using the Schönwetter weights) would come to 11.9 g. and that of the 49 four-egg sets to 9.7 g., a 2.2 g. difference. The difference in size is only a slight one, yet it is constant, and has to be taken into account in calculations as to the size and shape of eggs.

The weight of a set approximates half the weight of the female. Huxley, *88,* reworking Heinroth's, *74,* mass of material on egg-weight and body-weight in birds, records that in 12 species of Oscinine birds weighing between 20 and 27 g. and averaging 22.8 g., the average egg weight was 2.35 g. or 10.3 per cent of the body weight. This compares closely with the Song Sparrow where the egg averages about 11 per cent.

A wealth of data on the relation of the weight of the set to the weight of the bird is given by Heinroth, *74;* these values range from 1.4 per cent with the single egg of the Emperor Penguin (*Aptenodytes forsteri*) to 100 per cent with the large sets of 8 to 13 eggs of European Titmice, and even higher—110 to 120 per cent with the Goldeneye (*Bucephala clangula*), Golden-crested Wren (*Regulus regulus*) and several small shorebirds, 125 per cent with the Spotted Crake (*Porzana porzana*) and 130 per cent with the Harlequin Quail (*Coturnix dele-gorguei*).

E. INHERITANCE OF COLOR, SIZE AND SHAPE

There have been four instances where I could compare the eggs of mothers and daughters and one case of two sisters. Twice mother and daughter were present during the same year, but the other times I had to depend on the description of the eggs.

In the two cases where the mother was present only one year, the eggs of the daughters seemed to match the descriptions of their mother's eggs fairly well. But in the other two cases the eggs differed markedly. Some of K51's eggs were brown and muddy-looking, others bluish with small brown spots. The eggs of her daughter K80 were strikingly handsome, with green-blue ground color and large splotches of red-brown, crushed-strawberry and lavender. K187's eggs were greenish with small red-brown speckles all over the surface; K202's, on the contrary had large, handsome, irregular splotches.

As to size and shape, K51's eggs were wide and K80's elongated both years; K107's were more elongated than were her daughter's, while with the other relatives there was a striking difference in size.

K187 laid eggs slightly under normal size, 19.3 x 14.5 mm. with a Schönwetter weight of 2.13 g., but her daughter K202 laid astonishingly large eggs, 20 x 15.9 mm., averaging 2.5 g. in weight.

K152's eggs were nearly normal, 19.75 x 14.75 mm. with a Schönwetter weight of 2.2 g., but her daughter K181 laid very small eggs, 18 x 14 mm. with a Schönwetter weight of only 1.8 g. K152 herself was somewhat larger than average, with a wing of 62.5 mm. and a weight of 21.8 g. on March 30, 1933, but K181 was very small with a wing of 59 and weighing only 17.1 g. on April 9, 1934. The father and brother—a nest mate of K181's—were also small, the former (121M) having a wing measurement of 65 mm. and weighing 23 g. on March 18, and the latter (212M) with a like wing measurement, but weighing only 19.6 g. on April 16.

As to the two sisters, K123's eggs were much more finely speckled than were K131's that had large, irregular blotches. The shape differed also, K131's four eggs being long and pear-shaped and K123's five eggs small and more rounded. Atwood, *7,* found that the eggs of White Leghorn sisters varied in weight as much as random samples from the same flock.

At a meeting of the British Ooologists Association a discussion was held on the question "Are the characters and colouration of eggs hereditary?", *9,* but the talk was entirely theoretical, not a single fact being presented. This, perhaps, is no more than could have been expected, for if eggs are collected, there will be no offspring to show any inheritance.

Wynne-Edwards, *215,* suggests that the "factor for egg-colour" in the parasitic Cuckoos may be "sex-linked," but this view is criticized by Punnett, *149b.*

F. SUMMARY

1. Song Sparrow nests on Interpont contain 4 eggs in about 50 per cent of the cases, 5 eggs in about 30 to 35 per cent and 3 eggs in about 15 to 20 per cent.

2. A young bird typically lays four sets of 4 eggs each, although sometimes starting out with 3 or 5 eggs. An older bird may lay four sets of 4 eggs each, or two sets of 5 and probably two of 3.

3. The one set of 6 eggs found on Interpont appeared to have some eggs in it that should have belonged to an earlier set.

4. The addition of Cowbird eggs does not influence the number of eggs laid by the Song Sparrow.

5. When a nest is destroyed, the first egg of the next set is laid five days afterwards.

6. Forty-four fresh eggs varied in weight from 1.8 to 2.85 g., the average being 2.28 g.

7. Schönwetter's formula for finding the weight of an egg from its measurements and the weight of the egg shell is given.

8. There is no regular decrease or increase in size of the eggs within a set with the Song Sparrows.

9. The average egg in a four-egg set is 2 per cent longer and 4 per cent heavier than the average egg in a five-egg set (Table VIII).

10. When 17 early sets are compared with 17 later sets of the same birds in the same season, the eggs of the later sets are found to average 8 per cent longer and 13 per cent heavier.

11. When early sets of young and adult birds are compared, the latter are found to average 3 per cent wider and 7 per cent heavier.

12. When early sets of the same birds are compared two and three years in succession, an increase in width of 2.5 per cent is found.

13. Four small females laid very small eggs, while the 16 largest females laid eggs 41 per cent larger.

14. Some small and medium sized females have laid large eggs.

15. Although the eggs of young birds *average* narrower than those of old birds, measurements cannot be depended upon to give a clue to the age of a particular bird.

16. Five-egg sets ranged from 10 to 12.9 g. in weight, and four-egg sets from 9.6 to 10.5 g.

17. With Song Sparrows the weight of a set is approximately half the weight of the bird that laid it. With other birds the weight of the set may vary from 1.4 per cent to 130 per cent of the weight of the bird.

18. Evidence for the inheritance of color, shape, and size of eggs is negative.

CHAPTER XIII

Incubation

Incubation is performed by the female alone, but the male guards the territory and calls his mate off the nest by means of a special "signal song."

A. THE ROLE OF THE FEMALE

The incubation patch begins to appear from four to six days before the first egg is laid, at which time the area is entirely bare and liberally supplied with blood vessels.

Eggs are laid in the early morning on succeeding days. There has been but one exception—K202, the young bird with the very large eggs, laid May 1, 2, 4, and 5 so far as I know. The skipping of a day in this case is perhaps explainable by the unusual size of her eggs and of the character of the weather from April 30 to May 5, 1935, this period averaging 5° C. (9° F.) below normal.

Incubation usually begins before the set is complete, since it is most common for eggs to hatch on two days. In only 11 cases am I sure that all eggs hatched on the same day, although in 21 other cases this might have happened. In 42 cases they hatched during two days and in four cases on three days. A female may not be consistent in the matter of starting to incubate as the following data show: K2's second set hatched May 4 and 5, 1929, while her fourth hatched July 7, 8, and 9. The next year K7 hatched her first brood in one day, but her second brood in three days, while K20 hatched her first in one day and second in two.

1. *Length of Incubation*

Length of incubation calculated from the laying of the last egg to its hatching has taken 12 days in 17 cases, 13 days in 12 cases, 14 in two cases and 15 in one case. Eggs seldom hatch in exactly 12 or 13 days, usually taking a few hours more. One of the females that took 14 days to hatch her eggs was young—K17 with her first set; the other was at least two years old—K31, the bird whose sets contained only three eggs. The 15 day incubation will be discussed later.

Twelve and thirteen day incubations are not correlated with time of year, both appearing early and late in the season. K2 hatched her second and fourth sets in 1929 in 12 days, and her first set in 1930 in 13 days.

2. The Rhythm of Incubation

The female comes off the nest every 20 to 30 minutes, and stays off from 6 to 8 minutes as a rule. This rhythm is evidently correlated with hunger. Of 64 records of intervals between visits to a baiting place of 1M and K2 in March and April, 1929, 16 lasted between 7 and 17 minutes, *42 between 18 and 33 minutes,* and 6 between 35 and 45 minutes, *the median interval being 25 minutes.* The birds usually ate for about four minutes at a time.

Stevenson found that it took 2 hours and 14 minutes for a Song Sparrow to empty completely its stomach and intestines and that the average weight of stomach contents of adults was 0.261 g., and of juvenals 0.335 g., the maximum weight being 0.39 and 0.73 respectively. He calculates that in summer with 14½ hours of daylight the Song Sparrow would consume 7½ meals per day, totalling 1.947 g. "or 9.6 per cent of the body weight of the adult," *180.* But this is not the way a Song Sparrow behaves; it eats 30 to 50 times a day, but probably seldom eats as much as 0.26 g. at one meal except late in the day. We saw in Table I that the Song Sparrow averages 1 gram heavier at night than in the morning, which means it must eat a full gram of food late in the day. Stevenson's calculation would allow it less than a gram for all the rest of the day. A Song Sparrow must eat more than 10 per cent of its weight daily; I believe it eats 15 per cent or more of its weight. Groebbels cites a Chaffinch (*Fringilla coelebs*) weighing 22 g. as eating 3.18 g. of seeds per day or 13.2 per cent of its weight, *67*: p. 719, while Schildmacher found a Weaver bird (*Quelea quelea*) weighing 18 g. eating from 28 to 33 per cent of its weight, *170.*

Observations on four incubations of three females are given in Table IX; the same male is involved in the first three cases, but a different one in the fourth.

TABLE IX

Length of Periods On and Off the Nest During Incubation

Birds		Dates	Mean Temp.		No. Hrs. Watched	Periods On the Nest			Periods Off the Nest			Per Cent of time Spent on the Nest	Length of Incuba-tion Period
			C.°	F.°		No. Periods	Mean Length	Range	No. Periods	Mean Length	Range		
							in Minutes			in Minutes			
K7	1M	4:23-5:3'30	13.9	57	17	22	30.5	14-55	27	6.0	4-17	80.4	12¼ days
K2	1M	4:23-5:4'29	12.8	55	30	35	30.0	21-71	46	7.8	3-21	79.4	12¼ days
K2	1M	6:27-7:6'29	21.1	70	21	23	27.0	20-63	30	9.0	5-14	75.0	12 days
K3	4M	6:25-7:5'29	20.6	69	24	27	20.0	10-40	30	8.0	3-15	71.4	?

The two records early in the season, although of different females and different years, show almost the same mean period on the nest. It is of interest to note that the male was the same in both cases; this similarity may be significant because of his role in calling the female off the nest.

The two records later in the season show shorter periods on and longer periods off than the two early ones. With K2 this would seem to be an adaptation to warmer temperature, although there was no really hot weather during her last incubation. But K3 evidently had a different rhythm from the other two females, for she had a markedly shorter period on the nest. How much of this difference is due to the different male we do not know. K2 never normally spent less than 20 minutes on the nest, and K7 did so but once, but with K3 half of her observed periods ranged between 10 and 19 minutes. Two of K2's very long periods on—63 and 68 minutes—were both during storms, while the longest—71 minutes—occurred on a bleak and windy afternoon. K7's period of 55 minutes occurred from 5.40 to 6.32 A. M. April 26.

In every case but K2's second record the longer periods off came during the first two days of incubation. During K2's first incubation the periods on were longest at the beginning and end and shortest in the middle, showing in general an inverse relation to the temperature. The periods off consistently decreased in length, becoming very short the last day before hatching. However, her last incubation did not corroborate these findings.

Dr. S. P. Baldwin and Dr. S. K. Kendeigh very kindly sent me summaries of 5 records of Song Sparrow incubation taken near Cleveland, Ohio, by means of the potentiometer, an electrical device by which the temperature of the nest is shown and hence the periods of time spent by a bird on and off the nest can be studied, 95. A total of 29 days are represented extending between May 11 and August 8. No consistent change in routine is shown near the end of incubation, and no consistent relationship to *daily* temperature except that there is a tendency for the periods *off the nest to vary with the temperature*. For instance, in the May nest the daily average period off the nest was 4.1 minutes with a mean temperature of 43° F. and increased regularly to a maximum of 7.5 minutes when the temperature reached 54° F., but the other records are not equally consistent.

When the *average* of each of the 5 records is considered, we find a consistent relationship with the average mean temperature of the period of observation, as seen in the following resumé where the average length in minutes of the periods on and off the nest is given:

48° F.: periods off, 5.7; on, 19.3; number off per day, 30-39, averaging 33.

66° F.: periods off, 7.8; on, 24.9; number off per day, 17-34, averaging 28.

68° F.: periods off, 9.2; on, 28.5; number off per day, 23-28, averaging 27.

75° F.: periods off, 9.3; on, 36.1; number off per day, 18-24, averaging 19.

80° F.: periods off, 16.5; on, 42.4; number off per day, 14-21, averaging 15.

The numbers of days covered by these records were as follows: 6, 11, 3, 5 and 4 respectively; each extended to the day of hatching. The percentage of time spent on the nest during the day ranged between 76 and 80 for the first 4 records, but dropped to 72 in the last. In the first 2 cases the length of incubation was known, viz., 12 days.

It is evident from these averages that the cooler the weather the shorter were the periods both on and off the nest, while the warmer the weather, the longer both periods were. Perhaps the explanation is that the cooler the weather the oftener the bird feels hungry, yet at the same time low temperature stimulates her to return promptly to her eggs. The first 4 birds do not differ widely from my Song Sparrows, but the last one (nesting during the hot, dry weather of late July, 1930) exhibited a very much slower rhythm than any of the other birds in Cleveland or Columbus.

My records as shown in Table IX agree in the main with those from Cleveland except for the fact that periods on the nest were longer in cool weather than in warm.

During 1934, 1935 and 1936 I noted whether or not the female was on the nest at each visit during incubation. During the first year a total of 57 visits in May showed the bird incubating at 43 or 75.4 per cent. During 1935 a total of 102 visits in May and early June found the female on the nest at 76 or 74.5 per cent, and in 1936 62 visits found her on duty 47 times (75.8 per cent). The record of one female, however, is not included in the 1935 data—namely K181 who took 15 days in which to hatch her own eggs and 14 for the Cowbird; during the first nine days after her set was complete she was found on the nest twice and absent 7 times. A steam shovel working near her nest doubtless disturbed her; moreover she lost her mate and had to attach her neighbor. Her own baby disappeared two days after hatching and the Cowbird did not thrive, being an undersized creature that died at the age of 9½ days because not brooded at night when all normal birds would have been well feathered. (See Appendix IV.) The year before K181 had not been able to raise her own young besides a Cowbird, and the latter did not leave the nest till 12 days old. K181 nested early both years, but her incubating and caring-for-young instaincts appear to have been weak.

B. The Role of the Male

The male protects the territory, calls the female off the nest many times a day and guards both the nest and her during her absence; his superfluous energies find expression in a considerable amount of singing.

Some of his singing has a particular meaning during incubation, namely what I call the "signal song." The male stops his ordinary singing and disappears into the grass, then after some minutes he flies to a new perch and gives one or more songs suddenly and loudly. No particular song is preferred for this purpose; it is merely the manner of delivery and usually proximity to the nest that distinguish it. It may be given less than two meters from the nest and occasionally as far as 10 meters, but about 6 meters is a more common distance.

During two storms 1M gave no signal song until their cessation, although each lasted about an hour. Again when boys were near the nest, he failed to give it at the usual 20 to 25 minute interval (see the last period on April 29 in Table X). However, a male will call his mate off when an observer is standing within 5 meters of the nest, a situation in which the female refuses to return to the nest until the person withdraws.

The female often comes off the nest at once, but sometimes she merely answers with *ee-ee-ee* and remains; she may come off within a few minutes or stay until a second signal song some time later; or she may come off with no reference to her mate. In K2's first incubation she came off 29 times in answer to his songs and 13 times independently in the 30 hours that I watched her. During her third incubation—due to the anomalous situation in which her mate was not allowed in the vicinity of her own nest, since she had built over the border in 4M's land—she came off only 9 times in answer to his songs and 17 times of her own accord in 21 hours of observation. K3 in her last incubation left the nest 12 times in response to 4M's songs and 16 times by herself; in this case 4M had taken a temporary vacation from nesting duties at the far end of his territory.

Table X shows the number of times K2 and K7 came off the nest in response to 1M's signal song during several hours observation on one day. The regularity of most of the periods on the nest of each bird is of considerable interest.

TABLE X

Detailed Records of Incubation During One Day

	K2 on Apr. 29, 1929					K7 on Apr. 26, 1930			
	Activity of K2		Activity of 1M			Activity of K7		Activity of 1M	
Hours	Minutes On	Minutes Off	Sing-ing	Guard-ing	Hours	Minutes On	Minutes Off	Sing-ing	Guard-ing
7.55-		8		g	5.00-		6		
10.55	24		s		1.30	52			
		6		g			8		
	26		s			48			
		6		g			6		
	22		s			28		s	
		5		g			5		g
	27		s			27			
		6		g			5	s	g
	29		s			28			
		6.5		g			7		g
1.05-						27			
4.05	21		s				4		g
		5				29			
		7.5	s	g			5		
	21.5		s	g		29			
		8					7		g
	27.5		s			14		s	
		7.5					7		g
	21					21		s	
		5					5		
	33					32			
							9		
						35			
							6		g
						25			

This table shows 1M as a devoted guardian in 1929, but less zealous in this regard in 1930.

Both days give him a better record as to guarding his nest, i.e. remaining in close proximity, in the meantime singing, than occurred at other times. During K2's first incubation 1M guarded 20 out of a

possible 46 times while I watched, but during her third incubation he
could not guard at all until July 6, when he finally won from 4M the
area around the nest. 4M guarded K3's nest a good deal during her
third incubation, but very little during her last. Usually the male
guards for only a few minutes, leaving to join his mate and often
escorting her back.

Although I watched K2's nest a total of 30 hours during her first incubation,
only twice did 1M go to the nest during that time: on April 16 at 1:55 he went
to the nest, K2 said *ee-ee-ee* and left; he left at 2:02. On April 29 he visited the
nest at 3:38 P. M., just before his mate returned to it. (The young hatched May
4 and 5.) The next year he visited the nest after K7 had been incubating three
days; she was off the nest at the time and returned as he was leaving; he went
towards her making strange little noises. Only three times have I found other
males at nests containing eggs.

Incubation is a subject that has been much neglected. Bussmann,
31, gives sample records of incubation rhythm with a number of
species which he studied with the Terragraph, Kluijver, *97,* did similar
work on the Starling (*Sturnus vulgaris*) and Baldwin and Kendeigh,
13, on the House Wren (*Troglodytes aedon*), all of these birds showing many periods on and off during the day. The Bobwhite (*Colinus
virginianus*) comes off the nest only once a day, but stays off for
several hours, *182.*

C. Summary

1. Incubation is performed by the female alone.

2. The incubation patch begins to appear 4 to 6 days before the
first egg is laid, by which time the area is entirely bare.

3. Incubation usually lasts slightly over 12 or 13 days, but rarely
has taken 14 and 15 days.

4. The rhythm of incubation consists in 20 to 30 minutes on the
nest and 6 to 8 minutes off.

5. This rhythm seems to be related to hunger.

6. A Song Sparrow probably eats from 10 to 15 per cent of its
weight each day.

7. Table IX gives average periods on and off the nest for two
incubations of K2, one of K7 and one of K3, the mate in the first three
cases being 1M, in the last 4M.

8. The two incubations early in the season—with different females but the same male—showed a marked similarity in the periods on the nest and the total percentage of time spent incubating—80 per cent.

9. K2's incubation late in the season showed a shorter average period on the nest and longer periods off, the total amount of incubation coming to 75 per cent.

10. K3 showed a much shorter period on the nest than did the other two birds, her total amounting to 71 per cent.

11. During 1934, 1935 and 1936 incubating females (except K181) were found on the nest at 75 per cent of 221 visits.

12. K181 was found off the nest 7 out of 9 times during the first 9 days of incubation; her eggs took 16 days to hatch and her young did not thrive.

13. The male guards the territory, nest and mate, and does considerable singing.

14. He calls his mate off the nest with a sudden loud song.

15. Under normal conditions a female may come off the nest two-thirds of the time in answer to "signal songs" and one-third independently.

16. Table X gives detailed records of periods on and off the nest during two sample days for K2 and K7 with notations as to 1M's activities.

17. The male visits the nest only rarely while his mate is incubating.

CHAPTER XIV

Care of the Young

The young are cared for by their parents for some ten days in the nest and after that for 18 to 20 days longer.

A. Care of the Young in the Nest

The egg shells have been eaten by the three females I have watched, but were carried away by a bird in Ithaca, New York (Haldeman, 71).

A summary of the chief events in the nest life is given in Table XI.

TABLE XI
The Young in the Nest

Bird	Mo.	Time*	1st Day	2nd Day	3rd Day	4th Day	5th Day	6th Day	7th Day	8th Day	9th Day	10th Day	11th Day
Per Cent of Time Brooded													
K1	May	18	?	53.0	45.0	56.0	51.2	47.7					
K2	May	39	?	50.9	47.1	40.0	62.2	42.1	22.9	?	4.7	0	0
K2	July	38	64	59.6	56.4	54.2	14.4	5.2	0	7.5	0	0	0
Interval between Feedings in Minutes													
K2	July	38	20	36	24	24	20	16.1	15	10.9	6.6		
K7	May	13.5	60	45	30	15	12	5.4	3.7	3.9			
1M	Avg. of 5 broods	90.5	32.4	18	13	8.1	7.3	6.1	5.4	5.0	4.0	2.5	2.3
Median Number of Seconds Spent at the Nest in Feeding by 1M in 1929													
				36.8	28.3	25	19.3	16.8	15	13	14	10	
Average Weight of Young in Grams													
			1.75	3.0	4.8	5.7	8.8	10.2	12.8	15.1	15.5	16.8	17.8

*Time=Number of hours watched.

Real brooding is indulged in only by the female, although 1M with some of his broods stood over the young for several minutes at a time; this was not to shade them, as the sun never reached the nests. The amount of time spent in brooding on the 5th and 6th days of the first two broods shown in the table is high due to unusually cold weather both times, viz., 2.8° C. (5° F.) below normal in 1928, 5° C. (9° F.) below normal in 1929.

I watched 1M five times while he was engaged in caring for a brood: 18 hours in 1928 from May 29 to June 2 with two young (this nest was destroyed June 3) ; in 1929 39 hours from May 4 to 14, 17 hours from June 7 to 18, and 38 hours July 7 to 15; and in 1930 13.5 hours May 5 to 12, the last four broods each consisting of four young.

The rate of feeding increases with the age of the young. 1M showed himself a devoted father in every case while I watched, feeding more than did his mates and very much more than K2. K7 was an experienced, zealous mother and during the 5th to 8th days greatly outdid 1M in feeding the young, probably bringing a larger total of meals than he did by the end of nest life. We see here a reciprocal relation ; with K1 (apparently an old bird) 1M fed a moderate amount, with K2 he took the major part of the responsibility, but with K7 he fed less again.

K2 fed her first two broods very little until the last half of nest life, but with her 3rd brood she started feeding visible stuff from the first. Haldeman, 71, found the female Song Sparrow consistently more zealous in feeding than the male during two years in which the same pair was watched; during the all day observation July 5, 1928, of the three young at the age of about 6 to 7 days, the female brought 198 meals, the male 63.

The amount of time spent by the male at the nest in delivering food decreases consisten ly from the beginning to the end of nest life, reflecting the differ t manner of feeding by the parent and the increased skill in receiving food on the part of the young. Five hundred and fifteen of these periods in 1929 were measured by stop watch; the medians of these day by day started on the 3rd day with 36.8 seconds, dropped to 19.3 by the 6th, and 13 by the 9th, and to 10 by the 11th day. Near the beginning of nest life he averaged about half a minute at the nest in delivering the food, but by the end of nest life he averaged only 10 seconds.

The average daily weights given in the table are based on 127 different cases here on Interpont. I have found that young of the same age differ widely in weights. Young that have left the nest weighed as follows : one bird at 21 days 19.7 g., a nest mate at 30 days 19.9 g., while a bird from another nest was weighed four times—23 days 19.9 g., 25 days 20.4 g., 28 days 19.2 g., 31 days 19.6 g.

The young usually stay in the nest 10 days during May, rarely 11, but later in the season they are quite apt to leave at 9 days and even 8. Once (May 1932) a normal brood stayed 12 days. A small brood does not necessarily leave any sooner than a large one.

B. Intervals Between Broods

After a nest has been destroyed, there is a very regular interval before the fledging of the next brood as will be seen in Table XII.

TABLE XII
Length of Time Necessary to Fledge Young
DATES YOUNG LEFT AFTER PREVIOUS NEST DESTROYED

Birds		Date of Destruction	Date Young Left Nest	Number of Young	Interval
K2	1M	April 12, 1929	May 15	2	33 days
K8	2M	May 16, 1930	June 15	5	3c days
K16	12M	June 11, 1930	July 11	3	30 days
K26	23M	June 10, 1930	July 10	3	30 days
K27	24M	May 17, 1930	June 15	3	29 days
K41	4M	April 26, 1931	May 26	2	30 days
K47	23M	May 4, 1932	June 3	3	30 days
K154	10M	May 10, 1933	June 9	3	30 days

DATES YOUNG LEFT NEST IN TWO SUCCESSIVE SUCCESSFUL BROODS

Birds		Date First Young Fledged	Date Second Young Fledged	No. Young in Second Brood	Interval
K2	1M	May 15, 1929	June 18	3	34 days
K3	4M	June 15, 1929	July 16	4	31 days
K7	1M	May 15, 1930	June 25	3	41 days
K2	5M	June 8, 1930	July 15	2	37 days
K15	11M	May 18, 1930	June 26	?	39 days
K20	17M	May 15, 1930	June 14	5	30 days
K38	42M	June 21, 1930	July 26	2	35 days

In six of eight cases there was an interval of just 30 days. K27 and 24M were one day quicker since their young stayed in the nest only 9 days. 1M and K2 took 3 days longer than usual, since their second nesting was delayed two days in starting due to the bleak weather in mid-April.

The second part of the table shows a large variation between the dates of the young leaving in two successive broods—from 30 to 41 days, averaging 35.4 days. It is of interest to see that in one case—

K20—the time was exactly the same as when a nest is destroyed—30 days. K2's third brood in 1929 were due to leave in as short a period, but as we left Columbus on July 16, I cannot be sure.

It is interesting how this same bird the next year was so deliberate, a 37 day period intervening. It is not the male that made the difference, for in 1930 1M and his new mate gave the longest interval of all—41 days; K7 was a most devoted mother to the young both in the nest and afterwards.

Records of the exact number of days between the dates of leaving the nest of one brood and the first egg of the next one are 6, 6, 9, 10, 11, 14, 14, 19.

When the young are about 17 days old they are able to fly and come out of hiding. When 20 days old they get food and drink for themselves to a small extent, and pursue their father, especially when he sings. When 28 to 30 days old they become independent and the tie with the parents is entirely broken.

C. Summary

1. The young are brooded by the female for the first five or six days of nest life.

2. The rate of feeding increases with the age of the nestlings.

3. Near the beginning of nest life 1M averaged half a minute per visit at the nest in delivering food, but by the end of nest life he averaged only 10 seconds.

4. The nestling Song Sparrow increases its weight more than ten-fold in the first ten days.

5. Weights of birds 21 to 31 days old ranged from 19 to 20 grams.

6. The young usually stay in the nest 10 days.

7. After a nest has been destroyed, the young of the following brood will usually be fledged just 30 days later.

8. Periods between the fledging of two broods successfully raised have ranged from 30 to 41 days.

9. The first egg of the next set has been laid 6 to 19 days after the fledging of the first brood.

10. Young birds become independent at the age of 28 to 30 days.

CHAPTER XV
Nesting Success and Failure

The number of young fledged in a bird population depends on many factors: survival of adults during the nesting season; length of the nesting season, which is conditioned by the weather both at the beginning and the end; number of eggs laid and number of broods attempted; amount of food available for the young; efficiency of the parents; and degree of interference by a large variety of influences, including human activities, floods, parasitism by the Cowbird, and the various enemies—reptilian, mammalian, and avian—that prey upon the eggs and young.

A. The Number of Young Fledged per Pair in One Season

In 1929 at the time of our departure on July 17 I believed the nesting activities of the two pairs I was studying were practically over (although Song Sparrows occasionally nest into September). Each pair made four attempts; one pair had one failure and three successes, raising nine young, while the other had two failures and two successes, raising five young.

In 1930 the numbers of young fledged per pair by fifteen pairs that survived the season were as follows: 0, 2, 2, 3, 3, 3, 4, 4, 4, 4, 5, 6, 7, 7, 10—a total of 64, an average of 4.3 a pair. The last four figures represent two broods each; hence 18 broods were raised, averaging 3.6 young to a brood.

With 16 pairs the number of attempts at nesting was known: 4 made 4 attempts, while 12 made 3. The number of successes (a success meaning that at least one Song Sparrow was raised) ranged from 0 to 3, 8 pairs having one success each, and 6 pairs two. The average number of attempts was 3.25, the average number of successes 1.4.

During the year of 1930 there occurred in Ohio "the greatest drought of record" . . . "amounting almost to climatic disaster." The three months of the Song Sparrow breeding season were characterized by a "warm and abnormally dry" May, "the driest June save one in 47 years," and the "driest July in 77 years" (Alexander, *1*). The mean temperature in July was 25° C. (77° F.) or 1.2° C. (2.1° F.) above normal.

This extraordinary drought did not affect the young in the nest adversely, only two young in the season apparently dying of starvation. The July young left the nest at the normal time without loss from lack of food, but it is true that most of the broods were small to begin with—4 birds in only one nest, 3 birds in two nests and 2 birds in three nests.

But the drought must have brought on the molt of the adults some two weeks or more early and thereby put a stop to nesting. In 1929 I saw no signs of molt before our departure on July 16; in 1933 from July 25 to August 6, a few of the birds were starting to molt, while others were not (10M, captured on August 4, showed no signs of molt). In 1930, on the contrary, many adults were decidedly in the molt by July 16.

In 1930 fall singing began from 14 to 18 days earlier than it has in any of six other falls. There was far more singing in the fall of 1930 than in any other fall since I have been studying Song Sparrows (see Chapter VII).

In Cornwall, Ryves, *164,* observed that in 1929 Blackbirds (*Turdus merula*) and Song Thrushes (*Turdus philomelus*) failed to raise third broods, perhaps because of "a drought and heat wave late in June and almost the whole of July."

Poultrymen can bring on the molt in laying hens by reducing their water ration, by giving them only grain to eat and thereby upsetting their protein balance. Could something of this sort have happened with the Song Sparrows?

It has been suggested that the extraordinarily hot and dry summer of 1934 should have affected the birds in the same way. Since I was away all the summer, I have no method of checking the matter except by the start of singing in the fall. 4M began singing the end of September as he did every other fall except 1930. An examination of the weather reports shows that although June and July 1934 were far hotter than the same months in 1930, nevertheless they had more rain—14 cm. (5.68 in.) in contrast to 6.5 cm. (2.53 in.). So it would seem as if the drought and not the heat had been responsible for the early molt in 1930.

It is clear that the breeding season of 1930 was cut short at the end, but it started a week to ten days earlier than any of the seasons in the last five years. The raising of 4.3 young per pair may be representative of a short nesting season—beginning late or ending early—but in a long season more young should be fledged.

B. SIZE OF SETS AND SIZE OF BROODS

The size of sets found on Interpont from 1930 to 1935 is shown in Table XIII, and the size of the broods raised in Table XIV, the totals being shown in Chart XV. The sizes of the sets are given as far as possible as they were laid, and not as they stood after losses due to Cowbird activities as previously published, *137*. Cowbirds' eggs and nestlings are omitted.

TABLE XIII
Size of Song Sparrow Sets on Interpont
As LAID

	6 Eggs	5 Eggs	4 Eggs	3 Eggs	2 Eggs	1 Eggs	0 Eggs	Nests	Eggs	Avg. Set
1930 - - - - - -	0	15	26	18	1	1	0	61	236	3.9
1931 - - - - - -	0	14	13	6	1	1	1	36	143	4.2
1932 - - - - - -	0	14	28	8	0	0	0	50	206	4.1
1933 - - - - - -	1	10	20	2	0	0	0	33	142	4.3
1934 - - - - - -	0	4	7	1	0	1	0	13	52	4.0
1935 - - - - - -	0	5	11	2	0	0	0	18	75	4.2
Total - - -	1	62	105	37	2	3	1	211	854	4.05

PERCENTAGES

1930 - - - - - -	0	24.5	42.6	29.5	1.7	1.7	0
1931 - - - - - -	0	38.8	36.1	16.7	2.8	2.8	2.8
1932 - - - - - -	0	28.0	56.0	16.0	0	0	0
1933 - - - - - -	3.0	30.3	60.6	6.0	0	0	0
1934 - - - - - -	0	30.8	54.6	7.8	0	7.8	0
1935 - - - - - -	0	27.8	61.1	11.1	0	0	0
Average - -	0.5	29.4	49.8	17.5	0.9	1.4	0.5

NUMBERS BY THREE YEAR PERIODS

1st 3 Years - -	0	43	67	32	2	2	1	147	585	4.0
2nd 3 Years - -	1	19	38	5	0	1	0	64	269	4.2

PERCENTAGES

1st 3 Years - -	0	29.3	45.6	21.8	1.3	1.3	0.7
2nd 3 Years - -	1.5	29.7	59.4	7.9	0	1.5	0

TABLE XIV

Size of Broods Raised

	5 Young	4 Young	3 Young	2 Young	1 Young	Nests	Young	Avg. Raised
	——Numbers of Nest Containing——					——Totals——		
1930 - - - - - -	6	8	10	5	0	29	102	3.5
1931 - - - - - -	7	3	4	2	2	18	65	3.6
1932 - - - - - -	1	6	9	6	8	30	76	2.5
1933 - - - - - -	0	4	2	1	3	10	27	2.7
1934 - - - - - -	0	1	1	3	1	6	14	2.3
1935 - - - - - -	0	2	4	1	0	7	22	3.1
Total - - - -	14	24	30	18	14	100	306	3.0

PERCENTAGES

	5 Young	4 Young	3 Young	2 Young	1 Young
1930 - - - - -	20.0	27.6	34.5	17.2	0
1931 - - - - -	38.8	16.8	22.2	11.1	11.1
1932 - - - - -	3.3	20.0	30.0	20.0	26.7
1933 - - - - -	0	40.0	20.0	10.0	30.0
1934 - - - - -	0	16.7	16.7	50.0	16.7
1935 - - - - -	0	28.6	57.1	14.3	0
Average - - -	14.0	24.0	30.0	18.0	14.0

NUMBERS BY THREE YEAR PERIODS

	5 Young	4 Young	3 Young	2 Young	1 Young	Nests	Young	Avg. Raised
1st 3 Years - - -	14	17	23	13	10	77	243	3.2
2nd 3 Years - - -	0	7	7	5	4	23	63	2.7

PERCENTAGES

	5 Young	4 Young	3 Young	2 Young	1 Young
1st 3 Years - - -	18.2	22.1	29.8	16.8	13.1
2nd 3 Years - - -	0	30.4	30.4	21.8	17.4

Sets containing one and two eggs were destroyed when incomplete; the nest that contained no (Song Sparrow) eggs was deserted after the deposition of a Cowbird's egg. The large proportion of three-egg sets in 1930 is due to the fact that observations were carried that year to the end of the nesting season. The proportion of five-egg sets was unusually high in 1931; I thought the explanation might have been that the proportion of adult females was exceptionally high that year because of a lack of young birds due to the shortened breeding season the previous year. But the breeding seasons of 1932, 1933, and 1934 were all bad, yet the proportion of five-egg sets ran consistently from 28 to 31. It might have been merely a chance that there was an unusual proportion of females that laid five-egg sets during 1931.

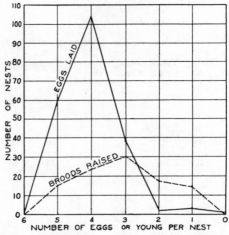

CHART XV. *Size of Sets Laid and Broods Raised from 1930 to 1935. See Tables XIII and XIV.*

The percentage of three-egg sets is comparatively low during the last three years. Perhaps the explanation is that during the first three I was too conservative in attributing damage to Cowbirds; the egg quotas of the first three years probably should be slightly higher than I have given them. Further experience has shown me that a three-egg set is an unusual occurrence among my Song Sparrows in the first two attempts. If only the early broods in 1930 are considered, we find 34.7 per cent of five-egg sets, 47.5 per cent of four-egg sets and 15 per cent of three-egg sets. The proportion of five-egg sets has been remarkably consistent during the past six years: if the observations are divided into three year periods, we find the average percentage of five-egg sets almost exactly the same, but four-egg sets are compartively more numerous and three-egg sets comparatively less numerous during the later periods. The average size of sets each year has been almost the same; if we count only the early part of the season for 1930, they have ranged from 4.0 to 4.3 eggs per set. The average of the first three years for these figures is 4.15 eggs, for the last three 4.2 eggs. I believe that the figure for the first period is a little low, because of too small an allowance for Cowbird depredations. It is of interest that there have been no significant fluctuations in the average size of sets during the six years; this matter will be discussed further in Chapter XX.

Although the size of the sets averaged so nearly the same from year to year, a very different picture is seen when it comes to the average size of the broods fledged. And here it should be stated that the first two seasons on Interpont showed good nesting success—what I should call a good normal course of events—that the third year was poor, and the next three very poor.

In 1930 there was a good percentage of nests raising five young, in 1931 a remarkable percentage, in 1932 only one nest did so, while since then not a single nest has achieved this proud result. In 1930, 1932, and 1935 there were more nests in which three young were raised than any other number, but in 1931, nests with five young were most numerous, in 1933 nests with four young and in 1934 with two young! But the numbers of successful nests during these last three years were very small.

In 1932 a surprising number—8, or more than one-fourth of the nests—raised only one young bird apiece. Conditions associated with the raising of only one and two nestlings per nest have been destruction of eggs by Cowbirds, addled eggs, a combination of Cowbird nest-mates and an early drought in 1932, and the removal by predators of all but one nestling from several nests.

The average number of Song Sparrows fledged per successful nest was 3.2 during the first three years and 2.7 during the last three.

C. Completely and Partially Successful Broods

Table XV gives the numbers and percentages of those broods each season that were entirely successful and those that were only partially so, only Song Sparrow eggs and nestlings being considered.

During the first two years nearly two-thirds of the successful nests raised their full quota, but matters have been very different since then; in 1932 only 13 per cent of the nests were completely successful, and in 1933 40 per cent, but during the last two years not a single nest has been completely successful. During the six years thirty-seven per cent of the successful nests raised their full quota.

TABLE XV

Completely and Partially Successful Nests

COMPLETELY SUCCESSFUL NESTS

Year						Number	Nests Percentage of Total Successful Nests	Eggs Laid	Young Fledged	Average per Nest
1930	-	-	-	-	-	18	62.1	73	73	4.1
1931	-	-	-	-	-	11	61.1	50	50	4.5
1932	-	-	-	-	-	4	13.3	17	17	4.3
1933	-	-	-	-	-	4	40.0	15	15	3.8
1934	-	-	-	-	-	0	0	0	0	0
1935	-	-	-	-	-	0	0	0	0	0
Total	-	-	-	-		37	37.0	155	155	4.2

PARTIALLY SUCCESSFUL NESTS

Year						Number	Percentage	Eggs Laid	Young Fledged	Average per Nest
1930	-	-	-	-	-	11	37.9	43	29	2.6
1931	-	-	-	-	-	7	38.9	27	15	2.1
1932	-	-	-	-	-	26	86.7	111	59	2.3
1933	-	-	-	-	-	6	60.0	25	12	2.0
1934	-	-	-	-	-	6	100.0	30	14	2.3
1935	-	-	-	-	-	7	100.0	31	22	3.1
Total	-	-	-	-		63	63.0	267	151	2.4

The average number of eggs per nest was the same with both the completely and partially successful nests, namely 4.2, but whereas the former raised an average of 4.2 young, the latter raised only 2.4 young per nest.

D. NUMBERS OF YOUNG RAISED IN 211 NESTS IN SIX SEASONS

A summary of the nesting success during the six years is given in Table XVI.

When I tabulated the results in 1931 and found them so closely similar to those of 1930, I thought there was a certain monotony in this study, I seemed to have discovered the formula the first year and it looked as if later years would be mere repetitions, some 70 per cent of the eggs hatching and 44 per cent being fledged. But I was soon disillusioned. The next season 60 per cent of the eggs were hatched and only 37 per cent were fledged—too many Cowbirds and a bad drought in May being the reasons. These results brought my averages down considerably, as published in 1933 and 1934, *135, 137.*

TABLE XVI

Numbers of Young Raised in 211 Nests in Six Seasons

THE NESTS

Year	Total Number of Nests	Number in which Eggs Hatched	Per Cent in which Eggs Hatched	Number in which Young Were Fledged	Per Cent in which Young Were Fledged
1930 - - - -	61	44	72.1	29	47.5
1931 - - - -	36	27	75.0	18	50.0
1932 - - - -	50	38	76.0	30	60.0
1933 - - - -	33	20	60.6	10	30.3
1934 - - - -	13	8	61.5	6	46.2
1935 - - - -	18	10	55.5	7	38.9
	211	147	69.7	100	47.4

THE EGGS

Year	Number Laid Total	Number Laid Per Nest	Hatched No.	Hatched Per Cent	Fledged No.	Fledged Per Cent	Average Fledged Per Total Nest	Average Fledged Per Successful Nest
1930 - - - -	236	3.9	161	68.2	102	43.2	1.7	3.5
1931 - - - -	143	4.2	103	72.0	65	45.5	1.8	3.6
1932 - - - -	206	4.1	125	60.7	76	36.8	1.5	2.5
1933 - - - -	142	4.3	72	50.7	27	19.0	0.8	2.7
1934 - - - -	52	4.0	18	34.6	14	26.9	1.1	2.3
1935 - - - -	75	4.2	31	41.3	22	29.3	1.2	3.1
	854	4.0	510	59.7	306	35.8	1.4	3.0
First 2 Years	379	4.0	264	69.6	167	44.1	1.7	3.6
Last 4 Years	475	4.1	246	51.8	139	29.3	1.2	2.6
First 3 Years	585	4.0	389	66.5	243	41.5	1.6	3.2
Last 3 Years	269	4.2	121	45.0	63	23.4	1.0	2.7

I thought 1932 had reached an all-time low, but 1933 was far worse—with only 19 per cent of the eggs hatched and fledged—an average of less than one bird for each nest. The unfavorable factors here were a great flood the middle of May and the plowing of Interpont in early June just when the new nests had young. In 1931 and 1933 almost exactly the same number of eggs were involved, but whereas in the former year 103 were hatched and 65 raised, in the latter 72 were hatched and 19 raised. Fortunately the Song Sparrows had high success in their third (or fourth) attempts; when we returned from a western trip in late July nine pairs had young out of the nest.

The next year only 13 nests were located before my departure May 24 for Europe; the Song Sparrows suffered from the heaviest Cowbird infestation of any year. This spring I collected most of the Cowbird eggs, thus giving the Song Sparrows a chance to raise a few young. Even with this help only 27 per cent were fledged, the lowest number except in 1933. If I had not interfered in the matter of the Cowbird eggs, probably only 10 Song Sparrows would have been raised instead of 14—or 19.2 per cent—just as in the year before. As for 1935 only 29 per cent of the eggs laid were hatched and fledged, Cowbirds still being the chief upsetting factor. It must be remembered that the figures for both these last years are based on only a small numbers of nests, early in the season; the success of early nests in my experience has always been less good than that of the later ones.

If we average the first two years we find that 70 per cent of the eggs hatched and 44 per cent were fledged, but in the last four 52 per cent were hatched and 29 per cent fledged. The average number of young raised in 1930 and 1931 per total nest was 1.7, per successful nest 3.6; from 1932 to 1935 it was 1.2 and 2.6 respectively. If we compare by three year periods we find 67 per cent hatched and 42 per cent fledged for the first 3 years; 45 per cent hatched and 23 per cent fledged for the last three. The average number fledged during the first period was 1.6 per total nest and 3.2 per successful nest; while for the last period the figures were 1.0 and 2.7 respectively.

I believe the first three years give conservative figures for average conditions, while the last three give a picture of a dwindling population unable to cope with too great odds—floods, human interference, and an over-population of Cowbirds.

1. *Comparison with Other Studies of Nesting Success*

The assumption that 23 per cent of success is decidedly too low to be typical is supported by the studies of other people as shown in Table XVII.

The studies in this table were made chiefly on Passerine birds nesting in the open. It is of great interest to find that in all of the 7 studies where the numbers of eggs are given except the last one, the percentage of fledging ranges between 40.5 and 46.7, averaging 43. These studies were made in the North Temperate Zone, three in Great

TABLE XVII

Success of Nesting in Eleven Studies; Mostly Open Nests of Passerine Species

Author	Bibliography Reference	Locality	Species	Nests	Eggs Laid	Eggs Hatched	Young Fledged	Successful Nests	Eggs Hatched %	Young Fledged %	Successful Nests %
a. Baron	15	England	11	71	265	160	124		60.4	46.7	
b. Nicholson	143	Scotland	?	156	687	420	300		61.1	43.7	
c. Praeger	149	Scotland	?	240				99			41.2
d. Clabaugh	39	California	13	38	187	103	76		55.0	40.6	
e. Clabaugh	40	California	17	39	168	104	68		62.0	40.5	
f. Pickwell	147	Illinois	1	30	102	79	46		77.4	45.1	
g. Potter	148	Pennsylvania	18	113				60			53.1
h. Walkinshaw	195a	Michigan	1	46				20			43.5
i. Nice	127a	Oklahoma	34	268				118			44.0
j. Nice	(1930-1932)	Ohio	1	147	585	389	243	77	66.5	41.5	52.4
k. Nice	(1933-1936)	Ohio	1	76	321	147	80	30	45.8	24.9	39.5
Total of Eggs in 6 Studies (a, b, d, e, f, j)				481	1,994	1,225	857		61.4	43.0	
Total of Nests in 5 Studies (c, g, h, i, j)				814				374			45.9

Britain and the rest in this country from the eastern to the western border. Since all of them except the last four years with the Song Sparrows are so consistent, it seems as if we can place considerable reliance upon this ratio of 40 to 46 per cent success for open nests of Passerines in the North Temperate Zone. No definite studies appear to have been made of this matter either in the Tropics or in the Arctic.

The number of successful *nests* is often easier to keep track of than the numbers of successful *eggs*. If we consider the five studies in which data on the success of nests are given (omitting the atypical results during the last four years with the Song Sparrows), we find that in 374 of 814 nests young were raised—45.9 per cent of success.

In various hole-nesting species the percentage of fledging is consistently higher. The percentage of success of 268 nests of the Bluebird (*Sialia s. sialis*) during three years was 68.6, *127;* of 133 nests of the House Wren (*Troglodytes a. aedon*) 68, *94;* of 54 nests of the Tree Swallow (*Iridoprocne bicolor*) in 1933 and 1934 71.5, *38;* of 175 nests of the same species 57 in two years, but only 38 the third year, *114.* Statistics on 283 eggs of the House Finch (*Carpodacus mexicanus frontalis*)—a species nesting in enclosed places—give 59 per cent of success, *19.* The publications of the Phytopathological Service at Wageningen, Holland, offer a wealth of data on hole-nesting birds, chiefly Titmice, but also Redstarts (*Phoenicurus phoenicurus*) and Starlings, the percentage of success ranging from 55 to 76, but the great majority of cases falling near 65, *138, 214*.

It is evident that birds nesting in the open suffer from many more nesting disasters than do those nesting in holes. How do the former keep up their numbers? In many cases they attempt more broods than the hole-nesters, although this is not universally true.

The Corn-Buntings (*Emberiza c. calandra*) studied by the Ryves show a very high percentage of fledging for ground-nesting birds, some 60 per cent for over 400 eggs, *165, 166*. These birds are typically single-brooded; their late nesting date, chiefly July, is evidently more favorable than one early in the season.

E. ANALYSIS OF THE LOSS OF EGGS AND YOUNG

In Table XVIII and Chart XVI the loss of eggs and young is analyzed for each of the six seasons from 1930 through 1935, the total number of eggs laid each year being the basis for all the percentages.

Under "Cowbird" come those cases where eggs were eaten, and young Song Sparrows crushed or crowded out, not cases of starvation

TABLE XVIII

Analysis of Loss in 211 Song Sparrow Nests

Year	Flood Eggs	Predator Eggs	Predator Young	Cowbird Eggs	Cowbird Young	S&A* Eggs	Parents Failed Eggs	Parents Failed Young	Man Eggs	Man Young	Parents Killed Eggs	Parents Killed Young	Young Starved Young	Total Loss Eggs	Total Loss Young	Both
1930																
Nos.	0	48	49	4	3	5	1	5	12	0	5	0	2	75	59	134
%	0	20.3	20.7	1.7	1.2	2.2	0.4	2.2	5.0	0	2.2	0	0.9	31.8	25.0	56.8
1931																
Nos.	0	23	29	2	0	9	3	3	0	0	3	5	1	40	38	78
%	0	16.1	20.2	2.9	0	6.3	2.1	2.1	0	0	2.1	3.5	0.7	28.0	26.5	54.5
1932																
Nos.	0	36	26	8	1	18	2	4	10	0	7	0	18	81	49	130
%	0	17.5	12.5	3.9	0.5	8.9	0.9	1.9	4.8	0	3.4	0	8.9	39.4	23.8	63.2
1933																
Nos.	21	23	43	5	0	5	1	0	6	0	9	0	2	70	45	115
%	14.8	16.2	30.2	3.5	0	3.5	0.7	0	4.2	0	6.4	0	1.4	49.3	31.7	81.0
1934																
Nos.	0	8	3	15	0	7	1	0	2	0	1	0	1	34	4	38
%	0	15.4	5.8	28.9	0	13.5	1.9	0	3.8	0	1.9	0	1.9	65.4	7.7	73.1
1935																
Nos.	4	18	6	12	0	5	0	1	1	0	4	0	2	44	9	53
%	5.4	24.0	8.0	16.0	0	6.6	0	1.3	1.3	0	5.4	0	2.7	58.7	12.0	70.7
Totals																
Nos.	25	156	156	46	4	49	8	13	31	0	29	5	26	344	204	548
%	2.9	18.2	18.2	5.5	0.5	5.7	0.9	1.5	3.7	0	3.4	0.6	3.1	40.3	23.9	64.2

*Sterile and addled eggs.

when Cowbirds were present. "Parental Failures" include the occasional disappearance of single eggs (8 cases), young carried off while hatching (7 cases), young pulled out of the nest (3 cases), or the last young deserted in the nest (3 cases). Under "Man" come two cases of nest robbery, the other damage having been done by plowing. When parents were killed and the nest undisturbed, boys were probably responsible in some cases and other enemies in others. A heavy rain drowned two nestlings in 1929, but no further damage occurred through this factor until the great floods of May 11 and 13, 1933 which must have destroyed the majority of the ground nests in the river valleys in central and southern Ohio. In 1935 a smaller flood affected only one nest that I had found.

As to the comparative loss of eggs and young, 344 eggs were lost and 204 nestlings, or 40.3 per cent loss of the original 854 eggs as eggs and 23.9 per cent as young. The egg stays in the nest from 12 to 18 days (the average of which is 15), the nestling 10 days; the average daily loss during the first three years was 2.1 per cent for the eggs and 2.5 per cent for the young. But the figures for the six years give a daily loss of 2.7 per cent for the eggs and 2.39 for the young.

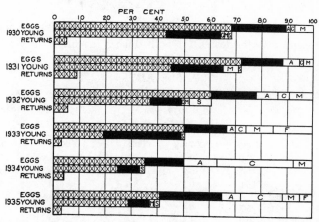

CHART XVI. *Analysis of Loss of Eggs and Young in 211 Song Sparrow Nests in Percentages of Numbers of Eggs Laid. X=eggs hatched, young fledged, and young "returning" the following spring. Solid black=loss from predators. A=addled and sterile eggs; C=loss from Cowbirds; F=loss from flood; M=miscellaneous factors—parental failures, man, and parents killed; s=starvation. See Table XVIII.*

The factor that affects only the eggs is that of sterile and addled eggs; the factor affecting only the young is that of starvation. The Cowbird also does considerably more damage to eggs than to young. The fact that floods and plowing and the killing of parents have destroyed many more eggs than young is largely a matter of chance.

Predators have taken exactly as many young as eggs—an average of 1.2 per cent for the 15 days the eggs are in the nest, and an average of 1.8 per cent for the 10 days the young are in the nest. Some enemies (cats for instance) prefer young to eggs. Often some enemy carries off the Song Sparrow eggs, leaving the somewhat larger Cowbird egg, although the Cowbird nestling is taken as readily as the Song Sparrow. Some predators may be attracted to the nest by the begging note of the young during the last few days of nest life. Yet at this same time they must be immune from the attacks of the smaller of their enemies, such as little snakes that would eat the eggs.

The loss from predators was high the first year—41 per cent, dropped the next two years to 36 and 30 per cent, reached its maximum in 1933 with 46 per cent, and fell again the last two years reaching only 21 and 32 per cent.

In Table XIX we see the loss for eggs and young during the six years and also the losses for both during the first two years and last four years.

TABLE XIX

Summary of Loss to Eggs and Young Divided Into Three Periods

	1930-1935 854 Eggs ——Per Cent Loss——			1930-1931 379 Eggs ——Per Cent Loss——	1932-1935 475 Eggs
	Eggs	Young	Total	Total	Total
Flood - - - - -	2.9	0	2.9	0	5.3
Predator - - - -	18.2	18.2	36.4	39.3	34.4
Cowbird - - - -	5.5	0.5	6.0	2.4	8.6
Sterile and Addled Eggs - - -	5.7	0	5.7	3.7	7.4
Parental Failure -	0.9	1.5	2.4	3.2	1.9
Man - - - - -	3.7	0	3.7	3.2	4.0
Parents Killed -	3.4	0.6	4.0	3.3	4.2
Starvation - - -	0	3.1	3.1	0.8	4.9
Total - - -	40.3	23.9	64.2	55.9	70.7

The total loss of eggs and young during 1930 and 1931 reached 55.9 per cent; during 1932 through 1935 70.7 per cent. (It must be remembered that most of the data was on the early part of the season, and that some of the great losses—at any rate in 1933—were made good later in the season.) What is the reason for the great increase in mortality during the last four years?

In the first place two factors have played a smaller role in the later years than earlier—predators (except in 1933) and parental failures. Wild predators have become increasingly scarce on Interpont— opossums, weasels, skunks and snakes. But all other factors have shown a large increase, and an entirely new one has been added, that of flood which amounted to a 5.3 per cent loss during the four years. Loss due to the killing of parents increased one-fifth, damage by man (entirely plowing) increased one-fourth, the percentage of sterile and addled eggs doubled, damage by Cowbirds mort than tripled, while death due to starvation increased six fold.

In normal seasons there is a very small loss of nestlings from starvation, and even in 1930 the drought did not injure the young in the nest. But in 1932 no less than 18 nestlings died, apparently from lack of food. This condition was correlated with a heavy Cowbird infestation and with a disastrous drought in May, for this month was the driest May in Columbus in the 54 years of the Weather Bureau's record, less than an inch of rain falling—2 cm. Thirteen of the 18 Song Sparrows had Cowbird nest-mates. There was no loss from starvation in the nestlings fledged before May 20, but in the next ten days only two broods were entirely successful, while eight suffered loss. In June no parents raised all the young hatched. No real rain came until June 27. Under normal conditions Cowbirds are usually raised without loss to the Song Sparrow young that are present; hence this early drought must have caused a lack of insect food that resulted in the death of 18 young Song Sparrows.

To return to the subject of predators. It may well be that the diminishing amount of damage by them reflects a real decrease in these animals. The very high loss in 1933 followed directly upon extended disturbance of the nesting area by plowing June 6 to 9. If I had not rescued the young they would have been destroyed by the tractor plow, but my activities in removing the threatened nestlings

(8 in number) and adding them to families in safe situations did little good, as most of these nests were robbed and only two of the transferred nestlings were fledged. Several nestlings were apparently taken by Bronzed Grackles (*Quiscalus quiscula aeneus*) that came in throngs to follow the plow. Here we have a similar situation to those reported by Errington, *55*, and Bennett, *17*, where disturbance due to man's interference and to exposure of nests was followed by a marked increase in predation.

Summing up the factors responsible for the excessive losses of the last four years, we find that man and the weather are chiefly to blame. Drastic reduction in cover brought about an unbalanced condition between Cowbirds and hosts, and exposed the adult Song Sparrows to increased dangers, while the late plowing brought an influx of new predators to prey upon the young. As mentioned in Chapter IX a higher proportion of well concealed nests have succeeded than of poorly concealed—namely 55 and 36 per cent respectively (omitting nests destroyed by floods or plowing). Extremes of weather—too little rain or too much—accounted for perhaps 8 per cent loss during the last four years (assigning half the loss through starvation to drought and half to Cowbirds).

The list of factors in Tables XVIII and XIX is a compromise, the best that can be done under the circumstances, but we know that in reality man is responsible for far more than 3.7 per cent loss. On account of his disturbing activities he should be charged with much of the predator loss (cats, rats, dogs, and in June 1933 Grackles), much of the Cowbird loss (see Chapter XVI), some of the killing of parents, and perhaps even the flood. Indeed, it is only drought, sterile and addled eggs, parental failures and part of the predator and Cowbird damage that cannot ultimately be laid at his door.

F. Summary

1. In 1929 two pairs of Song Sparrows each made four attempts at nesting, raising 9 and 5 young respectively.

2. In 1930 fifteen pairs raised from 0 to 10 young each, totalling 64 and averaging 4.3 young.

3. The great drought in 1930 cut the breeding season of the Song Sparrows short and brought on the molt more than two weeks early.

4. The proportion of five-egg sets in the early broods has been fairly consistent during the six years, ranging from 28 to 39 per cent, averaging 30 per cent.

5. The average number of eggs per nest in the early broods has been practically the same during the six years, ranging from 4.0 to 4.3 and averaging 4.1.

6. The average size of the broods fledged has decreased very much; in the first two years it was 3.6, in the next 2.7.

7. During 1930 and 1931 nearly two-thirds of the successful nests raised their full quota, but in 1932 only 13 per cent did so and in 1933 40 per cent. In 1934 and 1935 not a single nest was completely successful.

8. The average number of eggs per nest was 4.2 with both completely and partially successful nests. The former raised 4.2 young per nest, the latter 2.4.

9. The percentage of eggs hatched was 70 in the first two years, 52 in the next four years, and 60 during the six years.

10. The percentage of eggs raised and fledged was 44 during the first two years and 29 during the next four, 36 during the six years.

11. The average number of young raised per total nest was 1.7 during the first two years and 1.2 during the next four, averaging 1.4 for the six years.

12. The average number of young raised per successful nest was 3.6 during the first two years and 2.6 during the next four, averaging 3 for all six years.

13. Comparison is made with 9 other studies of Passerine birds building open nests; of 1,994 eggs 62 per cent were hatched and 43 per cent fledged. Of 814 nests 45.9 per cent raised young. A per-

centage of success of some 41 to 46 per cent of eggs and nests appears to be normal in temperate North America.

14. In hole-nesting species the percentage of success averages around 65.

15. The losses of eggs are analyzed for each of the six seasons under 8 headings.

16. The total loss of the original eggs amounted to 40 per cent as eggs and 24 per cent as young—64 per cent in all.

17. The average daily loss of eggs was 2.7 per cent and of young 2.4 per cent.

18. The percentage of the 854 eggs lost by the different factors was: flood 2.9; predators 36.4; Cowbird 6; sterile and addled eggs 5.7; parental failures 2.4; man—nest robbing, but chiefly plowing 3.7; parents killed 4; starvation 3.1.

19. The total loss during the first two years was 55.9 per cent; during the next four 70.7 per cent.

20. The damage done by predators decreased from 1930 to 1932, but reached a maximum in 1933 when conditions were greatly disturbed by the plowing of the whole of Interpont in June.

21. Floods occurred during the nesting season only in 1933 and 1935.

22. The heavy losses from 1932 to 1935 were due to interference by man, severe parasitism by the Cowbird, drought and flood.

23. The results in 1936 were not included in this chapter, as the changes made by the addition of 52 eggs are so slight as not to warrant the reworking of the tables. In brief, they are as follows: 12 nests, 5 with 5 eggs, 6 with 4 eggs, 1 with 3 eggs; 2 raised 4 young, 1 raised 3 young, 2 raised 2 young, and 2 one young. Fifty-two eggs; 26 hatched (50%); 17 young were fledged (32.7%). Average number eggs per nest 4.3; number young raised per total nest 1.4, per successful nest 2.4. Wholly successful nests only one (14.3%). Loss of eggs: 13 taken by predators, 6 by Cowbird, 2

addled, 5 destroyed by man. Loss of young: 6 taken by predators, 3 starved (with Cowbird nest-mates).

24. The total loss to eggs and young of the 906 eggs laid during the 7 years was: flood, 25 (2.8%); predators, 331 (36.7%); Cowbird, 56 (6.1%); sterile and addled eggs, 51 (5.6%); parental failure, 22 (2.4%); man, 36 (4%); parents killed, 34 (3.7%); young starved, 28 (3.1%); a total loss of 40.9% of the eggs as eggs, and 23.5% as young—64.4% in all.

CHAPTER XVI

The Cowbird in Relation to the Song Sparrow

Next to the European Cuckoo the Cowbird is the most famous brood-parasite; but although an immense literature exists on the former bird, the latter has been strangely neglected as a subject for study.

A. THE COWBIRD AS PARASITE

Cuculus canorus is highly specialized as a parasite, but this is not true with *Molothrus ater ater*.

1. *Non-specialization of the Cowbird*

The European Cuckoo is a large bird—the female weighing 100 g.—yet it parasitizes small birds, and its egg is comparatively small, averaging about 3 g., *74, 174*. The Cowbird female, on the other hand, weighs about 39 g. (see Appendix IV), and her egg is just about the same size as that of the Cuckoo. The Cuckoo is specific in its parasitism, its egg is abnormally small and hard shelled, and the nestling evicts eggs and young from the nest. The Cowbird is not specific in its parasitism, its egg is of normal size and shell-texture, the nestling does not "intentionally" evict its mates and finally *the incubation period is not shorter than that of some of its relatives.*

As to the relative size of Cowbird eggs and other Icteridae, Cowbird eggs on Interpont average 8.9 per cent of the weight of the bird that lays them. It is a difficult matter to check on the weights of American birds and their eggs due to the scarcity of data, but from two different articles by Bergtold, *20, 21,* and from information given me by Dr. L. E. Hicks, I found that the weight of an egg of a Red-winged Blackbird (*Agelaius p. phoeniceus*) comes to 8.9 per cent the weight of the female. Huxley, *88,* in re-working Heinroth's mass of material on weights of eggs and adults in 436 species found the eggs of oscinine species with a mean body weight of 37.9 g. averaged 9 per cent the weight of the adult.

a. *The Incubation Period of the Cowbird*

It has long been believed that the one respect in which *Molothrus ater ater* was specialized was that of a short incubation period—"only 10 days," "about the shortest period of any of our passerine birds," *58, 59*. In the first place, ten day incubation periods have been reported for the Red-winged Blackbird, *4, 30,* Bobolink (*Dolichonyx oryzivorus*) and Yellow-headed Blackbird (*Xanthocephalus xanthocephalus*), *20, 30*. In the second place, in my experience the Cowbird egg on Interpont has never hatched in 10 days; with the Song Sparrow as host, in 5 cases it hatched in 11 days, in 9 cases in 12 days, in 3 cases 13 days, and one case 15 days. The Song Sparrow egg normally hatches in 12 or 13 days; the Cowbird egg hatches with about one day less of incubation than the Song Sparrow. It never hatches two or three days before the first Song Sparrow egg, which would be the rule with a 10 day incubation period. In 24 cases it has hatched one day before; in 15 cases on the same day, three times one day later, and eight times two to five days later—in the last 11 cases having been laid after the set was complete.

2. *Relations to Its Own Species*

Cowbirds on Interpont have not entered my traps readily, so that I have caught only four males and nine females. All these were given colored celluloid bands, while the aluminum band was put on the left leg; all nestlings have been banded on the right leg. (Of 35 banded nestlings safely fledged up to June, 1935, not a single one has returned.) Three of the males were often recorded during the season of capture, but not seen in subsequent years. Three of the females (A11, A35 and C23) were present for two seasons, and two (B27 and B28) for three. (See Appendix IV.)

Cowbirds are notably gregarious creatures, and here in Columbus they are sociable even in the breeding season, although Friedmann found in Ithaca, N. Y., that they "scatter during the breeding season when they have no true social life except as parasites of other birds," *61*. With a small population of Cowbirds, this investigator found the species predominantly monogamous, with some tendency towards polyandry. But here on Interpont, with an abundance of Cowbirds, promiscuity prevails just as the older writers maintained.

A banded male has been seen with three different banded females and one unbanded female, while banded females are seen with varying numbers of males from one to five.

Far from driving off other members of their species the males regularly attend the females in small troops, while two females often accompany each other in the most companionable manner. Friedmann never saw Cowbirds fight, but I have recorded this behavior five times —April 7, 10, 1930, April 10, 11, 1933, April 12, 1935—the occasion being disagreements between males during communal courting parties.

3. *Relation to Its Breeding Area*

Although Cowbirds show no impulse to defend a territory, yet they appear much attached to their spring and early summer homes. My banded birds have had definite ranges on Interpont. One male was usually found from the third dike to Dodridge Street, but twice recorded on Central Interpont. Two others ordinarily confined their activities to Central Interpont. Three females frequented the same range for two years, the other two for three. The ordinary range of male and female was about 7 hectares (18 to 20 acres), but either may be seen on occasion over an area of 12 hectares (30 acres).

Cowbirds disappear from Interpont sometime in July, but from the middle of September to mid-October, some, at least, revisit their breeding grounds, at which time we hear the males' "song" once more. I have fall records of three of my females; A11 Sept. 13, 1931, and Oct. 2, 3, 1932; B27 Oct. 11, 1933, and C23 Oct. 14, 1935.

Several banders have found Cowbirds excellent subjects for homing experiments. An immature bird returned from 3 miles and an adult female from 20 miles (Gillespie, *64*), while Lyon, *116,* had a male return from 25 miles, and in later studies from quite extraordinary distances—80, 500, 850 and 1,200 miles (128, 800, 1,400 and 1,900 km.), as reported by him at the meeting of the American Ornithologists' Union at Pittsburgh, October, 1936.

4. *Relations to Its Hosts*

The Cowbird not only transfers the care of its offspring to its host—a situation that in itself may result in death to some of the young of the host—but it often carries away eggs of the host.

a. The Eggs of the Cowbird

The eggs of *Molothrus ater ater* are of a generalized type, usually finely speckled. A few individuals lay quite distinctive eggs, but many are so typical that it is difficult to decide which are from the same bird and which not, especially as I seldom collected the eggs. With five exceptions they have been larger than the largest of the Song Sparrow eggs. Measurements of 75 eggs on Interpont range from 20 x 16 mm. and 21.2 x 15 mm. to 25 x 18 mm., averaging 22.6 x 16.3 mm.

Weights of 24 fresh eggs ranged from 2.7 to 4 g., averaging 3.17 g. (Schönwetter, *174*, gives the average measurements of 625 Middle European eggs of *Cuculus canorus* as 22.4 x 16.5 mm., the average weight being 3.3 g.)

The earliest dates for Cowbird eggs on Interpont have been, Apr. 24, 1930; Apr. 25, 1931; Apr. 27, 1932; Apr. 24, 1933; Apr. 25, 1934; Apr. 22, 1935; and Apr. 29, 1936. Cowbirds appear to be less influenced by temperature than are the Song Sparrows. The average date for the first egg is Apr. 25, which happens to be the very same date as the average for the start of general laying with the Song Sparrows.

During 1930 and 1931, when nesting began early, the first nests of the Song Sparrows escaped parasitism, but since then the start of laying of the two species has synchronized excellently.

I believe that Cowbirds on Interpont lay three (and possibly four in some cases) "sets" of eggs with intervals of 6 to perhaps 12 days between "sets." Although females probably as a rule lay an egg every day, *59*, it may well be that an egg is sometimes held over, so that 5 eggs may be laid in 6 or 7 days. (On Apr. 28, 1933, I caught B28 and finding her weight to be 45.6 g., kept her in a cage until she laid, which was not until the night of the 29th-30th.) The following data are based on eggs that were decidedly distinctive, a date in italics meaning a positive one, the others being estimated, i.e., a nest with a fresh Cowbird egg might be found on a certain date, but I would not know exactly when it had been laid. Unfortunately, I never found all the Cowbird eggs laid on Interpont, nor did I find late eggs, because of leaving Columbus in June.

1932	Type A.	*Apr. 27, 29*, May 2	May 7, 9, *12, 13*	May **20, 24**
	Type B.	*May 7, 11, 12*, 13	May **25, 26**	June 9
	Type C.	(*May 4, 1931*)	*May 12, 1932*	June 9, *1932*
1934	Type D.	May *3, 5*, 6	*May 12*	
	Type E.	May 5, 6, 7, 8, 9		
	Type F.	May 1	*May 12*	
	Type G.	*May 4, 5, 7, 8*	May 28	
1935	Type G.	Apr. 28, 29, *30*	May 12	
	Type I.	*June 6*	*June 17*	

Types B and G were what I called "marbled" eggs, white and beautiful with brown and lavender spots, very different from the ordinary eggs. Type C is the strangest I have ever found from a Cowbird; they were large, with geenish ground color and unmarked except for a circle of red-brown speckles around the large end. I found all three examples in the region of the third dike, one in 1931 and two in 1932; they must have been laid by a bird whose usual range lay off of Interpont.

The dates of hatching of Cowbirds' eggs on Interpont appear to go in waves—1930: May 5, 10-18, May 28-June 1 (these were in Northern Yellow-throat nests), June 8-12; 1931: May 6, 9, 13-16; 1932: May 11, 14, 18-30, June 7, 8; 1933: May 10-15, 22, 23, June 4, 5; 1935: May 3, 9-20; 1936: May 10, 13, 15-17, 20, 21.

It will be noted that the chief time of hatching has been from the 9th to 20th each year except 1932, when it occurred from the 18th to 30th. Intervals between "waves" were 7, 7, 8, 10 and 12 days.

Two Cowbird eggs have been laid in the same Song Sparrow nest in 26 instances during this study, or 26.5 per cent of the cases; three eggs in one nest 3 times (3.1 per cent) and one egg in 69 nests (70.4 per cent). As a rule two eggs in a nest are laid by different females. On June 8, 1928, I found four Cowbird eggs in a Northern Yellow-throat's (*Geothlypis trichas brachidactyla*) nest on Interpont; these had been laid by two different birds and at different times for two were fresh and two nearly ready to hatch.

b. The Nestling Cowbird

The little Cowbird is strikingly different from its nest-mates, being covered with light greyish down instead of black. Unlike the young Cuckoo it is a peaceful occupant of the nest, and whatever damage it may do comes from its large appetite and rapidly increasing size, which are to be expected in view of the greater growth it must make in the

8 to 10 days of nest life. The Song Sparrow leaves the nest weighing 16 to 17 g., the Cowbird weighing about twice as much (averaging 33 g. according to Friedmann, *59*). At this time it weighs approximately half as much again as its Song Sparrow foster-mother or father, and more than twice as much as an adult of the next most favored host—the Northern Yellow-throat.

c. The Destruction of Eggs of the Host

The female Cowbird occasionally injures Song Sparrow eggs with her claws (only two eggs in the 98 parasitized nests in this study), but she often removes an egg. I have seen this happen twice.

On May 22, 1928, about 9:15 A.M. a male and female Cowbird came into 4M's territory; the female disappeared and shortly returned with an egg in her bill which she ate at her leisure, contents and shell, while the Song Sparrows protested.

On Apr. 26, 1934, at 8:45 A.M. a male and female Cowbird were watching 141M's territory while the Song Sparrows scolded; the male stayed in the elm above, but the female flew to a small locust, looked down intently, then descended to the ground where she was hidden in the grass. In a few seconds she reappeared with an egg in her bill and flew off, followed by the male. I examined the nest, finding three Song Sparrow eggs in it; the next morning it had been destroyed.

Blinco, *23*, reports a Cowbird carrying off a Robin's (*Turdus migratorius*) egg at 5:30 P.M. Roberts, *161*, witnessed the removal of eggs from nests of a Scarlet Tanager (*Piranga erythromelas*) and Chipping Sparrow (*Spizella passerina*). Dr. H. W. Hann (mss.) found that Cowbirds in Michigan laid 40 eggs in Ovenbirds' (*Seiurus aurocapillus*) nests and removed 34 eggs; they never took eggs at the time of laying which is at dawn, but sometimes removed them the day before, sometimes on the same day and occasionally on the following day.

The same Cowbird—to judge from egg type—will remove a Song Sparrow egg from one nest in which she lays and not from another. During the first three years I assigned the loss of 14 Song Sparrow eggs to the Cowbird, or about one-fifth the number of Cowbird eggs; but during the last four years the loss has been much greater—at least 34 Song Sparrow eggs lost for 61 Cowbird eggs gained—55.9 per cent of the times Cowbird eggs were laid. The loss throughout the seven years comes to 37.2 per cent of the times eggs were laid, but it was probably somewhat higher. Capek, *35,* reported a 36 per cent loss of eggs by removal in the case of the European Cuckoo, but Chance's, *36,* Meadow Pipit Cuckoo regularly removed an egg of her victim at the time of laying her own.

B. The Song Sparrow as Host

Melospiza melodia is a favored host of the Cowbird in many regions. "If being victimized carries with it any distinction, then the Song Sparrow is distinquished over a greater area than any other species, certainly in North America, and possibly in the world, few cuculine hosts having ranges coincident with that of their parasite at all comparable with that of *Melospiza melodia*" (Friedmann, *59*). Barrows writes for Michigan—"Probably this species rears more Cowbirds than any other bird which we have," *16*. As to Ohio, Hicks in summarizing the records of 599 parasitized nests found by him in Ohio says, "The Song Sparrow ranked first as host, furnishing 22 per cent of all the parasitized nests found." Of 398 nests of this species, 135 or 34 per cent held Cowbird eggs or young, *79*.

On Interpont the Song Sparrow serves as practically the only host for the early eggs of the Cowbird, the only other possible victims that nest in late April being a few pairs of Cardinals (*Richmondena c. cardinalis*). Later the Northern Yellow-throats share the burden, and probably Indigo Buntings (*Passerina cyanea*).

The Song Sparrows on Interpont are disturbed by the presence of adult Cowbirds on their territories, giving a note of anxiety, and attacking the female as she approaches the nest. Yet they are good foster-parents to the young Cowbirds, that ordinarily prosper under their care. Pickwell, *147,* reports that the Prairie Horned Lark is a poor fosterer, and the same seems to be true of the Ovenbird according to Dr. Hann.

The number of Song Sparrows raised in a nest with one Cowbird were as follows: 5 in one case, 4 in 3 cases, 3 in 9 cases, 2 in 5 cases, and one in 6 cases. Single Cowbirds were raised alone 4 times. There were 4 cases of 2 Cowbirds being raised in one nest: once alone, once with one Song Sparrow, and twice with two.

On June 13, 1932, I found a nest on Interpont containing a Cowbird and three Northern Yellowthroats ready to leave.

C. The Effect of the Cowbird on the Song Sparrow

The amount of parasitism during the seven years is shown in Table XX, as well as data on the Cowbird eggs and young. (I am including in this table *the results obtained in 1936,* since they constitute a significant addition to the data.)

TABLE XX

The Cowbird in Relation to the Song Sparrow

	Total	Song Sparrow Nests		Nests With			Cowbird Eggs and Young			
		No. Parasitized	%	1 Egg	2 Eggs	3 Eggs	Eggs Laid	Eggs Hatched	Young Fledged	Per Cent Success
1930	61	15	24.6	10	5	0	20	17	7	35.0
1931	36	10	27.7	8	2	0	12	7	2	16.6
1932	50	29	58.0	22	7	0	36	24	16	45.7
1933	33	12	36.4	9	3	0	15	5	2	12.3
1934	13	9	69.2	4	3	2	(16)*	(2)	(2)	(12.5)
1935	18	14	77.7	10	4	0	18	8	4	22.2
1936	12	9	75.0	6	2	1	12	11	5	41.7
	—	—	—	—	—	—	—	—	—	—
Total 223		98	43.9	69	26	3	129 [113	72	36	31.9]†

*13 of the 16 eggs in 1934 were collected.
†Results with 1934 omitted.

During the first two years the amount of parasitism ran comparatively low, being only some 26 per cent in contrast to the 34 per cent found by Hicks throughout Ohio for the Song Sparrow. After that the parasitism of the early nests increased strikingly, affecting 58, 45 (for 20 early nests in 1933), 69, 78 and 75 per cent. One reason for the comparatively light parasitism of the early nests in 1930 and 1931 (28 per cent early in the season), lay in the fact that most of the first sets were complete before the Cowbirds began to lay, but since then the majority of the first sets of the Song Sparrows and the start of Cowbird laying have coincided.

Of 113 Cowbird eggs (the 16 laid in 1934 being omitted since I collected most of them), 72 hatched, but only 36 were fledged—31.9 per cent of success.

In Table XXI the success of Song Sparrow nests in five years with and without Cowbird eggs is shown.

TABLE XXI

Success of Song Sparrow Nests With and Without Cowbird Eggs
ONLY NESTS THAT RAISED AT LEAST ONE SONG SPARROW INCLUDED

	——Non-Parasitized Nests——			——Parasitized Nests——		
	Number Nests	Number Young Fledged	Average Fledged per Nest	Number Nest	Number Young* Fledged	Average* Fledged per Nest
1930 - - -	24	86	3.6	5	16	3.2
1931 - - -	17	64	3.6	1	1	1.0
1932 - - -	15	46	3.1	15	30	2.0
1933 - - -	7	18	2.6	3	9	3.0
1935 - - -	3	11	3.7	4	11	2.8
	66	225	3.4	28	67	2.4

*Song Sparrows only.

Sixty-six successful nests without Cowbird eggs raised an average of 3.4 Song Sparrows, while 28 successful nests with Cowbird eggs raised only 2.4 young. *Hence each Cowbird would seem to have been raised at the expense of one Song Sparrow.*

What percentage of the eggs laid come to their ends through Cowbird activities? If we turn back to Table XVIII we find that 46 were removed by Cowbirds—5.5 per cent, while 4 young were crushed —0.5 per cent—6 per cent in all. If we add to this the 13 starved young in 1932 that had Cowbird nest mates, we get a total loss of 63 of the original 854 eggs or 7.5 per cent. This is probably a little low, since I do not believe I counted enough eggs as being removed by Cowbirds during the first three years, and in 1934 I collected most of the Cowbird eggs; perhaps 72 eggs or 8.5 per cent loss would be more nearly correct.

Friedmann says, "The Cowbird is probably one of the chief factors in checking the increase of the smaller Sparrows and Finches," *59*, p. 196. I do not feel that we know enough about the factors influencing survival and increase of our common birds to enable us either to accept or reject this statement.

a. The Incidence of Cowbird Parasitism on Interpont

Table XX shows the great increase in Cowbird parasitism during the course of the study. During four of the years I took nesting censuses (by counting the singing males) of all the birds on Upper Interpont, but unfortunately failed to do this in 1932 and 1933, an omission which greatly hampers me in trying to study the course of events.

There have always been on Interpont more pairs of Song Sparrows than of other possible hosts for the Cowbirds. In 1930 there were 52 Song Sparrow pairs and 41 pairs of other hosts, in 1931 48 Song Sparrows and 34 others, in 1934 25 Song Sparrows and 24 others, in 1935 25 Song Sparrows and 20 others. (See Appendix III.) The number of Cowbirds laying on the area has been about six during each of the four years. Thus during the early period each Cowbird had 14 to 15 pairs of hosts, but during 1934-'35 about 8. In 1936 the number of Cowbird females dropped to 4, but the Song Sparrows were so few in number (only 13 females), while the other hosts came to only some 22 pairs, that the situation was even worse than before for the Song Sparrows.

Fortunately, careful, detailed censuses were taken from 1924 to 1933 by L. E. Hicks on an 80 acre tract some 10 miles northeast of Interpont, *80;* by working over these figures and comparing them with his paper on Cowbird Hosts in Ohio, *79,* and by consulting with him, the following facts have been found: During the 10 years there was a total of 48 female Cowbirds and 604 pairs of suitable hosts, or one Cowbird to 12.5 pairs of hosts. Dr. Hicks found 301 nests of these hosts, of which 105 contained Cowbird eggs. Hence a population of one Cowbird to 12.5 pairs of hosts resulted in 35 per cent parasitism. Calculating on this basis, a supply of 8 pairs of hosts per Cowbird would result in 55 per cent parasitism. This would probably be somewhere near the truth, if the whole Cowbird season is taken into consideration and all the hosts, although my figures for the Song Sparrows in April, May, and early June, 1934, 1935 and 1936, run over 70 per cent.

A possible explanation of the very heavy parasitism during the last three years is this: the population of Cowbird hosts has greatly diminished, while the population of Cowbirds remained fairly stable. This does not, however, explain the sudden jump in 1932. I believe this was due to two factors: marked increase in the numbers of Cowbirds that year—I distinguished no less than 7 types of their eggs on Upper Interpont—and the lateness of the season which delayed the start of nesting of the Song Sparrows to the most favorable date for the

Cowbirds. That there was no scarcity of other hosts for later "sets" of the Cowbirds is shown by a note in my records that I estimated that 18 pairs of Northern Yellow-throats were present and 6 pairs of Alder Flycatchers.

In 1936 the decrease in Cowbirds was more than compensated for by the even greater decrease in Song Sparrows; the former were one-third fewer than before, the latter (i.e. the females) had dropped to half their numbers in 1935.

There are two factors in Molothrine character that have enabled the present unbalanced situation to develop: faithfulness in returning to the breeding grounds and, at the same time, the lack of the territorial safeguard.

D. THE SUCCESS OF THE COWBIRD ON INTERPONT

If we turn to Table XX, we find, contrary to expectation, that the Cowbird eggs have not succeeded as well as the Song Sparrow eggs, for only 31.9 per cent of the 113 Cowbird eggs have been fledged in contrast to 36.2 per cent of the 854 Song Sparrow eggs (data for 1934 being omitted for both species, but included for 1936). In only two years—1932 and 1936—did the Cowbirds succeed better than the Song Sparrows. The Cowbirds run all the hazards to which their hosts are subject except those imposed by the Cowbirds themselves in relation to the Song Sparrows; to compensate, they have some hazards of their own. Three of the 113 eggs were laid in deserted nests, and two in empty nests—one of which was promptly deserted—giving a 3.5 per cent loss. Eight eggs were laid in incubated sets hatching from two to five days after their nest mates, all these young perishing —giving a 7 per cent loss. So we have a 10.5 per cent loss of Cowbird eggs due to the exigencies of parasitism to offset the 8.5 per cent loss they inflict on the Song Sparrows.

My figures also show that parasitized nests—as nests—do not succeed as well as non-parasitized ones, even when we count the raising of Cowbirds alone as a success, for 56 per cent of 118 non-parasitized nests raised at least one young bird and only 40 per cent of 80 parasitized nests (data for 1934 and 1936 omitted), the percentage of success for the 198 nests being 47.8. This brings up the question as to the excellence of concealment of non-parasitized and parasitized nests;

we find that 71 per cent of the former nests were classed as excellent in regard to concealment and 62 per cent of the latter. We have already seen in Chapter X that (excluding 12 nests destroyed by flood and plowing) the success of 135 nests ranked excellent in concealment reached 55 per cent, while the success of the 64 ranked good, fair and poor reached only 36 per cent. These figures seem to show that Cowbirds do not find well concealed nests quite as readily as those poorly concealed, and that the same is true of predators. Incidentally this brings up the problem as to how the Cowbird finds her nests—by watching her victims build, or by direct search? I believe that both methods are used.

The Cowbird eggs hatched slightly better than the Song Sparrows —63.7 per cent in contrast to 60.7 per cent (1934 omitted, 1936 included), but fewer Cowbirds were raised, primarily because of the 8 that hatched too late to compete successfully with their nest mates.

It may well be that the Cowbirds as well as the Song Sparrows are suffering from Molothrine over-abundance. With a restricted supply of host nests, more eggs have to be laid in sets where incubation has begun, and more young perish. (Our figures do not show this, but larger samples of Cowbird and host populations might do so.)

This matter of relative success of parasite and host is a very interesting one. How does it stand with the smaller hosts where the Cowbird must do much more damage than it does to the Song Sparrow? If only 32 per cent of a Cowbird's eggs are fledged, how does it keep up its numbers so remarkably well?

My guess is that Cowbirds and Song Sparrows lay about the same number of eggs each year. I believe the Cowbird is a longer-lived bird than the Song Sparrow, that the young bird after becoming independent runs fewer dangers than does the young Song Sparrow, and that this is certainly true of the fully adult bird.

E. Summary

1. In contrast to the European Cuckoo, the Cowbird is not specialized for parasitism.

2. The Cowbird is not specific in its parasitism, its egg is of normal size and shell-texture, and the nestling does not deliberately evict its nest-mates.

3. The incubation period is not shorter than that of some of its relatives.

4. With the Song Sparrow as a host the incubation period of the Cowbird egg has been normally 11 to 12 days, sometimes longer, but never shorter.

5. Cowbirds are markedly social birds even in the breeding season in this region.

6. The Cowbirds on Interpont have shown no tendency to pair, but are promiscuous.

7. Fights between male Cowbirds have been recorded on five occasions.

8. Cowbirds show no disposition to defend a territory, yet they restrict their activities to an area of 20 to 30 acres during the breeding season.

9. Their attachment to their homes is shown by the reappearance in fall of banded females and also by homing experiments—some male Cowbirds returning from extraordinary distances.

10. The average measurements of 75 Cowbird eggs were 22.6 x 16.3 mm., the average weight of 24 fresh eggs being 3.17 g.

11. The earliest eggs of the Cowbirds have been found between Apr. 22 and 29, the average being Apr. 25.

12. There is evidence that some Cowbirds on Interpont lay three "sets" of eggs.

13. Two Cowbird eggs were laid in one Song Sparrow nest in 27 per cent of the cases during this study, 3 eggs in 3 per cent and one egg in 70 per cent.

14. The young Cowbird normally leaves the nest at 9 or 10 days weighing half as much again as its Song Sparrow foster-parent.

15. Cowbirds removed Song Sparrow eggs at least one-third of the times that they deposited eggs, but the host's egg is not taken at the time the Cowbird lays her egg.

16. The Song Sparrow is a favorite host of the Cowbird throughout most of its range.

17. In Ohio L. E. Hicks has found 34 per cent of its nests parasitized.

18. On Interpont the Song Sparrow is the most important host for the Cowbird.

19. Cowbird parasitism has increased very much during the course of the study, about 26 per cent of the nests being affected during 1930 and 1931, but from 58 to 78 per cent of the early nests in four out of the last five years (Table XX).

20. Sixty-six successful non-parasitized nests raised an average of 3.4 Song Sparrows, while 28 successful parasitized nests raised an average of 2.4 Song Sparrows (Table XXI).

21. A loss of at least 7.5 per cent of the original Song Sparrow eggs can be laid at the door of the Cowbird.

22. The numbers of Cowbirds and their hosts on Interpont are given for four years (see Appendix III).

23. On an 80 acre tract 10 miles northeast of Interpont Hicks found an average of one Cowbird to 12.5 pairs of hosts. Thirty-five per cent of the nests of these hosts were parasitized, *80*.

24. During 1930 and 1931, on Interpont there were approximately 14 to 15 pairs of hosts to each female Cowbird, but during 1934 and 1935 only about 8 pairs.

25. The population of Song Sparrows and other Cowbird hosts has greatly diminished during the last four years, but the Cowbird population remained almost stationary until 1936 when it decreased one-third.

26. Cowbird reproduction has been less successful than that of the Song Sparrow, 32 per cent of the eggs of the former having been hatched and fledged in contrast to 36 per cent of the latter.

27. Parasitized nests do not succeed as well as non-parasitized nests even when the raising of a single Cowbird is counted as a success.

28. Cowbirds apparently do not find well concealed nests quite as readily as those poorly concealed, and the same is true of predators.

29. The Cowbird offers a particularly rich field for research.

CHAPTER XVII

Survival of the Adults

From 1929 to the late summer of 1932 Interpont afforded optimum conditions for Song Sparrow settlement. If this area had been left undisturbed a most interesting study could have been made of the fluctuations of a population of this species in a fairly stable environment with the weather and ecological succession as the chief factors for change.

But the picture was greatly complicated by the wholesale destruction of cover on Interpont.

All along the river bank in the late summer of 1932 everything was cut down but the large trees, while the main body of Upper Interpont was taken over for gardens for the unemployed the following March, leaving only the dikes comparatively undisturbed, but the strip along the river was allowed to grow up to weeds. In the summer of 1934 even the dikes and this strip from the 3rd to the 4th dike were "cleaned up," so that the only areas available for Song Sparrows were our garden, the 1st and 2nd dikes, the space along the river bank between the 1st and 3rd dike and between the 4th dike and Dodridge street Bridge.

If this destruction had meant simply fewer territories and a proportionally smaller Song Sparrow population living under comparable conditions to those before, the problem would have been simple. But this was not the case. Cowbird infestation of the nests greatly increased especially in 1934, 1935 and 1936 while the mortality of adult Song Sparrows at all seasons became very heavy.

The study divides itself (as was clearly shown in Chapter XV) into three "good" and four "bad" years; during the first period both favorable and unfavorable conditions influenced a thriving, well-situated population, but during the last period too many unfavorable factors decimated an exposed and dwindling colony.

A. Survival of the Adult Males

Most of my data on survival and most of the calculations must be based on the males, since the females are not able to return as faithfully to their former homes as are the males. Yet they must survive practically as well as the males, since the sex ratio each spring is usually even or almost even.

The survival of the breeding males is a comparatively simple matter to follow in a relatively unchanging environment, for the males remain on or return to the approximate site of their territories with entire faithfulness. Hence if the birds are banded, the stability of the population can be followed from year to year and the season of the death of each bird be ascertained, particularly if the fall happens to be favorable for finding the birds.

It has been necessary to select several dates from which to reckon. April 6 is the most important; this is the point when I consider the breeding population as established, for all the males and practically all the females are present. A banded or otherwise positively known bird that is settled on or near Interpont on April 6 of any year is entitled to membership in that year's group; the few that arrived in May or June, are counted in the next year's. (In the 1930 group of males are two birds banded previously—1M in 1928 and 4M in 1929.) With the females the reckoning has to be a little more liberal, a few that arrived as late as April 18 to 21 being included with the April birds.

Early June is the next date, chosen largely because each year except 1930 and 1934 we left Columbus in that month. October is the month when the summer residents leave. It was possible in the fall of 1930 and 1931 to check up on the presence of all the banded adult males at this time, but not of the females; since then the censuses have been less satisfactory due to cold weather in early October during three of the years, while in 1934 the large scale destruction of cover that had taken place in the summer prevented an accurate count.

The survival of the six different groups of males is shown in Table XXII and Chart XVII.

It must be remembered that these six different groups do not represent the total new breeding population on Interpont each year; they are the *banded* representatives of these new breeding birds and, besides, a few of them nested to the north and west of Interpont.

It will be seen that the survival rate was excellent until October, 1932, from which date it rapidly decreased. The first rather unexpected finding is the mortality of the adult males during the breeding season, ranging from 11 to 16 per cent during the first three years, but accounting for a third of the birds in 1933 and nearly a half of them in 1934, dropping, however, to a fifth in 1935.

The returning ratios for the total population of males the first two years were high—59.3 and 65.1 for the whole population; in 1933 the ratio was 48, in 1934 it dropped to 23, in 1935 it was 30, and 1936 20. I believe that the first two percentages are typical for a thriving,

TABLE XXII

Survival of Banded Breeding Male Song Sparrows

NUMBERS

	1930 Apr. 6	1930 June	1930 October	1931 Apr. 6	1931 June	1931 October	1932 Apr. 6	1932 June	1932 October
1st Group	27	24	23	16	13	12	10	8	6
2nd Group				27	24	22	18	17	10
3rd Group							47	38	33
4th Group									
5th Group									
6th Group									
Total	27	24	23	43	37	34	75	63	49

PERCENTAGES

	1930 Apr. 6	1930 June	1930 October	1931 Apr. 6	1931 June	1931 October	1932 Apr. 6	1932 June	1932 October
1st Group	100	88.8	85.2	59.3	48.1	44.4	37.0	29.6	22.2
2nd Group				100	88.8	81.5	66.7	63.0	37.0
3rd Group							100	80.9	70.2
4th Group									
5th Group									
6th Group									
Total	100	88.8	85.2	100	86.0	79.1	100	84.0	65.3
"Returns"				59.3			65.1		

NUMBERS

	1933 Apr. 6	1933 June	1933 Oct.	1934 Apr. 6	1934 June	1934 Oct.	1935 Apr. 6	1935 June	1935 Oct.	1936 Apr. 6
1st Group	4	2	2	2	2	1	1	1	1	0
2nd Group	8	4	2	1	1	1	1	1	1	0
3rd Group	24	13	6	4	3	2	1	1	0	0
4th Group	20	17	10	6	2	2	2	2	2	2
5th Group				17	8	7	4	2	1	0
6th Group							6	5	2	1
Total	56	36	20	30	16	13	15	12	7	3

PERCENTAGES

	1933 Apr. 6	1933 June	1933 Oct.	1934 Apr. 6	1934 June	1934 Oct.	1935 Apr. 6	1935 June	1935 Oct.	1936 Apr. 6
1st Group	14.8	7.4	7.4	7.4	7.4	3.7	3.7	3.7	3.7	0
2nd Group	29.6	14.8	7.4	3.7	3.7	3.7	3.7	3.7	3.7	0
3rd Group	51.1	21.0	12.7	8.5	6.3	4.3	2.1	2.1	0	0
4th Group	100	85.0	50.0	30.0	10.0	10.0	10.0	10.0	10.0	10.0
5th Group				100.0	47.0	41.2	23.5	11.8	5.9	0
6th Group							100.0	83.3	33.3	16.6
Total	100	64.2	35.8	100	53.3	43.3	100	80.0	46.6	100
"Returns"	48.0			23.2			30.0			20.0

well-situated Song Sparrow population. It seems probable that the comparatively low figure for the spring of 1933 probably did not include all the males that were still living, some of them having been driven from Interpont in the late summer of 1932 by the destruction of all cover along the river bank. There were 13 males which I could not locate that fall; of these 8 had had territories in this region which had been rendered untenable. It may also be that in the spring some males returned to Interpont and finding their homes radically changed left to seek better quarters. The fact that there were some empty territories on Interpont each year after 1932 does not disprove this assumption, for we do not know that a dispossessed bird settles on the *nearest* suitable territory.

I believe that the very low return ratios of 1934 and 1935 largely reflect the heavy mortality from which the birds suffered during the previous nesting season—36 and 48 per cent of the nesting males during approximately two months.

In a secure population it would seem safe to calculate on a 60 per cent return ratio of breeding male Song Sparrows.

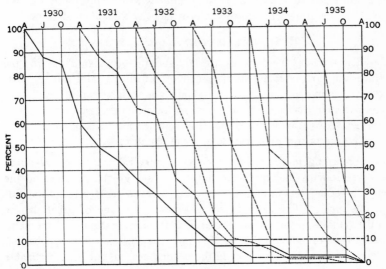

CHART XVII. *Survival of Adult Banded Breeding Males in Percentages of Total. A=April 6, J=June, O=October. See Table XXII.*

Because of the uncertainty of my October figures during the later years, we can be sure of the winter mortality only during 1930 to 1931 and 1931 to 1932. The first winter caused a comparatively heavy toll— a 26 per cent loss of the breeding males (October to April), but during the next winter only 14 per cent came to their ends during this period. Kendeigh, *94,* reports that after the winter of 1930 and 1931 the survival of the House Wrens (*Troglodytes aedon*) at Gates Mills in northern Ohio was very low, but the following winter it was good. He found a definite correlation between the survival ratio of his birds these two years and the average night temperature in the Wrens' winter range—southeastern United States, the average for 1930-31 being slightly below 10° C. (50° F.), that of 1931-32 reaching 15.6° C. (60° F.). In Columbus the three months of the first winter averaged 0.8° C. (33.5° F.) and of the second winter 4.4° C. (40° F.). But no Song Sparrows have died of cold on Interpont during our stay in Columbus, so far as I know. It might have been that some of the migrating birds in 1930-31 were caught in a storm, as mentioned by Lincoln, *103.* Another effect of severe weather is the increased predation on birds by Sparrow Hawks (*Falco sparverius*) and Screech Owls (*Otus asio*) when mice are protected by a blanket of snow.

B. SURVIVAL OF THE ADULT FEMALES

The data on the females are less satisfactory than those for the males, due to the fact that they cannot return so faithfully to their former nesting sites and are occasionally found far from home. Hence it is probable that some that return to the general region are not discovered. Also it may be that sometimes when a nest is broken up, the female deserts and joins a male at some distance.

According to these figures female "survival" is from two-thirds to three-fourths that of the males; there is a greater loss during the early breeding season and also a lower percentage of returns the following spring. The early breeding season is a time of great danger to the females, probably correlated with the fact that most of the nests are on the ground, and that the females take sole charge of incubation. I have no data on losses later in the nesting season, but it is reasonable to suppose that a bird would have a better chance of escape from a somewhat elevated nest than from the ground.

TABLE XXIII

Survival of Banded Breeding Female Song Sparrows

NUMBERS

	1930 April	1930 June	1931 April	1931 June	1932 April	1932 June
1st Group - - - -	20	15	8	8	4	4
2nd Group - - - -			24	18	10	7
3rd Group - - - -					50	35
4th Group - - - -						
5th Group - - - -						
6th Group - - - -						
Total - - - -	20	15	32	26	64	46

PERCENTAGES

	1930 April	1930 June	1931 April	1931 June	1932 April	1932 June
1st Group - - - -	100	75.0	40.0	40.0	20.0	20.0
2nd Group - - - -			100	75.0	41.7	29.1
3rd Group - - - -					100	70.0
4th Group - - - -						
5th Group - - - -						
6th Group - - - -						
Total - - - -	100	75.0	100	81.2	100	71.9
"Returns" - - -			40.0		43.7	

NUMBERS

	1933 April	1933 June	1934 April	1934 June	1935 April	1935 June	1936 April
1st Group - - - - -	2	0	0	0	0	0	0
2nd Group - - - - -	3	1	0	0	0	0	0
3rd Group - - - - -	17	10	3	1	0	0	0
4th Group - - - - -	25	17	3	2	2	2	1
5th Group - - - - -			16	12	3	1	0
6th Group - - - - -					11	6	1
Total - - - - -	47	28	22	15	16	9	2

PERCENTAGES

	1933 April	1933 June	1934 April	1934 June	1935 April	1935 June	1936 April
1st Group - - - - -	10.0	0	0	0	0	0	0
2nd Group - - - - -	12.5	4.2	0	0	0	0	0
3rd Group - - - - -	35.4	20.0	15.0	2.0	0	0	0
4th Group - - - - -	100	68.0	12.0	8.0	8.0	8.0	4.0
5th Group - - - - -			100.0	75.0	18.8	6.2	0
6th Group - - - - -					100	54.5	9.1
Total - - - - -	100	59.8	100	68.2	100	56.2	100
"Returns" - - -	34.4		12.8		22.7		12.5

When do the males run sufficient dangers to bring their losses up to those of the females? If we average the figures found for the banded males for the years 1930 and 1931 (Table XXII), we find a 20.4 per cent loss from November through March or 4.1 per cent per month; an 11.1 per cent loss in the early nesting season or 4.4 per cent per month and 5.5 per cent from mid-June through October or 1.2 per cent loss per month—a total loss of 37 per cent each year averaging 3.1 per cent each month. The most dangerous time is during the early nesting season, although the winter losses average rather high partly due to the high loss of migrating males in the winter of 1930-31, and partly due to the fact that in February and March the resident male is proclaiming territory.

There happened to have been 40 deaths of the resident males from the spring of 1930 to the end of 1932—a convenient coincidence as 40 is the calculated yearly loss of adult males in a secure population. The seasons of death of these 40 birds were as follows: from November to January—11 or 3.7 per month; in February and March— 9 or 4.5 per month; from April to mid-June—11 or 4.4 per month; mid-June through October 9 or 2 per month. These two sets of figures correspond very well with each other.

As to the females, we have few data on which to base calculations, for three reasons—first, the impossibility of checking on their presence in the fall; second, the impossibility of finding *all* the "returns" each spring; and thirdly, because of the possibility that some of the breeding season losses represent desertions rather than deaths. Perhaps the best we can do is to assign them a 10 per cent monthly loss during May and June and a 2 per cent monthly loss during the rest of the year which would bring their annual mortality to 40 per cent. (It is possible it may be somewhat higher, and the numbers are kept up by more first year females *surviving to start the breeding season* than their brothers that have been proclaiming territory for two months, but there is no way to check this problem at present.)

C. Losses and Replacements in the Population

As already shown in Tables XXII and XXIII there has been a considerable loss every year of breeding birds during the early nesting season. The losses in the whole population under observation (most of Central Interpont in 1930, most of Upper Interpont in 1931 and all of Upper Interpont after that) are shown in Table XXIV, and also the numbers of new birds of each sex that settled in the areas during the early nesting season. The last column shows the size of the June population of breeders in comparison to that in April.

Some of the birds were unbanded, but the fact of their disappearance was as evident as with banded birds, except in the case where an unbanded bird might have disappeared and been replaced in a day or two by another unbanded bird. It may well be that the losses of females have been even higher than shown in the table.

TABLE XXIV

Losses and Replacements in Song Sparrow Populations on Interpont
(Some of the Birds Were Not Banded)

	Total in April		Lost		New		Total in June		June Population Per Cent of Original Numbers	
	♂♂	♀♀	♂♂	♀♀	♂♂	♀♀	♂♂	♀♀	♂♂	♀♀
1930 - - -	30	30	4	10	1	5	27	25	90.0	83.3
1931 - - -	41	41	7	11	2	4	36	34	87.8	82.9
1932 - - -	69	65	10	20	2	6	61	51	88.4	78.5
1933 - - -	44	41	12	15	6	5	38	31	86.4	75.6
1934 - - -	29	25	10	9	5	0	23	16	79.3	64.0
1935 - - -	25	25	6	9	1	0	20	16	80.0	64.0
Totals -	238	227	49	74	17	20	205	173	86.1	76.2
1st 3 Yrs. -	140	136	21	41	5	15	124	110	88.6	80.9
Last 3 Yrs. -	98	91	28	33	12	5	81	63	82.6	69.2

The first columns of the table give us the sex ratio of these populations in April: in three years it was equal, in the others it showed an excess of males, giving a total ratio of 104.9 males to 100 females. By June, however, in every year there were unmated males—ranging from 2 to 10, the sex ratio at this time averaging 118.5:100 in the period from 1930 to 1935.

In 1936, however, the sex ratio was very high in April—18 males to 12 females—150:100. We have already seen in Chapter IV that the quota of summer resident males was only about half the expected number this year; the shortage of both males and females may have been due to the severity of the preceding winter. By June most of the unmated males had disappeared and the sex ratio was nearly even.

During the first three years the loss of males was 15 per cent, but during the last three double this figure. (The losses in 1933 and 1934 among the banded males on and off Interpont were even higher as shown in Table XXII.) The loss of females reached 30 per cent during the first three years and 35 per cent during the last three. These figures do not show the high death rate of the resident males—both old and young—that were new on Interpont in a particular winter and that disappeared *before* April 6. In 1934 there was a particularly high toll—six unbanded males that were proclaiming territory and four banded ones—more than a third as many as the breeding population in April. If we add these 10 potential breeders that were present in

March to the 29 males present on April 6, we have an original population of 39 that was reduced to 18 by the end of May—a loss of 54 per cent. There has clearly been something very much the matter with Interpont as a nesting place for Song Sparrows ever since the spring of 1933.

As to the gains in new birds, they were always much smaller than the losses; with the males they reached 24 per cent of the losses during the first three years and 41 per cent during the last three—a total of 34 per cent, i.e., for every three birds lost one new one came in. With the females replacements reached 37 per cent of the losses during the first three years, but only 17 per cent during the last three, the total being 29 per cent, or in other words 3 females gained for each 10 lost. It may be that the general region was disturbed by the changes induced by cultivation, so that males were being driven out of their territories in the surrounding country side. I have no explanation to offer for the lack of records of new females during the last two years, but since comparatively few females were banded, a change of unbanded females on North Interpont (provided it happened promptly) could have escaped my notice.

In every year but 1934 and 1936 the loss of females was greater than that of the males—the total loss through the six years being half as many more. The number of new females, however, was three times as great as that of the males in the first three years, but less than half as much in the last three. In 1936 5 of the 6 unmated males had disappeared by May 10; some were probably killed, but others may have given up their territories (see Chapter IX).

I believe that most of the males that disappeared were probably killed, but I am not sure about the females. It seems likely to me that some deserted after their nests were broken up, but I never found such a bird in a different location the same year, nor in any subsequent year. If she deserts she must go some distance away before joining a new mate (as did the Wheatear, *189a,* cited in Chapter IX), and the next year return to her new home. The comparatively large numbers of new females during the first four years would support this desertion theory.

This serious mortality of the breeding birds has, even in the best years, an important effect on reproduction; it is a factor that has to be reckoned with in calculations as to the possible increase of a population. It is more serious than mortality at any other time of the year because it cuts off the breeding birds when there is little chance of replacement. Adjustment is occasionally made through polygamy, but this is but a makeshift arrangement of rather doubtful success so far as the progeny is concerned.

How general this loss among breeding birds during the nesting season is we have no means of knowing. It has not been reported by other observers, so far as I know.

D. Proportion of First Year Birds in the Population

In 1930 all the males on about 20 acres of Central Interpont were banded, so that the next year I knew the status of the Song Sparrow population of this area. In 1931 every male on Central Interpont was banded, in 1932 and 1933 every male on both Central and North Interpont (i.e., Upper Interpont) and in 1934 every male on Central Interpont. Table XXV gives the numbers and percentages each year for these different areas of the population surviving from the previous year, of the new adults that moved in, and of the first year birds, as well as the survival ratio. In the last columns the numbers of adult and first year birds among the *resident* males on Interpont are given—for Central Interpont in 1930, for Upper Interpont afterwards.

Each year a few adult males came in—two late in the previous summer, the others in the winter or spring. It is possible that a few more of the summer residents which I assumed to be first year birds were really older. It was only in 1934 that this group assumed importance amounting to a fourth of the breeding males—a fact correlated with the widespread destruction in neighboring regions, particularly south of Interpont where a mile (1.6 kilometers) stretch bordering the river on which probably over 30 pairs were present April 16, 1932, and 25 pairs were recorded March 31, 1933, was so altered in character that exactly one pair could be located on April 23, 1934. Under such circumstances it is strange that Interpont and the woods opposite it were not filled to capacity; it seemed to me that spring that Upper Interpont could have accommodated about six more pairs than it did. Perhaps the floods of May, 1933, may have been partly responsible for the sparse population.

TABLE XXV

Proportions of Adult and Young Males on Interpont in April

Year	"Returns"*	New Adults	Young Males	Total	Survival Ratio April to April	Adult	Young
			Breeding Population on Central Interpont			Resident Males†	
1930—Numbers						8	6
Per Cent						57.1	42.9
1931—Numbers	18	1	4	23(+8)‡		16	8
Per Cent	78.3	4.3	17.4	100	59.3	66.6	33.3
1932—Numbers	19	1	24	44		20	21
Per Cent	43.2	2.3	54.5	100	61.3	48.8	51.2
1933—Numbers	19	1	9	29		14	5
Per Cent	65.5	3.5	31.0	100	43.2	73.7	26.3
1934—Numbers	6	5	8	19		5	5
Per Cent	31.6	26.3	42.1	100	20.7	50.0	50.0
1935—Numbers	6	2§	9§	17		1	6
Per Cent	35.3	11.8	52.9	100	31.6	14.3	85.7
BREEDING POPULATION ON UPPER INTERPONT							
1933—Numbers	30	3	11	44			
Per Cent	68.2	6.8	25.0	100	43.5		
1934—Numbers	11	6	12	29			
Per Cent	37.9	20.7	41.4	100	25.0		

*"Returns" signify survival of breeding males of previous year.

†Figures based on Central Interpont in 1930, on Upper Interpont afterwards.

‡Of the 33 males present on Central Interpont in June, 1930, 26 were banded. Of the 31 present in 1931 18 were "returns," 4 were known to be first-year birds, and one was a new adult resident. The percentages are based on the 23 birds whose status was known.

§Five of the new breeders were known to be young through the character of the song; the other two residents were adult. The 4 new summer residents were counted as first-year birds, although one or two might have been adult.

Turning to the numbers of "returns," i.e., survivals of birds present the previous year, we find a very high proportion in 1931, high in 1933, and low in 1932, 1934, and 1935. In order to analyze these percentages we must examine the survival ratios of the adults and here we see that the differing proportions for 1931 and 1932 depended not on the survival of the adult birds which was almost the same both years, but on the numbers of young present. In 1931 after the shortened breeding season of 1930 there were only 4 young birds present in the 20 acre tract, but in 1932 after the optimum breeding season of 1931 there were 19 first-year males on this tract and 24 on the 30 acres of Central Interpont. In 1933 the population of "returns" came the nearest to our theoretical figure of 60 per cent adult birds. Yet this figure resulted from poor survival of the adults and a low quota of young from the unsuccessful breeding season of 1932 and also (probably) a shortage of territories. In 1934 we find the worst survival and smallest percentage of old inhabitants for any year, while the figure for adults from outside is strikingly high. In 1935 the survival and quota of returns is again low, and the proportion of young high. It must be kept in mind that each year except 1932 there have been vacant territories on Central Interpont.

The figures for Upper Interpont (Central and North Interpont) for 1933 and 1934 show the same tendencies as those for Central Interpont.

As for the 26 males present on the 20 acres in June, 1930, 18 were present in 1931 (69.2 per cent), 11 in 1932 (42.3 per cent), 4 in 1933 (15.4 per cent), 2 in 1934 (7.7 per cent), one in 1935 (3.9 per cent) and none in 1936. (In connection with the very high rate of 69.2 per cent survival it must be remembered that this is reckoned from June to April, not April to April for which the ratio was 59.3 per cent as shown in the table.)

If we consider the proportions of young among the resident males we find that only in 1930 do we approach our expected 40 per cent. In 1931 and 1933 the proportions are low due to unsuccessful breeding seasons, in 1932 very high as we have seen in the total populations. The high proportions of the last two years result from the excessive mortality of the resident adults. It is a little disconcerting that we have no really "typical" year with 60 per cent adults and 40 per cent young, yet if we take the totals from 1930 through 1934 we get 58.4 per cent adults and 41.6 per cent young.

As to results on other species studied by means of banding, Uchida, *192,* in a four-year study of the Chimney Swallow (*Hirundo rustica gutturalis*) and Mosque Swallow (*Hirundo daurica nipalensis*) obtained a 46 per cent return of adults. A return ratio of some 48, *114,* to 52, *113,* per cent of adult Tree Swallows (*Iridoprocne bicolor*) on Cape Cod, Mass., is reported by Low. Another study on this same species in Princeton, Mass., gave 47.6 and 50 per cent return of adults (Chapman, *38*). Price, *149a,* obtained 52.4 per cent return of adults of the Plain Titmouse (*Baeolophus i. inornatus*) in California. In Kluijver's *98,* work with a colony of Starlings (*Sturnus vulgaris*) 49.6 per cent of the adults returned. Dr. S. P. Baldwin writes me that his breeding

House Wrens (*Troglodytes a. aedon*) give only a 35 per cent return ratio of adults.

It is interesting to note that the return ratios of the Swallows, Titmice, and Starlings range between 46 and 52.4 per cent.

It is the general belief that breeding birds return with great faithfulness to their former nesting sites, but is this always true? It cannot hold for species that are present one year and absent the next. It is natural that this impulse should be less strong in birds depending on specialized nest sites than on generalized sites. Bank Swallows (*Riparia r. riparia*) banded as breeding adults have been found in later years nesting at 13.5 kilometers (8 miles) distance in this country, *183*, and 15 kilometers (9 miles) in Germany, *185a*. Surprising results were obtained by Hicks with Purple Martins (*Progne s. subis*), *77b*; a female banded as a breeding bird was taken the next year on June 5, 17 kilometers (10 miles) south of the place of banding, while a male that nested for two years was found 210 kilometers (125 miles) southwest on May 5 the third year. So it is possible that these ratios of 35 to 50 per cent return of adults do not represent *all* the surviving adults.

If I calculate the return ratios of both sexes of my Song Sparrows for the first two years, I get 51 and 56 per cent respectively. But I know that this is too low a figure, for I am sure that all the surviving females do not return to Interpont.

E. Summary

1. During the first 2 years Interpont offered optimum conditions for the Song Sparrows, but after that cover was destroyed on a large scale.

2. The first three years show a thriving, well situated population, the last four an exposed and dwindling population.

3. The survival of the adult breeding males was excellent during the first part of the study, averaging over 60 per cent from one April to the next, but in the spring of 1932 it dropped to 48 per cent, and after that to 23, 30 and 20 (Table XXII).

4. There was a loss from April to June of 12 to 16 per cent of the banded males during the first three years, but during the next two it ranged from 36 to 47 per cent. This heavy loss during the

nesting season was largely responsible for the very low return ratios from 1934 to 1936.

5. During the somewhat severe winter of 1930-31 there was an appreciably greater loss among the migrating Song Sparrows than during the following winter. After the markedly severe winter of 1935-36 there was a striking shortage of summer residents, both male and female, in the breeding population.

6. The returns of the females never exceeded 44 per cent and in 1934 fell to 13 per cent. Their mortality from April to June ranged from 19 to 44 per cent, exceeding that of the males each year except in 1934 (Table XXIII).

7. From two sets of data the monthly loss per 100 adult males is estimated to average: from November through January 3.7, February through June 4.4, July through October 1.2-2.

8. The sex ratio of the breeding Song Sparrows on Interpont was 104.9:100 in April and 118.5:100 in June for the first 6 years, but in 1936 it was 150:100 in April, and nearly even in June.

9. The heavy loss of both males and females during the first months of the breeding season is shown in Table XXIV; it averaged 15 per cent of the males in the first three years and 30 per cent during the next three.

10. The loss of females averaged 30 per cent during the first three years and 35 per cent during the next three.

11. The proportion of first-year males in the population ranged from about 26 to 55 per cent (Table XXV).

12. In populations of six other species the percentages of adult birds that returned are reported as ranging from 35 to 52.

CHAPTER XVIII

Survival of the Young

The problem of the survival of the newly-hatched nestling for the first ten days of its life was treated in some detail in Chapter XV. What becomes of the 60 per cent of hatched birds that leave the nest in safety? Due to the retiring nature of the young Song Sparrow, to the fact that I seldom used colored bands on nestlings, and also to my preoccupation with other stages of the nest life, my information on the number of young leaving parental care at the age of 26 to 28 days is rather meager. In 10 broods, 70 per cent of the fledged young reached independence.

The present chapter is concerned with those fledged nestlings that reach adulthood; first with those that "returned," and second with a discussion of problems of survival.

A. RETURN OF THE FLEDGED YOUNG

Nearly 13 per cent of the Song Sparrows, banded in the nest and safely fledged, have later been found in the region as breeding birds. Let us examine the facts in regard to these particular birds and then turn to the question of the homing of young birds in general.

1. *The Number of Nestlings that Returned*

Forty birds banded as nestlings—26 males and 14 females—returned as breeding birds as shown in Table XXVI.

TABLE XXVI

"Returns" of Banded Nestlings in the Following Spring

Year Banded	Total Banded and Fledged	Total Returns as Breeders	Per-centage	Males R*	SR*	Un*	Females R*	SR*	Percentage Tot. Banded ♂♂	♀♀
1929 - -	11	1	9.1				1			9.1
1930 - -	102	12	11.8	7	1			4	7.9	3.9
1931 - -	65	13	20.0	4	4	1	1	3	13.8	6.2
1932 - -	76	10	13.2	4	3		1	2	9.2	4.0
1933 - -	27	2	7.4	1				1	3.7	3.7
1934 - -	14	1	7.1				1			7.1
1935 - -	22	1	4.5	1					4.5	
Totals	317	40	12.6	16	9	1	3	11	8.2	4.4

*R=resident, SR=summer resident, Un=status unknown.

The percentage of returns of the fledged young varied from 4.5 to 20. The highest figure occurred after the favorable winter of 1931 to 1932, when the return percentage of the adult males reached 65. The lowest figure occurred after the exceptionally severe winter of 1935 to 1936. The scarcity of summer resident males in the 1930 brood corresponds with the high mortality of the adult summer resident males that same winter as mentioned earlier in Chapter XVII.

The 39 young that returned from the 1930 to 1935 broods constitute 4.5 per cent of the 856 eggs laid.

a. The Sex Ratio of the Returned Nestlings

Almost twice as many male Song Sparrows were located as females. Kluijver, *98*, on the contrary, reports that his returning Starlings (*Sturnus vulgaris*) banded as nestlings were equally divided as to sex.

Most of my banding was done early in the season. Jull, *92*, found with the domestic fowl that the earliest eggs produced more males and the latest more females, although Callenbach, *34*, could not substantiate these results. Riddle, *152*, writes that, when pigeons "are induced throughout the year to lay large numbers of eggs," more males are produced in winter and early spring and more females in summer. This matter of sex ratio of nestlings might well be investigated in House Sparrows and Starlings, as Friedmann, *60*, suggests.

I do not know, of course, whether there were more males than females among the 317 Song Sparrow nestlings banded. It seems probable to me that the main reason for the disproportionate numbers of the sexes among the returns of these birds may be that the females do not come back as faithfully to the place of their birth as do their brothers, for even if they should have the impulse to do so, their late arrival in the spring would often make it impossible.

2. *The Distances from the Birth Place at Which the Young Birds Settled*

As already mentioned in Chapter VIII, the great majority of returning nestlings did not settle far from their birth places. The distances in meters for the males were as follows: 6 between 100 and 180; 5 between 225 and 270; 5 between 300 and 340; two at 450; one at 580, two at 640 and one at 1,400. The females were found at the following distances in meters: one at 45; one at 135; 5 between 220 and 270; and one each at 330; 410; 450; 800; and 1,300. Thus 82 per cent settled within 450 meters of their birth places, and 91 per cent within 800 meters.

But since the six birds which I did not capture were found on South Interpont and just outside Interpont, they could not have settled more than 800 meters from their birth place. *Hence 38 of the 40 nestlings located within 800 meters of the birth place, i.e., 95 per cent..*

How thoroughly was the region within 1,600 meters of Interpont covered? Of course it could not be censused as carefully as Interpont itself, but I feel that the suitable ground was covered fairly well on the east bank of the river for about 1,600 meters to the south, which was as far as the cover extended, and on the west bank of the river directly across from Interpont and north of Interpont for some 800 meters, beyond which region there were not many Song Sparrows. I never was able to check the few Song Sparrows that lived to the east in the city. The country suitable for this species was mainly situated along the river and not especially difficult to cover. One source of error in my methods is that some of the young females probably arrived after I had finished my censuses outside of Interpont.

3. *Do Young Return to Their Birth Place?*

This much discussed problem is answered in the affirmative by some and the negative by others. Dupond, *50,* for instance, concludes from the results of banding in Belgium, that "This rule of return to the birth place is a principle that holds true for all birds." Lincoln, *104,* on the other hand, takes the extreme view that "homing instinct in most birds does not operate until after they have nested for the first time, and that the selection of the first nest-site is fortuitous, anywhere within the natural range of the species."

On the whole, the percentage of returns of banded nestlings to the birth place has not been high. Of the 980 nestlings Starlings banded by Kluijver in 1931 and 1932, 81 or 8.3 per cent had returned by December, 1934, *98.* Low obtained an 11 per cent return of Tree Swallows, *113, 114,* but Chapman only 3.3 to 6.25 per cent, *38,* while other banders of different species of Swallows get very low returns—Uchida, *192,* 1.5 per cent, and Thomas, *189,* the same with *Hirundo r. rustica* in England, while Stoner, *183, 183a,* with the Bank Swallow (*Riparia r. riparia*) in Iowa got almost no returns of either adults or young. There has also been a very low percentage of returns of House Wrens banded as nestlings at Gates Mills, Ohio—"2.6 per cent of a total of 648," *94*. Only 2 of 145 young of the Plain Titmouse (*Baeolophus inornatus*) were later found breeding—1.3 per cent, *149a*.

However, there is one record of a remarkably high percentage of return, namely of the Mallards (*Anas p. platyrhynchos*) that were hatched in Finland from English eggs, 34 out of 62 birds returning to their place of hatching—55 per cent (Välikangas, *192a*).

Whittle, *202, 205*, points out two reasons why "returns" of birds banded as nestlings are comparatively infrequent: first, banders do not search over the surrounding country-side for possible returns, and, second, if the adult birds pre-empt the available territories, the young birds—arriving later—have to move elsewhere.

In connection with the first point, it is of interest to note that only five of my 40 "returning" birds were captured in our garden, or 1.6 per cent of the 317 banded nestlings.

As to the second, although it is supported by Whittle's own experience with Song Sparrows, yet on Interpont returning nestlings have *not* filled empty niches. In 1932 with the highest percentage of returns of adults, there was at the same time the highest percentage with the young.

Let us return for a moment to Lincoln's theories. His supposition, in explanation of the "occasional return of a young bird to its natal area," that "the immature birds of many (if not most) species migrate in company with their elders" is not supported by recent studies. It is well known that old and young in many species migrate at different times, and careful life-history studies of many Passerine birds have shown the breaking up of the family as soon as the young were independent. Sherman writes "in more than a score of years given to an intensive study of the forty-four species nesting close at hand I have found the bonds between parents and their young are of very short duration," *179*. Butts, *33*, discovered that even the flocks of the Black-capped Chickadees (*Penthestes a. atricapillus*) were not composed of family parties.

Geese and Cranes are notable examples of an enduring family bond, but I can find very few instances of this in Passerine birds. The only certain record that I can find of the keeping together till late fall of a family in a Passerine species in America is that of the Eastern Bluebird (*Sialia s. sialis*), *82a;* Dr. Hicks tells me that he has also noted this in Ohio.

Lincoln believes that non-return of the young "is but the operation of a natural law to prevent much of the inbreeding that might result were the offspring to return with their parents to the home-site of the previous year," *104.* However, despite all the banding that has been done in this century, only three undoubted cases of inbreeding in the wild appear to have been reported: two of brother and sister— Shelley's Downy Woodpeckers (*Dryobates pubescens*), *178,* and my Song Sparrows (see Chapter IV), and one of father and daughter— Clobes' Swallows (*Hirundo r. rustica*) in Germany, *40a.* (Schenk, *169,* mentions a case of two Long-tailed Tits (*Aegithalos caudatus*) banded in the same nest found feeding young together the following year (Lambert, *99a*), but he does not consider this absolute proof that the two birds in question were the parents of the young, a number of instances having been reported of several adults of this species feeding young at one nest. He rejects two reported cases of brother and sister Swallows (*Hirundo r. rustica*) nesting together the summer of their birth.)

It would seem that inbreeding does not often happen with wild birds, even though great numbers of young have been proved to have returned to their birth places. So far as I know there is no reason with the majority of birds why it should not occur except that of chance, and on account of the high mortality of birds of all ages the chance is small. With certain Geese (*Anser* and *Casarca,* for instance) the family keeps together for a long time; the birds know each other personally, and brothers and sisters, although remaining friendly throughout life, do not mate with each other (Heinroth, *73a,* Lorenz, *112*).

The matter of the return of the young hinges partly on the question as to when the homing faculty arises. Dr. Hicks tells me that it does not develop in homing pigeons until an age of several months is reached. Could this be the explanation why one Song Sparrow settles

180 meters from home, another 800, and still another further away—
that these were the areas they had reached in their early wanderings
and where they had settled in the late summer? The return in the
spring of certain young banded males to the places where they had
warbled in the fall (Chapter VII) makes this seem reasonable. Perhaps young Song Sparrows linger in the vicinity of their birth places
longer than do the young of some other species.

To sum up. Young are certainly far less *ortstreu* or faithful to
their homes than are adults. Young of many species do scatter widely,
although I never will believe that they scatter over the whole "natural
range of the species," or even subspecies. In some cases a substantial
proportion of the surviving young has been found to return to the
vicinity of the birth place. Kluijver considers it is 44 per cent with
his Starlings, *98;* I believe in some years it has been higher than that
with my Song Sparrows.

B. Survival of the Fledged Young

We have been considering the *return* of the nestlings to their
birth place; let us now turn to the question of their survival. What
percentage of the fledged young can be expected to survive?

If 50 to 60 per cent of the adults normally survive each year, a
stable population should contain from 40 to 50 per cent of first year
birds. Hence from 100 pairs 80 to 100 young should survive to the
following spring, or an average of 0.8 to 1 young per pair.

1. *What Percentage of Fledged Young Should Survive Till the Following Spring in Order to Maintain the Population?*

In 1930 15 pairs that survived the season laid 195 eggs and raised
64 young (4.3 per pair), of which 7 (or 8, if we assign one of the
uncaptured juvenal females to this group) were found the following
spring, i.e., a return of .45 to .53 young per pair. The breeding season
of 1930, although beginning early, was shortened at the end by the
great drought; we do not know whether or not, in seasons that have
begun late, as small an average as 4.3 birds are fledged per pair. In a
favorable season of greater length the number should be larger. There
was a shortage of young birds in the population in 1931, as shown in

Table XXV, but we do not know how great a part the rather severe winter played here.

In a normal season I estimate that each female Song Sparrow in this region averages about 16 eggs. In seasons shortened either at the beginning or the end, the average might be nearer 12.5. During the first three years the female population (including replacements) was reduced by June to 80 per cent of the original number, and in no case did a lost female raise a brood successfully before her disappearance; hence if we calculate the history of 100 pairs we will have to multiply the average number of eggs laid by each female per season by 80 instead of 100.

TABLE XXVII

Number of Young That Must Survive in Order to Maintain the Population

Number Young Fledged per 100 Pairs			No. Per Pair	Survival Fledged Young to 1 Year of Age				
Eggs ♀♀	Eggs	Young		12%	15%	18%	20%	25%
Short Seasons	12.5 x 80=1000 x 36%=360		(4.5)	43	54	65	72	90
	12.5 x 80=1000 x 42%=420		(5.3)	50	63	76	84	105
Long Seasons	16 x 80=1280 x 42%=538		(6.7)	65	81	97	108	135
	16 x 80=1280 x 45.5%=582		(7.4)	70	87	104	116	146

In Table XXVII there are calculations on the number of young fledged per 100 pairs under various circumstances; there are two short seasons and two long seasons each with a different percentage of success. The first line allows 36 per cent success, which—although low—was the average found on Interpont during six years of observations. The next figure is the average for the first 3 years on Interpont—42 per cent—and the last—45.5 per cent—is the very best that occurred in any one year. In parentheses the average number of young fledged by each of the 80 pairs is given for each of these seasons.

In the second part of the table the number of young that might survive to adulthood are given according to different percentages. Remembering that 80 to 100 young birds are needed in the population, we see that 12 per cent survival is too low under any circumstance. Fifteen and 18 per cent meet the requirements after the two favorable seasons. A 20 per cent return results in 84 young birds with the second of the shortened seasons, but it takes nearly 25 per cent to get the quota with the poorest nesting of all.

Or we may calculate in another way. In the next chapter we will see that Song Sparrows that reach breeding age have an average length of life of something over two years. In order to maintain the population each pair must replace itself every two years on the average. If a female lays 16 eggs per year and 40 per cent of these are fledged, that would mean 6.4 young leaving the nest per year; one survivor would represent 16 per cent. But if she averages 12.5 eggs per year and only 36 per cent are fledged, then only 4.5 young would be raised and one survivor would represent 22 per cent. For the 15 pairs in 1930 one survivor per pair would have meant a survival ratio of 23 per cent.

It seems as if our present knowledge of breeding success of the Song Sparrow in this region points to an average survival ratio of the fledged young somewhere around 20 per cent.

Kendeigh, *94*, makes the following calculations for the House Wren (*Troglodytes a. aedon*): "in a two-year life span, 18 eggs will be laid," of which 68 per cent or 12 will be hatched and fledged. "If the House Wren population is to remain constant, only 2 of these 12 birds, or 17% will live to reproduce and replace the adults."

Kluijver, *98*, arrives at the same percentage for Starlings (*Sturnus vulgaris*); in 1931 and 1932 519 banded young were fledged in the colony at Wageningen; 38 young had returned to breed in 1933 and 1934, besides 49 other new birds, making 87, which is 17% of 519. He assumes that 87 represents the number surviving of the 519, believing that 56% of the surviving young may have settled in other localities. His calculations are complicated by the fact that only about half the birds breed at the age of one year.

Still another way in which to approach the problem of the number of young that survive to the age of one year, is to examine banding statistics. Stadie, *179a*, reports that of 300 recoveries of the Black-headed Gull (*Larus ridibundus*) 75 per cent were of birds less than a year old, while Schenk, *168*, found the same proportion with 140 examples. In a later paper, *169*, Schenk tabulates the captures of 1,354 birds of 80 species (most of the individuals being non-passerine) ringed as nestlings and finds that 73.5 per cent were taken in the first year of life. This would mean a 26.5 per cent survival to the age of one year of birds banded somewhat before fledging; the percentage of survival of fledged birds would be slightly higher.

Severtzoff, *175a,* states that in birds 10 per cent of the young that hatch survive to breed. This is a difficult matter to check, as statistics on the number of eggs laid per female and number hatched are seldom to be found. I believe this estimate is a little low for the Song Sparrow. In Table XVI we have seen that 510 young were hatched in the 211 nests from 1930 to 1935; if 10 per cent, or 51 survived to the next spring, that would be only 16 per cent of the 306 birds fledged, which, according to the calculations in Table XXVII, is too small a proportion on the average. If 20 per cent survived of the 306 fledged—61 birds—that would amount to 12 per cent of the 510 hatched.

Now that we have a tentative estimate of the percentage of fledged young that should survive, let us turn back to Table XXVI, which shows that 12.6 per cent of the fledged young were found the following spring on Interpont or in the vicinity—40 birds out of 317. If 17 per cent of the fledged young (55 birds) *survived,* then three-fourths *returned* to their birth place. If 20 per cent (63 birds) survived, then three-fifths returned. If these seem high proportions for return to birth place, let us assume that more young survived. If 25 per cent survived (79 birds), half returned; if 30 per cent (95 birds), two-fifths; and if 50 per cent (159), one-fourth.

We cannot escape the conclusion that a substantial proportion of the young Song Sparrows returned to the place of birth. According to the best of our knowledge, this proportion included *one-half to three-fifths of the birds that survived.*

C. Summary

1. Twenty-six males and 14 females out of 317 fledged nestlings were later found as breeders. The percentage of return ranged from 4.5 to 20, averaging 12.6. This was 4.5 per cent of the number of eggs laid.

2. The question is raised as to whether the preponderance of males was partly due to a high sex ratio in the early broods. The late arrival of young females may offer difficulties in the way of return to

the birth place, and also would have prevented my finding any returning to the vicinity of Interpont.

3. Twenty-eight of 34 returned young (82%) settled within 450 meters of their birth places, and 38 of 40 (95%) within 800 meters.

4. Only 5 of these birds—or 1.6 per cent of the total banded—were ever caught in our garden.

5. The percentage of banded nestlings of other species returning to breed in their birth place has ranged from 1.3 to 11, except for one wholly exceptional case of 55.

6. Our present knowledge indicates that birds rarely migrate in family groups.

7. Inbreeding in the wild apparently has been proved in only three instances.

8. Young return to their homes much less faithfully than do adults, yet a substantial percentage of the young of some species have been found to do so.

9. In order to maintain a stable population, from 15 to 25 per cent of fledged young should survive to breeding age (Table XXVII).

10. With House Wrens and Starlings it has been calculated that 17 per cent of the fledged young survive.

11. With Song Sparrows it is estimated that an average of 20 per cent of the fledged young should survive to adulthood, if the population is to be maintained.

12. Banding statistics from three sources show a loss during the first year of some 75 per cent of birds banded as nestlings.

13. Severtzoff states that in birds 10 per cent of the young that hatch survive to breed. It is estimated that in Song Sparrows this percentage is nearer 12 per cent.

14. It is believed that one-half to three-fifths of the young Song Sparrows that survived, returned to their place of birth.

CHAPTER XIX

Age Attained By Song Sparrows

When one attempts to calculate the average age of a bird, it must be made clear as to which portion of the population one is considering. The average age of the nestlings is a very different thing from that of those birds that reach sexual maturity, and a much more difficult problem. Magee, *117,* does not believe that "the average life of Purple Finches, eliminating the mortality among the young birds before they are able to fly, is much, if any, over two years." With most species it would be very difficult to calculate the average life from this starting point.

Much more satisfactory results will be obtained by considering those birds that are present on their breeding grounds the spring following their birth (in a species breeding at one year of age). My calculations will have to be confined to the males; the disappearance of a male once well established on his territory nearly always means his death, unless the territory has been made untenable, or he has failed to get a mate after proclaiming territory for two months or so (see Chapter IX).

A. The Average Age of Song Sparrows

Average ages of a bird population may be calculated in two ways— by averaging the known age at death of individuals, and by means of a formula based on the annual mortality of the breeding birds.

The average of the ages attained by the 27 banded males in the 1930 group reached 2 years and 9 months. This is somewhat less than the true average since several of the males must have been two or more years old when I first knew them. The ages of the 27 males of the 1931 group averaged 2 years and 6 months, the average of the 54 birds being 2 years and 7 months. The average age of 17 males banded in the nest in 1930 and 1931 came to 2 years and 1 month; of 8 banded in the nest from 1932 to 1934, 1 year and 6 months. The longevity of these birds was influenced by the high mortality of the last three years.

Burkitt, *29,* gives a formula for calculating average age: the number of surviving young must equal the number of adults that die yearly;

so if a bird lives n years, there die 1/n birds. If we count the yearly death rate of adult male Song Sparrows at 40 per cent, we have .4=1/n, and N=2.5 years.

Hence both sets of data agree in giving an average age of 2½ years for a breeding male *in a well situated population* of Song Sparrows.

But a very different picture is given during the latter part of the study. By calculating on the return ratios, we find that the average of the 1932 group was 1 year 8 months, and of the 1933 and 1934 groups only 1 year 5 months.

If we average the return ratios (April to April) from Table XXII, we obtain the following figures from which we can calculate the average length of life according to Burkitt's formula.

First two years: return ratio 62.9%; average life 2.7 years. (27 + 16 + 27 = 70 = totals; 16 + 10 + 18 = 44 = returns. 44/70 = .629 = survival. 1.00 — .629 = .371 = mortality. 1/.371 = 2.7 years.)

First three years: return ratio 55.2%, average life 2.2 years.

Third, fourth, and fifth years: return ratio 36.0%, average life 1.6 years.

Fourth, fifth and sixth years: return ratio 24.8%, average life 1.3 years.

All six years: return ratio 43.2%, average life 1.7 years.

The figures for the later years and consequently for the total of six years are probably too low, for, because of the destruction of cover, we cannot be sure that all surviving males returned to Interpont.

It is impossible to work on the records of the females, as I am sure that all the survivors are not located. If females have a 55 per cent survival rate in secure populations, then their average age is 2 years 2½ months; if it is 50 per cent, their age is 2 years.

Burkitt calculated the average age of his Robin Redbreasts (*Erithacus rubecula*) to be 2.8 years, *29,* and of Rooks (*Corvus frugilegus*) "as either ten or seven years," *29a*; Kluijver, *98,* dealing with a bird with which only about half breed at one age, estimated the average life of Starlings that reach the breeding age as 3 years.

Hoffmann's, *84,* estimate of only 1½ years as the average age of his Blue Jays (*Cyanocitta cristata*) was based on the numbers of banded birds recaptured by him, but how could he be sure that all of the survivors entered his traps? Let me take an example from my Song Sparrows. Twenty-six of the birds captured in our garden in the fall of 1931 and spring of 1932 were later found nesting on or near Interpont; exactly two of these were retrapped in our garden. This would give a 92 per cent annual mortality of these 26 birds, and *an average age of 1 year and 1 month,* whereas it really reached somewhat over two years. I would expect the Blue Jay—a large bird that raises but one brood—to have a longer average life than a Song Sparrow.

In an interesting set of calculations Lewis, *102a,* estimates that in a colony of 200 Common Murres (*Uria aalge aalge*) 100 young will be hatched each year of which 12.5 per cent will survive to breed, while 6.25 per cent of the adults will die each year; that some birds will live to be 17 years old, while the average length of life will be 9 years.

B. Potential Age

The "average age" as we have seen it is just another way of expressing survival rate. The potential length of life is a very different thing. Small Passerines in captivity have lived from 12 to over 24 years (Gurney, *68,* Flower, *57,* Witherby, *210,* Brown, *26*), while banding has shown that they sometimes reach 10 or more years in the wild, *140a.*

As to records of old Song Sparrows, there are three of birds at least 7 years old: one in New England (Weeks, *195b*), one in Colorado (Benson, *18*), and one in California (Grinnell, *65*), the first being a migratory bird, the other residents. 4M, banded as an adult in June, 1929, was at least 7½ years old at the time of his death in December, 1935.

I am practically sure that this famous individual was present in 1928, for his territory was occupied by a bird of his pugnacious character, four of whose songs I recorded, and which matched 4M's songs when I came to study them the next year. Moreover, his treatment of 1M upon the return of the latter in March, 1929, was typically that of an old, established male. Although I did not study Song Sparrows intensively until February, 1929, when I began to record 4M's singing, yet I was much interested in all cases of Song Sparrow warbling with which I met, and I never heard 4M warble. I believe he was adult when he came to Columbus in the fall óf 1927, which would make him at least 9½ years old by December, 1935, but he might have moved in from elsewhere in the early spring of 1928 after having out-grown his warbling, in which case he would have been 8½ years old. He was an aggressive, dominating bird in 1929 and 1930, but since then became less quarrelsome. I did not notice any diminution in singing zeal until the fall of 1934, when he sang much less than in previous falls; while in the fall of 1935 he hardly sang at all. Nevertheless, on May 11, 1935, while mateless, he gave 2,305 songs during the day.

The oldest Song Sparrows I have known among the males were: 8-9 years 4M; nearly 6 57M; 5 years 10M; at least 4 years 2M, 23M, 131M, 176M, 183M; at least 3 years 17 individuals; at least 2 years 45 individuals. As to the females, only three were known to have been present for 4 years: K24, K28 and K135. Nine were recorded 3 years and 31 2 years.

C. Age Composition of a Song Sparrow Population

If we assume that a certain proportion of adult breeding birds survives each year and that this proportion remains stable to the end of the potential life of the bird, what percentage in the population should represent each age class? Table XXVIII gives these percentages for 11 different rates of survival for birds breeding at the age of one year from the very high one of 75 per cent to the very low one of 25 per cent.

Sixty is the percentage of survival estimated for Song Sparrows in a secure population, 50 is that found with three species of Swallows and the Plain Titmouse, and 35 that reported for House Wrens, as cited in Chapter XVII. As to the very high and very low percentages, it may be that the Alpine Swift (*Micropus m. melba*) is a representative of the former, since this species raises but one brood of 2-3 eggs and individuals of 7, 8 and 9 years have been found breeding in their birth-places, *169a.* Lewis, *102a,* calculates an even higher survival rate —93.5 per cent—for *Uria a. aalge,* but do these birds breed at one year of age? As for the very low rates of survival, perhaps Titmice in Europe with their immense broods (often *averaging* more than 10 eggs, *138, 213, 214*) fall into these categories. But there appear to have been studies with only a few species of survival of banded breeding birds on which calculations can be based. Kluijver, *98,* found a 50 per cent return with Starlings, but here the late average age of breeding complicates matters, so that his birds are not directly comparable with species breeding at one year.

TABLE XXVIII

Theory as to Age Composition of a Population of Breeding Birds. Theoretical Numbers of Each Age According to Annual Survival Rate

(Species Breeding at One Year of Age)

Percentage Survival	75	70	65	60	55	50	45	40	35	30	25
Age in Years	——Number of birds in each age class in a population of 100——										
1 - - -	25	30	35	40	45	50	55	60	65	70	75
2 - - -	19	21	23	24	25	25	25	24	23	21	19
3 - - -	14	15	15	14	14	13	12,	10	8	6	5
4 - - -	11	10	10	9	8	6	5	4	3	2	1
5 - - -	8	7	7	5	4	3	2	2	1	1	0
6 - - -	6	5	5	3	2	2	1	1	0	0	0
7 - - -	5	4	3	2	1	1	0	0	0	0	0
8 - - -	4	3	2	1	1	0	0	0	0	0	0
9 - - -	3	2	1	1	0	0	0	0	0	0	0
10 - - -	2	1	1	1	0	0	0	0	0	0	0
11 - - -	1	1	1	0	0	0	0	0	0	0	0
12 - - -	1	1	0	0	0	0	0	0	0	0	0
13 - - -	1	0	0	0	0	0	0	0	0	0	0
Total -	100	100	100	100	100	100	100	100	100	100	100
Avg. Length of Life in Years - -	4	3.3	2.8	2.5	2.2	2	1.8	1.7	1.5	1.4	1.3

In birds with 75 per cent annual survival one bird out of a hundred should live to be 13 years old, while with only 25 per cent survival the oldest bird would be only 4 years. (Perhaps 25 per cent survival is too low an average for any species; it may be that 30 or 35 is the lowest rate.)

It is of interest to notice that the proportions of two year old birds does not differ greatly throughout the whole table.

Sixty per cent survival gives an extreme longevity of 10 years, which fits well, I believe, with the case of the Song Sparrow; that of the Swallow reaches 7 years and of Wrens 5 years. It may well be that the survival rate rises somewhat in the later years as the birds become more experienced, yet are fully vigorous; this would increase the number of years that the last survivors would live. A banded Swallow (*Hirundo r. rustica*) has attained the age of 9 years, *210*.

Let us see how the survivals of the Song Sparrows fit with these expectations. Instead of trying to calculate the age composition of each year's population (which would be rather unsatisfactory because of the uncertainties as to the ages of some birds), let us take three groups of males—the 54 birds in the 1930 and 1931 groups (see Table XXII and Chart XVII), the 10 males hatched in 1930, and the 144 breeding males banded from 1928 to 1935—; we will treat each of these sets of individuals as a unit, and *show how many birds were present one year, how many two years, etc.* (Since it is only with the 10 males that I am sure of the year of birth of all the birds, the other two sets of males do not get quite all the credit due them for the number of years lived.)

TABLE XXIX

Age Composition of Three Groups of Banded Male Song Sparrows

NUMBERS AND PERCENTAGES OF BIRDS PRESENT ONE, TWO, THREE, ETC., YEARS

No. Years Present	54 Males 1930-1931 Groups No.	%	10 Males Hatched in 1930 No.	%	144 Males Banded 1928-1935 No.	%
1 - - - - - - - - -	20	37.0	3	30	75	52.1
2 - - - - - - - - -	16	29.6	3	30	45	31.2
3 - - - - - - - - -	13	24.1	3	30	16	11.1
4 - - - - - - - - -	2	3.7			5	3.5
5 - - - - - - - - -	2	3.7	1	10	2	1.4
6-8 - - - - - - - -	1	1.9			1	0.7
	54	100	10	100	144	100

The first two sets of birds show a high percentage of survival the second and third years, but after that there is a sudden falling off. Although the 54 birds start out midway between the 60 and 65 per cent survival groups in Table XXVIII, yet their numbers surviving two and three years are far too high for any group in the whole table. This comes, of course, from the increased mortality from 1933 on; a number of the birds that survived only two and three years should have lived several years longer. As to the 10 males, they fail to fit in with any group; their survival was excellent at first, but only one bird lived after July, 1933. The results with the 144 males correspond fairly well with the 45 per cent survival column in Table XXVIII, although the two year class is too large.

Let us treat these three groups of Song Sparrows in a different way so as to find out *the percentage that survived each year from the original population.*

TABLE XXX

Actual Survival Compared with Theoretical in Three Groups of Song Sparrows

NUMBERS ALIVE EACH YEAR ON APRIL 6

	Theoretical Percentage	60 Per Cent Survival — Actual Survival 54 Males 1930 and 1931 Groups		10 Males Hatched in 1930		45 Per Cent Survival Theoretical Percentage	45 Per Cent Survival Actual Survival 144 Males Banded 1928-1935	
		No.	%	No.	%		No.	%
I year - -	100	54	100	10	100	100	144	100
2 years - -	60	34	62.9	7	70	45	69	47.9
3 years - -	36	18	33.3	4	40	20	24	16.7
4 years - -	22	5	9.3	1	10	9	8	5.6
5 years - -	13	3	5.5	1	10	4	3	2.1
6 years - -	8	1	1.9	0	0	2	1	0.7
7 years - -	5	1*	1.9	0	0	1	1*	0.7
8 years - -	3	1†	1.9	0	0	0.4	1†	0.7
9 years - -	2	?‡	?	0	0	0.2	?‡	?
10 years - -	1	?	?	0	0	0	?	?

*4M was banded as an adult in 1929 and nested in 1935, hence survived 7 years at the lowest calculation.

†4M was almost certainly a breeding bird in 1928, which gives him a survival of 8 years.

‡4M might have been even older than 8 years.

In Table XXX we first see the theoretical percentage that should survive each year with a 60 per cent survival rate. After this are given the numbers and percentages of the 54 males, and the 10 males hatched in 1930; then the theoretical survival for a population with a 45 per cent survival rate is shown, and finally the figures for the 144 males.

We see that in the first two sets of males survival was better than expectation the second year and about the same the third. But during the fourth and fifth years it was less than half what it should have been, and after that even lower. This is contrary to what one would expect on theoretical grounds, for with experienced birds still in full vigor the survival rate ought to increase slightly for a few years. Our figures show the great increase in mortality that occurred on Interpont after the change in conditions.

The total number of males shows a somewhat better survival than 45 per cent the first year, but after that lower percentages. It is probable that my figures do not quite do justice to the survival of the birds, since a few of them probably took up territory elsewhere after the destruction of cover that started in the summer of 1932.

If the 60 per cent survival rate had been maintained on Interpont throughout the study, 33 of the 138 males in the 1930 to 1934 groups should have been living in April, 1935. Actually there were only 9. And of the 135 females banded during these same years, only 5 were present. Now—May, 1936—there are only three Song Sparrows on Interpont that were banded as adults in previous years: 183M banded in 1933, 223M banded in 1935 and his mate K204 banded the same year.

D. Mortality Factors

What are the factors that kill off so many healthy adult Song Sparrows each year? My guess would be predators of various kinds as the large factor. In 1930 and the spring of 1931, boys shot a number of Song Sparrows, but I was able to stop this to a large extent after getting a commission and badge as a Special Game Protector. Barrows, *16*, says, "It is one of the species most often killed at light houses," although this danger ought not to affect Ohio Song Sparrows. He also says "undoubtedly thousands of these valuable and innocent birds have been killed for the bounty which Michigan has unwisely offered for so many years on the English Sparrow." It is probable that this very thing is happening in Ohio at present during the Pest Hunts, where points are given for "sparrows." Lincoln, *103*, gives the cause of death of a number of banded Song Sparrows: 2 killed against windows, 5 killed by automobiles, 6 caught in traps for animals, and several migrating birds caught in an autumn storm in Virginia and North Carolina.

I have never seen any evidence of disease in Song Sparrows and only three cases of abnormalities: one of 68M's young in 1931 was deformed on one side, one male had a tumor near the cloaca, while a third lost his feathers all around his bill and on the top and sides of his head in 1932, but returned in 1933 in normal condition. There have been only three cases of partial albinism noted: two in breeding birds, but both came to their ends before raising young.

E. Summary

1. The average age of the 27 males in the 1930 group was at least 2 years, 9 months; and in the next group 2 years, 6 months.

2. The average age of 25 males banded as nestlings came to 23 months.

3. By Burkitt's formula the average age of the adult male Song Sparrow in a secure population should reach 2½ years.

4. The average age of the males during the last three years has been only 1.3 years.

5. Calculations of average length of life in several other species are cited.

6. Small Passerines in captivity have lived from 12 to 24 years.

7. Three Song Sparrows have been known to have reached the age of 7 years, while 4M's age was at least 7½ years and perhaps 9½ or more.

8. Table XXVIII shows the theoretical numbers of individuals of each age that should be present in populations according to 11 different survival rates.

9. The age classes of three groups of male Song Sparrows are shown in Table XXIX.

10. Actual survival is compared with theoretical in these groups in Table XXX.

11. If the 60 per cent survival rate had continued throughout the study, 33 of the 138 males in the 1930 to 1934 groups of banded breeders should have been living in April, 1935; actually there were only 9.

12. Mortality factors in this species are touched upon, also the few cases of abnormalities and albinism that have been observed in the course of the study.

CHAPTER XX

Some Population Problems

Let us first examine the factors that influence the size of Song Sparrow populations, then consider the course of events on Interpont and compare this with other studies, and finally discuss some theories on population problems.

A. FACTORS INFLUENCING THE SIZE OF A SONG SPARROW POPULATION

The size of a Song Sparrow population in a favorable region depends on three factors:

1: Survival of adults, during the breeding season and over winter.

2: Number of young surviving to the following spring, depending primarily on the success of the breeding season, its length and percentage of fatalities, and also on the subsequent mortality of the young until breeding age is reached.

3: Number of birds coming in from outside, both adults and young.

The first factor is greatly influenced by the amount of cover and to some extent by persecutions from boys, and also by weather in the winter.

The second factor depends closely on the weather during the breeding season and in winter, also on the amount of cover, and perhaps on the numbers of predators.

The third factor varies inversely with the first and second factors, and directly with the amount of destruction of cover in nearby regions.

Severtzoff, *175a,* believes the number of young hatched makes little difference in the next year's population, on the principle that predation varies with the number of prey and that the more little birds there are, the more there will be eaten. Although this may be true with comparatively long-lived game birds, I do not believe it holds with the Song Sparrow, where the first-year birds form an important part of each year's breeding population, as shown in Table XXV and Chapter XVII.

B. The Course of Events on Interpont

In Table XXXI figures are given as to the breeding population present each year on Interpont on April 6; the numbers are of males, the numbers of *pairs* averaging some 5 per cent less (see Table XXIV). The percentages of the Upper Interpont populations are given in terms of the maximum in 1932.

TABLE XXXI
Number of Breeding Males Present on Interpont on April 6

		1930		1931		1932		1933		1934		1935		1936	
North	⎫	17	⎫	17	⎫	25	⎫	15	⎫	10	⎫	8	⎫	7	⎫
	⎬ Upper		52		48		69		44		29		25		18
Central	⎭	35	⎭	31	⎭	44	⎭	29	⎭	19	⎭	17	⎭	11	⎭
South		14		12		18		14		6		8		7	
Total		66		60		87		58		35		33		25	

PERCENTAGE OF MALES ON UPPER INTERPONT IN TERMS OF THE 1932 POPULATION

1930	1931	1932	1933	1934	1935	1936
75	70	100	64	42	36	26

NUMBER OF MALES ON CENSUS AREA OUTSIDE INTERPONT

1932	1933	1934	1935	1936
58	52	9	15	10

PERCENTAGE IN TERMS OF THE 1932 POPULATION

1932	1933	1934	1935	1936
100	90	16	26	17

Interpont used to afford optimum conditions for Song Sparrow settlement. Let us take the peak of numbers—the population in 1932—as 100 per cent and compare the years. In 1930 Upper Interpont was filled to 75 per cent of its capacity, but this year because of the great drought had a shortened breeding season. In 1931 the area was filled to 70 per cent capacity with a population largely adult—66 per cent (Table XXV). An optimum breeding season in 1931 and a favorable winter resulted in a 100 per cent population in 1932 with 50 per cent of first year birds, although the survival of the adults had been very high—65 per cent of the birds present the previous spring (Table XXII).

The tide now turned with a poor breeding season due to too many Cowbirds and an early drought, but if Interpont had been left alone, the following year might have reached the 1930 level. However, the destruction of cover, added to the small number of young raised in the previous season, brought the population in April, 1933, down to 64 per cent of its level a year earlier. After that conditions went from bad to worse; between floods, Cowbirds, and the elimination of cover, adult mortality rose to unprecedented heights and reproduction became almost nil. In 1933 the mortality of the breeding males during the first two months of the nesting season reached 36 per cent, while reproductive success—thanks to floods and large scale plowing—was the least of any year, only 19 per cent.

The population in 1934 dropped to 42 per cent of that in 1932; this year adult mortality reached its peak—47 per cent of the males during the early nesting season, while Cowbirds placed a heavy burden on the survivors. The population of 1935 was even smaller, reaching only 36 per cent of that of 1932; adult mortality was less serious—20 per cent—but the Cowbirds were far too numerous for the depleted population of Song Sparrows. The disturbance of cover was less, and I had hoped that conditions might improve once more. However, the severe winter of 1935-36 reduced the number of summer resident males by about half the expected quota, so that the breeding males reached only 18, or 26 per cent of the 1932 number. Upper Interpont could easily accommodate double the number of pairs with excellent territories.

That the population of Song Sparrows in the immediate region of Interpont has suffered even greater losses than that on Interpont itself is shown by the last two sets of figures on Table XXXI, which give data on about 50 hectares (some 120 acres) adjoining Interpont to the south, west, and north. The number of pairs in this area is less than a fifth of what it was in 1932. The greatest loss has come on the stretch directly south of Lane Avenue which four years ago supported more than 30 pairs, but since the complete and permanent "clean-up" in the summer of 1933 has not had more than 1 or 2 pairs. The rest of the region has lost less than a third of its possible territories, but seems to be filled with Song Sparrows to only 40 per cent of capacity. (In 1932 it had a population of 28 pairs, and now should be able to support from 18 to 20 pairs, but actually had only 8 in April, 1936.)

I believe that we have with the Song Sparrows what Errington, *52, 53, 54, 54a,* has so ably shown for the Bob-white (*Colinus virginianus*), namely, that a well-situated population is practically immune to predation, while a badly situated one suffers heavy losses; in

other words that survival is "largely determined by the carrying capacity of the land."

It may be that the heavy mortality of the adult birds is traceable
to the depletion of cover, and particularly to the lack of safe tangles
for nesting purposes, thus exposing the birds to predation at night,
perhaps from Screech Owls (*Otus asio naevius*) and cats.

The high mortality of adult Song Sparrows that has gone hand
in hand with the destruction of cover seems to indicate that a Song
Sparrow will return to or stay by its former home, even after this has
been so changed by removal of cover that it no longer affords safety
from predators. Yet this does not explain the taking up of these lethal
territories by new birds. Perhaps in lieu of anything better, they
adopted territories that had a certain amount of cover, yet lacked safe
sleeping places.

C. Comparison with Other Studies

On an 80 acre tract of bottom-land 10 miles northeast of Interpont Hicks made thorough censuses of the nesting population for 10
years, *80*. The number of pairs of nesting Song Sparrows from 1924
to 1933 were as follows: 21, 20, 24, 18, 28, 33, 31 (1930), 23, 17, 27.
It will be noted that his peaks of population do not agree with mine,
since, in the four comparable years (1930 to 1933) 1930 was the highest and 1933 next highest, with 1932 the lowest of all, having only 55
per cent as many pairs as 1930. This is quite in contrast to the conditions on Interpont, which had by far the largest population in 1932,
and the smallest during this same period in 1933.

The explanation of our directly opposite results would seem to
be due to the different effects of the 1930 drought, which were only
temporary on Interpont, but were far reaching in the following years
on the Westerville tract, with its "permanent pools of stagnate water,"
due to "the resultant lowering of the water table, reduced cover and
food, and over-grazing." This last condition, fortunately, is not a
factor on Interpont.

Chart XVIII shows the opposite trends of the Song Sparrow populations in these two bottomland areas in the same county, demon-
strating how important local conditions are in such matters.

Another census, taken from 1928 to 1934 on 220 acres on an island off the coast of Wales, shows a remarkably stable population, "the variation at the greatest not exceeding about 6 per cent," the numbers ranging from 210 adults in 1929 to 224 in 1934. "The stability of the more numerous species, such as meadow pipit, wheatear, hedge-sparrow, and oyster-catcher, is of considerable interest, influencing greatly as it does the stability of the total population. It is quite possible that this stability is ensured more easily on an island than on a mainland heath because any gaps in the territories of the regular breeders are more rapidly filled from the ranks of the great numbers of migrants which pass through the island in spring and autumn," Lockley, *110*.

Elton's, *51b,* statement that "The chief cause of fluctuations in animal numbers is the instability of the environment" would seem to be supported by the history of these three populations, for the environment in Skokholm which appear to have remained fairly stable, while those in Ohio experienced drastic changes.

It has been suggested that solar radiations influence populations, not only of the well known "cyclic" species in the north, but of Passerines as well (De Lury, *47,* Wing, *208*). In Chart XVIII the numbers of sunspots as given by De Lury are plotted, and also the number

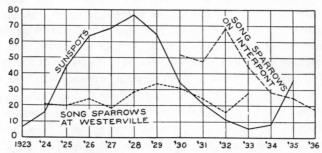

CHART XVIII. *Fluctuations in Two Song Sparrow Populations Compared with Sunspot Numbers.*

——— *Annual Sunspot Relative Numbers (Wolf-Wolfer-Brunner).*

— — — *Number of Song Sparrow Males Holding Territory on Upper Interpont.*

- - - - - *Number of Song Sparrow Pairs on 80 Acre Tract in Westerville (L. E. Hicks).*

of pairs of Song Sparrows in Hicks' and my populations. I do not deny that variations in solar radiations may have an effect on plants and animals, but I fail to see any relationship between the 11 year cycle of sunspots and the fluctuations in these two populations of Song Sparrows in Franklin County, Ohio. In neither case do we need to invoke the influence of changes on the sun's surface, for we can trace the increases and decreases of birds to definite effects of weather and changes in cover conditions.

D. Some Theoretical Considerations on Population Problems

Two interesting articles on population theories have recently appeared, one by a Russian, the other by an Australian. Severtzoff, *175a,* believes that species increase as fast as they can, until decimated by a "plague," which may be abiotic, an effect of weather or of changes wrought by man, or it may be epidemic disease. He states that "the current notion that one pair of progenitors is replaced by one pair of descendants proves to be an erroneous one," and considers that, "Those individuals that have survived the period of juvenile mortality forming a stable population, the duration of life of the individuals of each species must correspond to the period between two consecutive plagues, this period being characteristic for each species."

A. J. Nicholson, *141,* on the contrary emphasizes the *balance* of populations, believing that competition is the only factor than can produce balance. "For balance can be produced only if increasing density decreases the chances of survival of an average individual." He says: "If an attempt be made to assess the relative importance of the various factors known to influence a population, no reliance whatever must be placed upon the proportion of animals destroyed by each. Instead, we must find which of the factors are influenced, and how readily they are influenced, by changes in the density of animals." He mentions "the territory habit" as producing "a stable equilibrium of the population density," but does not develop the proposition.

How do my experiences with *Melospiza melodia* fit in with these theories?

Both authors emphasize that crowding is dangerous, the former stressing the role of epidemics, the latter the lack of sufficient food and nesting sites for all and the ease with which the animals can be found by enemies.

Now a fundamental trait of the Song Sparrow is that *it does not allow itself to be crowded*. If its numbers increase greatly, the surplus must spread into new areas.

According to Severtzoff's ideas, Song Sparrow populations should increase for a period of perhaps 5 to 10 years and then suddenly dwindle. But with an annual mortality in the adults of at least 40 percent, after 5 years there would be only 13 birds left of an original population of 100 breeding birds and at the end of 10 years only one (Table XXVIII). Severtzoff's experience has been with game birds and his picture of events fits them much better than it does this small Passerine.

Nicholson believes that too great density is the special evil to be avoided. But with the Song Sparrows, one trouble in recent years has been their *lack of density,* which has resulted in a concentration of parasitism by the Cowbird.

As to applying his ideas of "balance" and "steady states" in populations to these Song Sparrows, the difficulty has been that in only one of the 8 years did the population ever reach its optimum. *In the 7 other years all those factors which Nicholson considers of negligible importance have kept their numbers well below this figure.* But it is true that once the Song Sparrows do attain the happy state of a full population, it is competition—in this case, territorial behavior—that prevents them from increasing beyond this number.

Nicholson is an entomologist and conceives of populations that are always threatening to be *over*-populations, as Errington terms them. But I have been dealing with populations that except for one year have been *under*-populations.

In an excellent appraisal of "The Malthusian Principle in Nature," McAtee, *120a,* shows that, "Malthusian theories that 'population is necessarily limited by the means of subsistence' and 'population always increases where the means of subsistence increase' do not normally function in nature."

He concludes that: "Malthus's postulated geometric increase of population is not the rule in nature; it is merely a potentiality, rarely realized. Populations usually are checked far short of a subsistence limitation. Automatic restriction by lowering of birth rate in response to density and by a great variety of self-limiting phenomena, together with sweeping indiscriminate destruction of immature forms, involving little or no actual competition either among themselves or with adults, seem to be the principal factors involved in maintaining the stability of populations."

This "lowering of birth rate" seems to take place in some cases, but many more observations are needed. Errington, *55*, cites King's unpublished observation on an inverse relationship between density of population and size of clutch in the Ruffed Grouse (*Bonasa umbellus*). Severtzoff, *175a*, mentions "the increase in the numbers of the issue brought forth by the herd as a whole" in depleted populations of Capercaillie (*Tetrao urogallus*) and roe-deer (*Capreolus caprea*).

I am not convinced that Kendeigh's figures, *94*, on reproduction in the House Wren show "that the number of broods per female per season tends to vary inversely with the total population." His population was small,—ranging from 6 to 14 pairs per year—, and he has not taken into account lateness or earliness of the seasons, nor the number of females coming in after nesting was well started. I would commend to the interested reader an examination of Wing's manipulation, *208*, of this same data by smoothing, whereby a *positive correlation* is found between the number of broods per female and the total population!

No change in the average number of eggs per set took place with the Song Sparrows on Interpont, no matter how large or small the population (Table XIII).

But the Song Sparrows do possess a "self-limiting" device in territorial behavior, and they certainly experience "sweeping, indiscriminate destruction" of the immature.

In 1903 Moffat, *126*, published an important paper which was largely over-looked; in it he described territory in birds, believing its purpose to be the limitation of "the number of breeding pairs to a fairly constant figure."

As I look at it, territory is one of the basal factors that must be reckoned with in population questions with Song Sparrows and many other territorial birds. It ensures that there will be no crowding, and no over-population, since surplus birds must go elsewhere. This I would call Nicholson's "controlling factor." But climate and many other factors may keep the numbers of a species in a region so low, that territorial behavior has no chance to limit population.

Perhaps we can conceive of a Song Sparrow population in a modified version of both Nicholson's and Severtzoff's ideas: the upper limit of the population is fixed by territorial behavior; the population may increase to this maximum when a majority of the factors are favorable, any surplus seeking new quarters; but there are so many possibilities of unfavorable factors—major "plagues" of droughts, floods, and severe winters, and local "plagues" such as man on Interpont—that the numbers of the birds are reduced at irregular intervals.

I have one chief criticism of theories on population questions—Severtzoff's, Nicholson's, Volterra's, 38a, Wing's and others; they all present too much theory based on too few facts. Their authors generalize too much, simplify too much. Each man looks at the world from his own special angle and assumes that all (or most) animal species behave in the same way as the few with which he is acquainted.

This is not so much their fault as that of naturalists the world over in not giving them data on which to work. We need a great body of facts intelligently and conscientiously collected before we can safely launch into elaborate theories.

E. Summary

1. Three factors influencing the size of a Song Sparrow population are survival of adults, survival of young, and additions from neighboring regions.

2. The course of events on Interpont from 1930 to 1936 is briefly summarized, the yearly populations being compared in percentages of the maximum of 1932.

3. It is believed that this Song Sparrow population illustrates Errington's principle that a well-situated population is almost immune to predation, but that an exposed one suffers heavy losses, so that survival is "largely determined by the carrying capacity of the land."

4. The population fluctuations of the Song Sparrows on Interpont are compared with those of another Song Sparrow population in the same county and also with censuses in Wales.

5. The relation of the changes in these two populations of Song Sparrows to the 11 year period of sun-spots is discussed.

6. Severtzoff believes that populations increase as fast as they can, so that when the catastrophe comes there will be as large a population as possible to meet it; A. J. Nicholson considers that populations are kept in balance by competition; McAtee emphasizes "self-limiting" devices; while Moffat suggested that the limitation of population was the chief purpose of territory.

7. These theories are discussed in the light of the experiences with the Song Sparrows on Interpont and some general conclusions drawn.

SUMMARY

This study on the Song Sparrow is an example of the modern technique based on banding, the unique advantages of which are *the opportunity to examine the subjects in the hand,* weighing, measuring and noting details of plumage, and the possibility of *absolute identification in the field* through the means of colored bands.

It was undertaken on a common bird, by one individual with no institutional support (save for library facilities) and no apparatus except that in use at any well-equipped banding station. The present volume is a report of a portion of the scientific findings from eight years of study on this particular species. The study could well have been pursued for many more years, since experimental techniques had hardly been started upon.

Other common species should prove equally rewarding.

In the course of this research no birds were killed and no eggs collected, the activities of the observer tending rather to the protection of the birds than their exploitation.

Detailed summaries have been given at the end of each chapter. At this time the attempt will be made to give in a few words a picture of the Song Sparrow on Interpont and its responses to its environment.

A. Response of the Song Sparrow to Climatic Influences

The most important factors in regulating the Song Sparrow's calendar are changing day-length and changing temperatures.

Low temperature stimulates migration in the fall, and flocking in winter. It inhibits song in spring and fall, migration in spring and territorial activities; and delays nesting.

High temperature delays, and perhaps in some cases inhibits, migration in fall. It stimulates song in spring and fall, migration in spring, territory activities, and nesting.

All these activities are fitted into a time schedule. Warm weather in December will not start singing, warm weather in January and early February will start singing but not migration, the very same temperature in late February will stimulate migration, but it is not until April that nesting will start, no matter how high the thermometer rises.

There are decreasing temperature thresholds for these activities, closely similar ones for taking up of territory (start of singing) and migration, but coming a month and a half apart, starting at about 54° F. (12° C.) and decreasing about ¾ of a degree Fahrenheit each day till normal, and later sub-normal, temperatures are reached.

For nesting, the threshold starts higher (65°-73° F.) and falls about twice as fast—approximately 1½ degrees Fahrenheit for 2 to 2½ weeks.

The birds will undertake these activities at the normal time at normal temperatures, and later at sub-normal temperatures, but are stimulated to begin them earlier by high temperatures.

Although the increasing and decreasing length of day appears to be of fundamental importance in regulating the activities of these birds, yet the percentage of sunshine during a particular season, or portion of a season, does not seem to have any significance.

Precipitation influences the Song Sparrow indirectly by its effect on the growth of the vegetation and the abundance of insects. The drought in June and July, 1930, brought on the molt prematurely, while during the drought in May and June, 1932, many young starved in the nest. The flood in mid-May, 1933, destroyed a great many of the ground nests in the river valleys in central and southern Ohio.

B. Relations to the Flora and Fauna of the Habitat

The flora of the habitat provides food, shelter, singing posts, and nesting sites. The Song Sparrow in this region fits into a variety of niches—bottom-land weed associations with some trees and shrubs, gardens, and even open woods.

The Song Sparrow is both predator and victim; he eats a great variety of invertebrate forms, and in turn is parasitized by other invertebrates. He dominates the small birds about him, but he and his eggs and young are preyed upon by many creatures; hence the necessity of his high "biotic potential" to cope with the "resistance of the environment," *38a.*

He serves as chief host for *Molothrus ater ater* and in this capacity suffers considerable loss to his progeny, especially of late years, when the Cowbird population has been disproportionately large.

C. Territory

The holding of territory is a fundamental trait with these birds, ensured by innate behavior patterns consisting of song, display and fighting. Territorial behavior in these Song Sparrows is essential for the undisturbed carrying out of the reproductive cycle.

Although highly territorial for over half the year, and inclined, if a resident, to remain on or near his territory permanently, yet in fall and winter he becomes somewhat social, particularly in times of severe weather and snow.

The sedentary disposition of the Song Sparrow is evidenced by his attachment to his territory throughout the year, even though defending it for only half the year; by the large proportion—probably more than half—of the surviving young that settle near their birth place; and finally by the fact that half the breeding males and a fifth of the females fail to migrate south in winter.

D. Relations Between the Pair

Although male and female have similar plumages, their roles are unlike. The male defends the territory, mate and nest, and feeds the young. The female builds the nest, incubates the eggs, and broods and feeds the young. The male dominates his mate by "pouncing" and protective behavior, yet she tyrannizes over him in many ways. They appear attached to each other and usually remain together throughout one season, although remating for a second season has not often happened on Interpont.

E. Some Physiological Responses

The Song Sparrow during spring and summer usually eats about once every 20 to 30 minutes. This rhythm of hunger may underlie the female's rhythm of building the nest and of incubation, and to a lesser extent (because interrupted by the male's visits to the nest), of brooding the young.

The weights of the Song Sparrows change as follows: from "standard weight" in fall they start to increase in December, reaching their maximum in January, and then gradually decrease to standard in April. The female's weight increases just before and during egg laying, probably remains somewhat above standard during incubation, but decreases while feeding the young, the male also losing weight at this time.

F. POPULATION PROBLEMS

The Song Sparrow is a hardy, adaptible bird, but only by devoting its energies to reproductive activities for more than a third of the year is it able to keep up its numbers.

Territory is a basic principle in population problems with this species for maintaining "balance" and preventing over-crowding. Perhaps because of this "self-limiting device," the birds on Interpont did not lay any larger sets when their numbers were few than when they were at the peak.

Population problems have proved to be complex and dependent on a wide variety of factors with just one species in one small area over a period of seven years, while the trend of another population of the same species during the same period ten miles away was quite different due to an initial dissimilarity in environment.

During the first three years of the study, conditions were favorable for the Song Sparrow, but after that grew progressively worse. Thus we have a picture first of a well situated, thriving population with an excellent survival, but later of an exposed population, subjected to many perils and unable to reproduce itself.

APPENDIX I

The Technique of the Investigation

My Song Sparrow study started partly by accident and only gradually developed from being one item in my bird study interests into my chief occupation, demanding the major part of my time and attention. We moved to Columbus from Oklahoma in September, 1927, at first renting the house which we later bought. During the first year and a half I spent much time studying all the birds on Interpont and recorded with considerable interest all cases of Song Sparrow "warbling" that I heard, this being a new experience for me. The only birds banded during this period were those captured in a small shelf trap next our house.

A. The Course of the Study

On March 26, 1928, I banded a Song Sparrow that was caught in my shelf trap; later I found that he lived next to us (he was 1M) and I studied his second nesting for 18 hours until the young were destroyed. In the meantime I became acquainted with 4M, his next door neighbor, and recorded four of his characteristic songs, although not banding him until the following year.

In February, 1929, I became very much interested in 4M's singing, and my enthusiasm for *Melospiza melodia* was greatly aroused by the return of 1M on March 9 and the sight of the territory establishment activities between him and 4M the following morning. From then on I concentrated on Song Sparrows, chiefly the two pairs nearest me, but also on 5M to a small extent, the bird next to the west. I spent some hours every day watching the activities of 1M and K2, 4M and K3, my studies much facilitated by the tameness of the birds. We stayed in Columbus until July 16, except for a 12 days' absence during K2's second incubation. The three adult males and two females mentioned above were banded, also 11 of their young. This intensive study was an essential foundation for the extensive work done in later years; I discovered the normal course of the birds' nesting cycle and found out the meaning of their notes and postures.

In 1930 four young males trapped in January took up their territories at various points over Central Interpont, and my one return from the nestlings—K17—settled at the west end of dike 2, so I gradually became interested in all the pairs in Central Interpont including a few south of dike 1—40 pairs in all; of these 27 males and 20 females were banded. Sixty-one nests were found and a total of 102 nestlings that left the nest in safety banded. An attempt was made to study the first nesting of 1M and K7, but the demands of the extensive study precluded much time being spent on one pair. The whole of this summer was spent at Columbus except for one week in late July and the last three weeks in August.

In 1931 four of my banded nestlings settled in North Interpont, so my field of operations had to be still further extended. This season every single male on Central Interpont was banded and all but 5 of the females—a total of 38 banded males and 30 females, besides 65 fledged nestlings from 40 nests. The spring migration was unusually delayed and my absence from Columbus April 3 and 4 caused uncertainty in the arrival dates of a number of the birds. We left Ohio June 6, but my husband came back to Columbus on June 15 and banded the five nestlings of 72M and K63, three of which survived to adulthood. We returned September 1, and I was able to trap many juvenal birds in our garden in the early fall, at this time beginning to measure and weigh the birds.

In 1932 I attempted to band every adult on Upper Interpont; I succeeded with the males—69 in number—and almost succeeded with the females, banding 67, but 6 were missed. These figures include only those birds that survived till April 6, plus those that appeared later. This season I measured the eggs in the nest. Sixty nests were found and 76 banded nestlings were fledged before our departure June 14. We returned September 27. 1932 proved to be an unfavorable nesting season with a late spring, an early drought that caused starvation of the nestlings, and very heavy Cowbird parasitism.

On March 1, 1933, Interpont was taken over for gardens for the unemployed, and although at that time I was able to save the dikes and several patches of shrubbery from destruction, ever since then Interpont has been a comparatively unfavorable place for Song Sparrows and other birds nesting in low situations. Several resident pairs were driven from their territories the first week in March; other males that returned were either killed shortly or left for better habitats. Forty-three of the 44 males present on Upper Interpont April 6 were banded, and 38 of 41 females. Thirty-three nests were found, but only 27 banded nestlings fledged, two great floods in May and the plowing of Interpont in June working havoc with the nests. We were absent from Columbus from June 18 to July 24, and from August 7 to September 14.

Twenty-eight of the 29 males present on Upper Interpont in 1934 were banded and 18 of the 25 females. Cowbird parasitism was very heavy this season. Only 14 nests were found and 14 nestlings fledged before my departure for Europe on May 22. During the summer a great amount of destruction of cover took place and many young must have perished in their nests. We returned September 20.

During 1935 I did not try to trap in the field in winter as I had done since January, 1931; 14 of the 25 breeding males were banded and 16 of the 25 females. Twenty-two nests were found and 22 nestlings fledged. We left Columbus June 19, returning September 11.

The following winter was much the coldest we had experienced in Columbus, and a number of Song Sparrows were trapped in the winter, mostly by the house. Nine of the 18 males on territories were banded and four of the 12 females.

To sum up the seven years: the first year was spent in intensive observation of two pairs; the next three on an ever enlarging population study and the last four on a steadily dwindling population. It was unfortunate that the work could not have been carried on through the summers, although nest finding becomes increasingly difficult due to the rank growth of vegetation and the quietness of the parents. A very interesting study of the population of Interpont could have been made if there had been a number of students and institutional support.

B. Trapping the Birds

It is necessary to trap most of the birds on their own territories. I use four different traps; a small pull string; a large pull string "flat trap," and 2 types of "government sparrow trap" (Lincoln and Baldwin, *105*). The two latter are my most useful traps, being easily transportable and automatic; i.e., the bird goes through a funnel and cannot find its way out. In the fall and winter I trap a number of Song Sparrows in our garden; many of these are transients and never seen again, but others are winter residents, while still others breed on Interpont or nearby.

Song Sparrows come readily to a mixed bait of baby chick feed, rolled oats, canary bird seed, millet, hemp, cracker and bread crumbs. In order to trap the birds out in the field, I choose a place where the trap can be fairly well concealed from passers-by and yet where the bird will be likely to discover the food, usually near one of his singing posts. Here I place an odd piece of chicken wire and bait every day or so, perhaps for a few days, perhaps longer before I put out the trap itself. Winter and early spring are the best times to trap, although I have caught birds throughout the nesting season. If I have caught an unmated male on his territory, I continue to bait, so as to be able to trap his mate soon after her arrival.

Sometimes birds can be captured by using rivals as decoys, i.e. if I have caught a male and place him in the trap on his neighbor's territory, the latter may enter the trap, or a female may be caught in the same way by using a next-door female. But this method is successful only with birds that know each other, for otherwise a Song Sparrow cannot tell the sex of one of its kind in the trap any more surely than a person can, and the presence of a strange Song Sparrow in this situation usually arouses little interest on the part of the male owner of the territory and even less from the female. In some cases in March and early April this method has proved helpful, but in others neighbors have failed to become sufficiently aroused to go into the trap.

An expedient which I adopt only under necessity is that of using the young as bait, either by placing the large trap over a favorably situated nest when the young are about 6 days old, or by putting young that are ready to leave the nest in a small cage inside the trap. The first method involves some risk due to disturbance of the surrounding vegetation.

A scheme that promises to prove increasingly helpful is to use the young Cowbird (*Molothrus ater ater*) from 7 to 10 days old for the capture of his foster parents. I have found it possible to introduce this parasite for a day or even two hours into a nest, then to place him in the trap beside the nest and thus catch the new foster parents, afterwards returning the little bird to his first home.

With all these methods of using nestlings as bait, both parents as a rule are quickly caught, but a few birds refuse to enter the trap.

After being caught, each bird is brought to the house in the small gathering cage which has a black cloth wrapped around it; the bird is banded, weighed, its wing and tail measured, and then it is released from the window, whence it quickly makes it way back to its territory.

C. Banding Methods

All the birds are banded with the numbered aluminum bands supplied by the United States Biological Survey. With nestlings the band is always placed on the right leg, while all birds caught in the garden and all adults trapped on their territories are banded on the left leg. The best time at which to band nestlings is at the age of six to seven days. All trapped birds are also given colored bands, but this has been done with only a few of the nestlings. Nestlings that survive to breed the following year are trapped and then given colored bands.

Colored celluloid bands were used by Burkitt, *27,* in his study of the Robin Redbreast (*Erithacus rubecula*) and later by Butts, *32,* on various American birds: the latter described in detail his method of manufacture and this I followed until 1932, since when the Biological Survey have been making such bands, thereby earning my profound gratitude.

The best colors for Song Sparrows are red, blue, green, black, and yellow; vivid colors should be used, and above all they should not fade. Celluloid toys can be used, but their manipulation is difficult and the colors often not dependable. I found poultry bands far more satisfactory, cutting them down to the proper size. (For larger birds the bands for baby chicks can be used without change.) I made my bands 14 mm. x 5 or 10 mm. which allowed an overlap of 3 or 4 mm., which was not sufficient, since a few of the birds removed the bands. The survey bands overlap much more, since they are 25 mm. long, and they have proved eminently successful. The wide bands (10 mm.) can be seen at a greater distance than the narrow ones, but it is not possible to use two of these on the same leg with the aluminum band as can be done with those 5 mm. in width.

I shaped the pieces of celluloid around a nail of the proper size, holding them in place by means of the next larger aluminum band. The nail with its celluloid and aluminum bands was placed in boiling water for one minute and then into cold water. For adjusting the bands on the birds I open them with fine pointed scissors, slip the latter out and squeeze the band together again as tightly as I can.

It is a good plan to use two celluloid bands on each bird, so that if one is lost, the fact is apparent and there is no confusion with other birds. With two bands of the same color or two bands of different colors a great many combinations can be made, according to the position of the color above or below the aluminum, whether it is on the right or left leg, etc. With five colors 210 combinations are possible. If narrow bands also are used so that two can be put on one leg with the aluminum band, further possibilities are opened. Or narrow bands can be used duplicating the formulas with the wide bands, for the two widths are easily distinguishable.

D. Nomenclature and Records

In dealing with large numbers of subjects the technique of record keeping is of much importance.

The first problem is that of nomenclature. The band numbers are impracticable for every day use, because too cumbersome and too difficult to read, hence every nesting adult is given a "field number" in the order with which I become acquainted with it. In most cases the birds have been banded, but a few have not been; for instance, the males from 31M to 39M nesting in Central interpont and to the south in 1930, a few males off of Interpont that have had banded mates, a few parents of banded nestlings, and a number of breeding birds during the last four years.

Each field number belongs to one bird only, a successor on the territory being given a new number. The males are designated 1M, 2M, etc. Females are called K1, K2, etc. In practice, however, a female is usually known by her "married name"—the number of her mate followed by f and the year. Thus K2 was 1f29 one year and 5f30 the next. I had believed, *129*, that these married names would be sufficient designation for the females, but have found them too complicated for birds with a varied or long history. But for my every day use in one season I pay little attention to the K numbers, simply calling a pair, for example, 12M and 12f.

Since field numbers are not given until a bird's status as a nester is assured, temporary numbers are often necessary. Thus this last spring the new summer residents were called Z1, Z2, etc., as they appeared, keeping the Z until banded. When a juvenal male banded on the right is found, he is called N1, N2 (Nestling), until trapped and his identity settled. Unbanded juvenal males that appear to be settled on territories in the fall are called U1, U2 (unbanded).

Another problem is presented in the fall and winter by those birds trapped in the garden or in various places over Interpont; in this case I know the band number (because of the colored bands), but I do not know whether the bird is a transient or summer resident in the fall or a resident or winter resident in the winter. These birds hence are called by the last two figures of their aluminum band numbers prefixed by a letter, as B93, C47, B being used for the first series of band numbers that I was using in the fall of 1931 and C for the next series I used, etc. Those birds that prove to be nesters are promoted to the field numbers.

I have gradually evolved a number of different schemes for keeping my records, each method supplementing the others.

1. *The Banding Record*

A chronological list is made of the birds as banded with the band number, field number, colored band scheme, date, hour, measurements, state of molt, etc., etc. This is chiefly useful, not for my nesting adults, but for the birds of unknown status caught in the garden and also as the record of the banding of the nestlings.

When I catch a banded bird whose identity is unknown to me, I can always find its history in this list where the bands are listed in order.

2. Card Catalog

Here the arrangement is by sex and field number and year of first nesting. A summary of all the most important data is given on each card, all that mentioned above, including weights and measurements each time captured; status as resident or summer resident; dates of arrival and departure each year if the latter; dates of arrival of mate and her K number; dates of taking up territory in the spring; of singing in the fall; etc. The female's cards are much the same, both K and married names being given; the number of eggs laid is noted and their measurements given on the back of the card. Ancestry is told whenever it is known.

3. Key Tables

The key tables consist of one series of sheets for the males and another for the females. Here the males are listed in order by their field numbers, the years from 1929 on being represented in vertical columns and divided into four seasons. The period of time during which I am acquainted with each bird is shown by a horizontal line, blue for the residents, red for the summer residents. The females are listed by their K numbers, but their mates' numbers are given each year, this being a convenient method for me to keep track of the two designations of these birds.

4. Daily Record

This is kept in my Roll Book in the same way as the record of all the different species seen, only in the case of the Song Sparrow each nesting pair has a space. Each day all the individuals I have seen or heard are noted, with s if the bird sang, 1 for male if merely seen, f if the female was seen. When a bird is surely identified by sight of the bands or by a known song, the notation is underlined; when a bird is trapped, it is underlined twice. One of the most useful features of this scheme is the record of the beginning and ending of song in each individual; it is also helpful in dating the death of a bird, and at times in serving as an index to the extended notes in the large field note book.

5. Field Note Book

The detailed record of activities is kept in a large book that I carry with me in a school satchel along with a sack of bait and my Game Protector's badge. Inside the front cover there is a map of Upper Interpont on which each pair with each bird's banding scheme is shown in color in its respective territory. Inside the back cover are many columns showing possible banding combinations in color with the bird's field or abbreviated band number (if it has no field number) opposite; this serves as my guide for further banding schemes, and can be consulted in the field when I meet one of the fall or winter banded birds. Daily summaries of the most important events on several pages near the back constitute an important feature of this book.

6. *Maps*

A large supply of mimeographed maps of Interpont has proved of great assistance particularly from January through April. On these maps residents are shown in blue crayon, summer residents in red, winter residents in brown and birds of unknown status in pencil. During the arrival of the Song Sparrows in the spring a new map is filled in nearly every day. Later in the season nests are indicated.

7. *Nest Record*

During the nesting season I carry with me folded inside the field note book sheets of lined paper divided into 10 or 12 columns. Each vertical column is devoted to a pair in the order in which nests are found, each horizontal line to a day, so that each page gives a brief account of the nesting activities of 10 or 12 pairs for some three weeks.

E. PLAN OF WORK

Since some of my birds stay here the year around, observations should be made every day. I usually spend from one to two hours (sometimes more) each morning in the late fall and winter, going over Interpont to record what birds I can and to bait any new birds. From February on I plan to visit every portion of Upper Interpont every morning to look for new arrivals of either sex. In the spring and summer practically the whole morning is devoted to the birds, and sometimes part of the afternoon or evening too. Although most of my time is spent on Upper Interpont, I have to take occasional censuses on South Interpont, below Lane Avenue bridge, for three-quarters of a mile, across the river and above Dodridge Street Bridge for a quarter of a mile to examine every Song Sparrow for bands, a slow process, especially with the ground-haunting females. One such census I try to take in mid-winter, and another about the 20th of February for resident males, one in March for summer resident males, and one the second week in April to examine the females. After this it is too difficult to see the birds, and no time can be spared from the studies on Upper Interpont. A few Song Sparrows nest to the east of us in town, but these I have never been able to check.

My census methods on Interpont depend on *personal identification* of each bird and the recording of its location on the map. Resident males should be located as early as possible in the fall or on mild days in January and February, while mid-winter trapping usually brings rewards for the earlier the residents are caught and banded the better. The arrival of a summer resident male is announced by his singing and by the territory activities of his neighbors; his clean plumage is quite in contrast with the sooty appearance of the residents. The arrival of a female is shown by the sudden silence of the male and also by his attitude of anxiety; a little search on his territory will soon be rewarded by the sight of his new mate.

As for the censuses off of Interpont the best time to examine the females is from their arrival in late March to the middle of April. At this time the pair keep together, the female is not yet incubating and the leaves are not out; after nesting has begun it is a tedious task to wait for the female to leave her nest (unless one wishes to find the latter). The limits of a territory can be found by following the birds; they will go ahead for a certain distance, but double back when they reach their boundary. The male can be distinguished by his tendency to keep behind and above his mate as if guarding her; she stays near the ground and it is no easy matter to make sure whether or not she carries a band.

The scheme of counting singing males (Cooke, W. W., *44*, Cooke, M. T., *41*) is unreliable with Song Sparrows, because of the fact that the singing of the male after the arrival of a mate is of irregular occurrence, depending on the stage of the nesting cycle.

APPENDIX II

Some Statistics Concerning Song Sparrow Banding on Interpont

A. Total Song Sparrow Population Given M and K Numbers, 1928-1935
All Breeders, or Prospective Breeders,

i.e., They Had Established Territory or Joined Mates

| | Total Numbers | Total Banded | | | Unbanded | In Nesting Groups (All Banded) |
		As Adults	As Nestlings	Total		
Males - - - -	231	151	25	176	55	144
Females - - -	207	146	14	160	47	146
Totals - - -	438	297	39	336	102	290

B. Returns of Birds Banded, 1928-1935

Nestlings

353 Nestlings banded. 40 reached breeding age   11.3%.
                       3 others found in fall and winter.
                       —
                       43   12.2%.

(Table XXVI shows a total of 317 nestlings; this was the number fledged.)

| | | Adults Yearly Returns | | Individual Returns | |
		Number	Per Cent	Number	Per Cent
Breeders - - - - - - - -	336	199	59.2	119	35.4
Transients - - - - - -	147	0	0	0	0
Winter Residents - - - -	74	5	6.7	2	2.7
Totals - - - - - -	557	204	36.6	121	21.7

517 Song Sparrows were banded as adults from 1928 through May, 1935; 40 nestlings that survived to start the breeding season are added to those banded as adults, making 557.

If we add the 353 nestlings to the 517 adults, we have a total of 870 Song Sparrows banded; yearly returns were 207 (23.8%) and individual returns 125 (14.3%).

In the "Yearly Returns" all the "returns" are totalled; for instance 4M counted 6, 10M 4, 1M 2, etc. Adults banded in the fall and returning in the spring or surviving to the spring are included. The interval is 6 months in 30 cases, in the others a year, *but never 3 months*.

In the "Individual Returns" each bird that returned or survived as mentioned above is counted only once, no matter how many years he may have lived. It will be seen that a third of the breeders "returned" and a fifth of all the banded adults. By dividing the number of yearly returns by individual returns we find that the average number of returns for each bird was 1.7.

Mr. M. J. Magee of Sault Ste. Marie, Mich., writes me that he has banded 1,178 Song Sparrows, and that his yearly returns were 105 (8.9%) and individual returns 76 (6.77%). Mr. and Mrs. F. W. Commons in Minnesota, *161*, banded 1,488 Song Sparrows and had 3.8% return ratio. I believe the explanation of the very high percentages obtained on Interpont lies in the technique of the study, which was based on the use of colored bands, trapping on each territory, and constant search for the birds.

As already stated, I have had no recoveries away from Columbus of the 870 birds banded up to May, 1935. Magee has had none from the 1,178 he has banded, nor Wharton, *201*, any from 1,429 banded in Groton, Mass.

One recovery out of more than 1,200 banded is reported by Broun, *25*,—a bird banded October 9, 1932, on Cape Cod, Mass., and killed at Stedman, S. C., December 18. A Song Sparrow banded at Gates Mills, Ohio, June 8, 1932, by S. P. Baldwin was taken in Janesboro, Ga., December 25, 1933.

APPENDIX III

Nesting Censuses on Upper Interpont.
(40 Acres)

	Number of Pairs			
	1930	1931	1934	1935
Eastern Green Heron				
Butorides v. virescens - - - - - - -		1		
Eastern Sparrow Hawk				
Falco s. sparverius - - - - - - - -	1	1		
Eastern Bob-white				
Colinus v. virginianus - - - - - - -	6	4	6	4
Ring-necked Pheasant				
Phasianus colchicus torquatus - - - -	1			
Killdeer				
Oxyechus v. vociferus - - - - - - -		1		
Spotted Sandpiper				
Actitis macularia - - - - - - - - -	2	1	1	1

		Number of Pairs		
	1930	1931	1934	1935
Eastern Mourning Dove				
Zenaidura macroura carolinensis - - - -	18	12	13	13
Yellow-billed Cuckoo				
Coccyzus a. americanus - - - - -		1		1
Black-billed Cuckoo				
Coccyzus erythropthalmus - - - - - -	2	1		
Ruby-throated Hummingbird				
Archilochus colubris - - - - - - -	2			
Northern Flicker				
Colaptes auratus luteus - - - - - -	4	4	4	4
Northern Downy Woodpecker				
Dryobates pubescens medianus - - - -	1	1	1	1
Northern Crested Flycatcher				
Myiarchus crinitus boreus - - - - - -			1	1
*Alder Flycatcher				
Empidonax t. trailli - - - - - - -	2	2	2	6
Northern Blue Jay				
Cyanocitta c. cristata - - - - - -	1	1	1	2
Carolina Chickadee				
Penthestes c. carolinensis - - - - - -			1	
Ohio House Wren				
Troglodytes aedon baldwini - - - - -	4	4	4	7
Carolina Wren				
Thryothorus l. ludovicianus - - - - -		1		
Catbird				
Dumetella carolinensis - - - - - -	6	6	4	4
Brown Thrasher				
Toxostoma rufum - - - - - - - -	2		1	1
Eastern Robin				
Turdus m. migratorius - - - · - - -	25	25	23	30
*Wood Thrush				
Hylocichla mustelina - - - - - - -	2	4	2	1
Starling				
Sturnus v. vulgaris - - - - - - - -	3	4	8	12
*Red-eyed Vireo				
Vireo olivaceus - - - - - - - - -	3	2	2	2
*Eastern Yellow Warbler				
Dendroica a. aestiva - - - - - - - -	1		2	1
*Northern Yellow-throat				
Geothlypis trichas brachidactyla - - - -	13	9	6	4
English Sparrow				
Passer d. domesticus - - - - - - -	30	30	12	12
Eastern Meadowlark				
Sturnella m. magna - - - - - - - -	3	4	1	
Baltimore Oriole				
Icterus galbula - - - - - - - - -			1	2
Bronzed Grackle				
Quiscalus quiscula aeneus - - - - - -	3			

		Number of Pairs		
	1930	1931	1934	1935
Eastern Cowbird				
Molothrus a. ater - - - - - - - -	6	6	6	6
*Eastern Cardinal				
Richmondena c. cardinalis - - - - - -	5	6	4	3
*Indigo Bunting				
Passerina cyanea - - - - - - - - -	11	7	6	3
Eastern Goldfinch				
Spinus t. tristis - - - - - - - - -	6	9	4	3
*Eastern Chipping Sparrow				
Spizella p. passerina - - - - - - -	2	1		
*Eastern Field Sparrow				
Spizella p. pusilla - - - - - - - -	2	3		
*Mississippi Song Sparrow				
Melospiza melodia euphonia - - - - -	52	48	25	25
Total Species - - - - - - - -	30	29	26	25
Total Pairs - - - - - - - - -	219	199	133	150
Total Pairs of Cowbird Hosts - - -	93	82	49	45
Number Pairs per Acre - - - - -	5.5	5.0	3.3	3.8

*Species commonly parasitized by the Cowbird in central Ohio, according to Hicks, 79.

APPENDIX IV

Futher Data on Cowbirds: Returns and Weights.

A. RETURNS

Adults: 4 males banded; no returns. 9 females banded: 3 returns—1; 2 returns—2. Percentage of returns on 13 adults banded 1931-1935: 7 yearly returns (53.8%); 5 individual returns (38.5%). Percentage of return of the 9 females: yearly returns 77.8%; individual returns 54.4%.

Nestlings: 35 banded and safely fledged. No returns. All nestlings were banded on the right leg and all adults on the left. All Cowbirds on Interpont were hopefully scrutinized for bands on the right leg, but without result.

Other banders, however, have had returns from young banded Cowbirds. Mrs. Marie Dales, Sioux City, Iowa, writes me of an "immature Cowbird banded July 14, 1924," that "returned May 3, 1929." Mr. O. L. Austin, Jr., informs me that at the Austin Ornithological Research Station on Cape Cod, they have many records of locally raised young of this species returning in May, some of them repeating in the traps throughout the summer.

B. WEIGHTS

1. *Weights of Young Raised by Song Sparrows*

May 16, 1932. 7 days. 21.8 g.   May 26, 1935. 8 days. 31 g.
May 25, 1936. 10 days. 31.5 g.   May 31, 1933. 14 (?) days. 28 g.
May 20, 1935. 9 days 17 g. In K181's nest; died the next day.

2. *Weights of Adults in Grams*

 5 weights of males, Apr. 4-May 13 :   48.2-51.7, average 50.7
14 weights of females, Apr. 4-May 11 : 34.2-45.6, average 39.8.
 4 weights of laying females :   40.2-45.6, average 42.7.
10 weights of non-laying females :   34.2-44.8, average 38.7.
 3 weights of "returning" females :   41.5-44.8, average 43.0.   (Non-laying).
 7 weights of new females :   34.2-39.3, average 37.1.   (Non-laying).

The greater weight of the birds known to be more than a year old is of interest.

Dr. L. E. Hicks has given me data as to weights of Cowbirds collected by him in Perry County, Ohio, Apr. 4, 1934.

> 10 males :   44.2-50.9, average 47.03 g.
>
> 5 females : 35.7-44.1, average 39.3 g.
>
> 2 juvenal males : June 18, 1935, 41.9 g.; July 10, 1935, 46.6 g. "Very well developed but still being fed by a Redstart and Prothonotary Warbler."

APPENDIX V

Meteorological Data for Columbus.

A summary of the average temperature, precipitation, and amount of sunshine in Columbus is given in Table XXXII. These figures are from the United States Weather Bureau which has kept records for this locality extending over 41 to 57 years.

TABLE XXXII

Average Temperature, Precipitation and Amount of Sunshine at Columbus, Ohio*

TEMPERATURE IN FAHRENHEIT; PRECIPITATION IN INCHES

(From the United States Weather Bureau Records)

Month	Temperature					Pecipitation		Sunshine	
	Average Daily Maximum	Average Daily Minimum	Average	Absolute Highest	Absolute Lowest	Average Total	Average Snowfall	Total Hours	Per Cent
January	36.4	21.7	29.0	72	—20	3.08	7.9	114	38
February	38.2	22.9	30.6	72	—20	2.72	5.8	128	42
March	48.5	31.4	40.0	84	0	3.44	3.4	176	47
April	60.7	41.5	51.1	90	15	2.89	1.1	212	56
May	71.9	52.0	62.0	96	31	3.53	T.	276	62
June	80.5	60.8	70.6	101	39	3.36	0	299	67
July	85.0	64.9	75.0	106	49	3.55	0	321	70
August	82.5	62.8	72.6	103	42	3.21	0	286	67
September	76.8	56.7	66.8	99	32	2.50	0	240	64
October	64.4	45.4	54.9	90	20	3.18	0.1	200	58
November	49.8	35.4	42.1	77	— 5	2.75	1.5	130	44
December	39.2	25.6	32.4	67	—12	2.70	4.2	96	33
Year	61.2	43.3	52.3	106	—20	36.19	24.0	2,477	54

*Length of record : Temperature, 57 years ; Precipitation, 51 years ; Amount of Sunshine, 41 years.

Ecologists tell us that it is not the mean temperatures that are most significant but the extremes. In Table XXXIII the temperature and precipitation during the period of study are shown, the absolute highest and lowest temperatures reached each year being given as well as the average. The lowest temperature during the period of study was 16 degrees below zero (Fahrenheit) on Jan. 22, 1936.

TABLE XXXIII

Temperature and Precipitation at Columbus During the Period of Study
(From Records of the U. S. Weather Bureau)

Year		Temperature in Degrees Fahrenheit			Precipitation in Inches
		Average	Absolute Highest	Absolute Lowest*	
1929	- - - - - - - - - -	51.7	92	—2	42.27
1930	- - - - - - - - - -	53.9	101	—8	21.60
1931	- - - - - - - - - -	55.4	98	13	35.54
1932	- - - - - - - - - -	53.8	99	—4	30.03
1933	- - - - - - - - - -	54.4	99	—6	32.02
1934	- - - - - - - - - -	53.7	106	—8	22.03
1935	- - - - - - - - - -	52.6	95	—4	35.35
Average of 7 Years - - -		53.6			31.26
Average of 55 Years - -		52.3			36.19

*Lowest in 1936 —16° F.

BIBLIOGRAPHY

1. ALEXANDER, W. H. 1931. Ohio Section, Year 1930. Climatological Data. 35:49.

2. 1932. Ohio Section, Year 1931. Climatological Data, 36:6.

2a. 1933. Ohio Section, Year 1932. Climatological Data, 37:48.

3. 1935. Annual Meteorological Summary with Comparative Data 1934, Columbus, Ohio, U. S. Department Agriculture Weather Bureau.

4. ALLEN, A. A. 1914. The Red-winged Blackbird: a Study in the Ecology of a Cat-tail Marsh. Abstract Proc. Linnaean Society of New York, 24-25:43-128.

5. ALI, S. A. 1930. The Nesting Habits of the Baya (*Ploceus philippinus*). Jour. Bombay Natural History Society, 34:947-964.

6. ATWOOD, H. 1914. Some Factors Affecting the Weight, Composition and Hatchability of Hen Eggs. West Virginia Univ. Agri. Exp. Sta. Bull., 145:73-142.

7. 1926-27. The Resemblance of Sisters in Respect to the Mean Weight of their Eggs. Poultry Science, 6:91-93.

7a. 1928. Observations concerning the Time Factor in Egg Production. Poultry Science, 8:137-140.

8. BAASCH, K. W. 1927. A Permanent Resident Song Sparrow. Bull. Northeastern Bird-Banding Ass., 3:19.

9. BAKER, E. C. S. 1927. Are the Characters and Colouration of Eggs Hereditary? A Discussion. Bull. British Ool. Assoc., 1:131-139.

10. 1930. On Abnormalities in Eggs. Bull. British Ool. Assoc., 3:28-32.

11. BALDWIN, S. P. 1921. Recent Returns from Trapping and Banding Birds. Auk, 38:228-237.

12. 1921. The Marriage Relations of the House Wren. Auk, 38:237-244.

13. BALDWIN, S. P., and S. C. KENDEIGH. 1927. Attentiveness and Inattentiveness in the Nesting Behavior of the House Wren. Auk, 44:206-216.

14. 1932. Physiology of the Temperature of Birds. Sci. Publ. Cleveland Mus. Nat. Hist., 3:1-196.

15. BARON, S. 1934. Nest Mortality. British Birds, 28:77.

16. BARROWS, W. B. 1912. Michigan Bird Life. Michigan Agricultural College, 822 p.

17. BENNETT, L. J. 1935. A Comparison of Two Iowa Duck Nesting Seasons. Trans. Am. Game Conf. New York City: 277-282.

18. BENSON, A. 1932. Returns. Bird Banding Notes, 2:86.

19. BERGTOLD, W. H. 1913. A Study of the House Finch. Auk, 30:40-73.

20. 1917. A Study of the Incubation Periods of Birds. Denver, Colorado, 109 p.

21.   1929. Egg Weights from Egg Measurements. Auk, 46:466-473.

21a. BERNEY, F. L. 1928. Effect of Drought upon Bird Life. Nature, 122:328-329.

22. BERNHARDT, P. 1930. Erfahrungen und Beobachtungen bei Raubvogel-Beringungen. Mitt. Vereins sächs. Ornithologen, 3:10.

22a. BIGGLESTONE, H. C. 1913. A Study of the Nesting Behavior of the Yellow Warbler (*Dendroica aestiva aestiva*). Wilson Bulletin, 25:48-67.

22b. BISSONETTE, T. H. 1931. Studies in the Sexual Cycle in Birds. IV. Experimental Modification of the Sexual Cycle of the European Starling (*Sturnus vulgaris*) by Changes in the Daily Period of Illumination and of Muscular Work. Jour. Exp. Zool., 58:281-314.

22c. BLANCHARD, B. D. 1936. Continuity of Behavior in the Nuttall White-crowned Sparrow. Condor, 38:145-150.

23. BLINCO, B. J. 1935. A Cowbird Removes a Robin's Egg. Wilson Bulletin, 47:158.

24. BOYD, A. W. 1931. On Some Results of Ringing Greenfinches. British Birds, 24:329-337.

25. BROUN, M. 1933. Some Interesting Recoveries. Bird-Banding, 4:157-158.

26. BROWN, C. E. 1928. Longevity of Birds in Captivity. Auk, 45:345-348.

27. BURKITT, J. P. 1924. A Study of the Robin by Means of Marked Birds. British Birds, 17:294-303; 18:97-103.

28.   1925. Ibid., 18:250-257; 19:120-129.

29.   1926. Ibid., 20:91-101.

29a.   1936. Young Rooks, Their Survival and Habits. British Birds, 29:334-338.

30. BURNS, F. L. 1915. Comparative Periods of Deposition and Incubation of Some North American Birds. Wilson Bulletin, 27:275-286.

30a. BURTCH, V. 1925. Notes from Branchport, N. Y. Bull. Northeastern Bird-Banding Ass., 2:20.

31. BUSSMANN, J. 1933. Experiments with the Terragraph on the Activities of Nesting Birds. Bird-Banding, 4:33-40.

32. BUTTS, W. K. 1930. A Study of the Chickadee and White-breasted Nuthatch by Means of Marked Individuals. I. Bird-Banding, 1:149-168.

33.   1931. Op. cit. II. Ibid., 2:1-26.

34. CALLENBACH, B. W. 1929. The Relation of Antecedent Egg Production to the Sex Ratio. Poultry Science, 8:230-234.

35. CAPECK, V. 1896. Beiträge zur Fortpflanzungsgeschichte des Kuckucks. Ornithologisches Jahrbuch, 7:41-72; 102-117; 146-157; 165-183.

36. CHANCE, E. 1922. The Cuckoo's Secret. London, Sidgwick and Jackson, 239 p.

37. CHAPMAN, F. M. 1928. The Nesting Habits of Wagler's Oropendola (*Zarhynchos wagleri*) on Barro Colorado Island. Bull. Amer. Mus. Natural History, 58:123-166.

38. CHAPMAN, L. B. 1935. Studies of a Tree Swallow Colony. Bird-Banding, 6:45-57.

38a. CHAPMAN, R. N. 1931. Animal Ecology. McGraw-Hill. N. Y. 464 p.

39. CLABAUGH, E. D. 1925. Casualties among Birds. Condor, 27:114-115.

40. ———— 1926. Op. cit. Ibid., 28:128.

40a. CLOBES, D. 1936. Rauchschwalbenberingung. Vogelring, 8 (1):23-24.

40b. COLE, L. J. 1933. The Relation of Light Periodicity to the Reproductive Cycle, Migration and Distribution of the Mourning Dove (*Zenaidura macroura carolinensis*). Auk, 50:285-296.

41. COOKE, M. T. 1923. Report on Bird Censuses in the United States, 1916 to 1920. U. S. Dept. Agri. Dept. Bull. 1165. 36 p.

42. COOKE, W. W. 1885. Mississippi Valley Migration. Ornithologist and Oologist, 10:33-35.

43. ———— 1913. The Relation of Bird Migration to the Weather. Auk, 30:205-221.

44. ———— 1916. Second Annual Report of Bird Counts in the United States with Discussion of Results. U. S. Dept. Agr. Bull. 396. 20 p.

45. CSÖRGEY, T. 1929/30. Vogelschutz-Studien aus den Jahren 1922-1930. Aquila, 36-37:220-231.

46. DAVIS, W. B. 1933. The Span of the Nesting Season of Birds in Butte County, California, in Relation to their Food. Condor, 35:151-154.

47. DeLURY, R. E. 1934. Fluctuations in the Numbers of Birds Revealed by Bird-Banding. Eastern Bird Banding Quarterly, 1:6.

48. DROST, R. 1930. Vom Zug der Amsel (*Turdus m. merula L.*). Vogelzug, 1:74-85.

49. ———— 1935. Ueber das Zahlenverhältnis von Alter und Geschlecht auf dem Herbst und Frühjahrszuge. Vogelzug, 6:177-182.

50. DUPOND, C. 1934. Quatre Années de Baguage d'Oiseaux (1930-1933). Ornithologie, Nos. 77-82:1-15.

51. EATON, R. J. 1933. The Migratory Movement of Certain Colonies of Herring Gulls. Bird-Banding, 4:165-176.

51a. EISENHUT, E., and W. LUTZ. 1936. Beobachtungen über die Fortpflanzungsbiologie des Feldsperlings. Mitt. über die Vogelwelt: 1 ff.

51b. ELTON, C. 1927. Animal Ecology. N. Y. Macmillan. 207 p.

52. ERRINGTON, P. L. 1933. The Nesting and Life Equation of the Wisconsin Bob-white. Wilson Bulletin, 45:122-132.

53. ———— 1933. The Wintering of the Wisconsin Bob-White. Trans. Wisconsin Acad. Sciences, Arts and Letters, 28:1-35.

54. 1934. Vulnerability of Bob-white Populations to Predation. Ecology, 15:110-127.

54a. 1935. The 1934 Drought and Southern Iowa Bob-white. Iowa Bird Life, 5:18-21.

55. ERRINGTON, P. L., and F. N. HAMERSTROM, JR. 1936. The Northern Bob-white's Winter Territory. Iowa Agri. Exp. Sta. Research Bull. 201:301-443.

56. EUSTIS, G. D. 1931. Some Song Sparrow Returns. Bird-Banding, 2:184.

57. FLOWER, S. S. 1925. Contributions to our Knowledge of the Duration of Life in Vertebrate Animals. IV. Birds. Proc. Zoological Soc., London: 1366-1422.

58. FRIEDMANN, H. 1927. A Case of Apparently Adaptive Acceleration of Embryonic Growth-Rate in Birds. Biol. Bull., 53:343-345.

59. 1929. The Cowbirds. Springfield, Ill. Thomas. 421 p.

60. 1931. Bird Distribution and Bird-Banding. Bird-Banding, 2:45-51.

61. 1935. Bird Societies. In C. Murchison's "Handbook of Social Psychology." Clark Univ. Press: 142-184.

61a. GAULT, B. T. 1902. A Song Sparrow Nest. Wilson Bulletin, 14:15-16.

62. GABRIELSON, I. N. 1922. Factors Contributing to the Destruction of Birds' Nests and Eggs. Bird-Lore, 24:136-139.

62a. GIBSON, E. 1918. Further Ornithological Notes from the Neighbourhood of Cape San Antonio, Province of Buenos Ayres. Part I. Passeres. Ibis, Series 10, 6:363-415.

63. GILLESPIE, J. A. 1927. Four and Five Year Old Catbird and Crested Fly-catcher, and Probably Resident Song Sparrow. Bull. Northeastern Bird-Banding Ass., 3:13.

64. 1930. Homing Instincts in Cowbirds. Bird-Banding, 1:42.

65. GRINNELL, H. W. 1931. Minutes of Cooper Club Meetings. Northern Division. Condor, 33:262.

66. GROEBBELLS, F., MÖBERT, F., and TIMMERMANN, G. 1930. Ueber die Beziehungen zwischen Eigewichten und Legefolge. Beitr. z. Fortpflb. d. Vögel, 6:91-92.

67. GROEBBELLS, F. 1932. Der Vogel. Bau, Funktion, Lebenserscheinung, Einpassung. I. Berlin. Borntraeger. 918 p.

68. GURNEY, J. H. 1899. On the Comparative Ages to which Birds Live. Ibis, Ser. 7, 5:19-42.

69. HAECKER, V. 1926. Ueber Jahreszeitliche Veränderungen and klimatisch bedingte Verschiedenheiten der Vogel-Schilddrüse. Schweizer. Med. Wochenschr. 7 (15):337-341.

70. HAIGH, G. H. C. 1935. On Pink-Footed Geese. British Birds, 28:367-369.

71. HALDEMAN, D. W. 1931. A Study of the Eastern Song Sparrow, *Melospiza melodia melodia*. Auk, 48:385-406.

71a. HAMILL, L. C. 1926. Notes on the Mating of Song Sparrows and their Range-Limits during the Nesting Season. Bull. Northeastern Bird-Banding Ass., 2:7-10.

72. HAUN, M. 1931. Statistische Untersuchungen über die Eierzahl in Gelegen der drei Lerchenarten (*Alauda arvensis, Galerida cristata* und *Lullula arborea*) sowie der Goldammer (*Emberiza citrinella*). Beitr. z. Fortpflb. d. Vögel, 7:135-138.

73. HAVERSCHMIDT, F. 1933. Beobachtungen in der Kormorankolonie bei Lekkerkerk. Beitr. z. Fortpflb. d. Vögel, 9:1-14.

73a. HEINROTH, O. 1910. Beiträge zur Biologie, namentlich Ethologie and Psychologie der Anatiden. V. Int. Orn. Kongress: 589-702.

74. ———. 1922. Die Beziehungen zwischen Vogelgewicht, Eigewicht, Gelegegewicht und Brutdauer. Jour. f. Ornithologie, 70:172-285.

75. ———. 1924. Lautäusserungen der Vögel. Jour. f. Ornithologie, 72:223-244.

76. HEINROTH, O. and M. 1924-1932. Die Vögel Mitteleuropas. 3 vols.

77. HENDERSON, G. 1934. My Neighbors in Franklin and Decatur Counties. Audubon Year Book. Indiana Audubon Society: 33-47.

77a. HEYDWEILLER, A. M. 1935. A Comparison of Winter and Summer Territories and Seasonal Variations of the Tree Sparrow (*Spizella a. arborea*). Bird-Banding, 6:1-11.

77b. HICKS, L. E. 1933. Returns of Purple Martins. Bird-Banding, 4:113.

78. ———. 1934. Individual and Sexual Variations in the European Starling. Bird-Banding, 5:103-118.

79. ———. 1934. A Summary of Cowbird Host Species in Ohio. Auk, 51:385-386.

80. ———. 1935. A Ten Year Study of a Bird Population in Central Ohio. Am. Midland Naturalist, 16:177-186.

81. HICKS, L. E., and C. A. DAMBACH. 1935. Sex Ratios and Weights in Wintering Crows. Bird-Banding, 6:65-66.

82. HICKS, L. E., and F. B. CHAPMAN. 1933. A Statistical Survey of Ohio Winter Bird Life. Ohio Jour. Science, 33:135-150.

82a. HIGGINS, A. W. 1925. Bluebird Behavior at Highland View Farm. Bull. Northeastern Bird-Banding Ass., 1:2-4.

82b. ———. 1926. Nesting Records of Song Sparrows 25935 and 39235. Bull. Northeastern Bird-Banding Ass., 2:39.

83. HOESCH, W. 1934. Nester und Gelege aus dem Damaraland. I. Jour. f. Ornithologie, 82:325-339.

83a. ———. 1936. Op. cit. II. Ibid., 84:3-20.

84. HOFFMAN, E. C. 1929. Longevity of the Blue Jay. Bull. Northeastern Bird-Banding Ass., 5:56-58.

231

85. HOWARD, L. E. 1920. Territory in Bird Life. London. 308 p.

86. 1929. An Introduction to the Study of Bird Behaviour. Cambridge. 136 p.

87. HOWELL, A. H. 1932. Florida Bird Life. Coward-McCann. N. Y. 579 p.

88. HUXLEY, J. S. 1927. On The Relation between Egg-weight and Body-weight in Birds. Jour. Linn. Soc., Zool., London, 36:457-466.

89. 1932. Field Studies and Physiology: a Correlation in the Field of Avian Reproduction. Nature, 129:166.

90. JUDD, S. D. 1899. The Efficiency of Some Protective Adaptations in Securing Insects from Birds. American Naturalist, 33:461-484.

91. 1901. The Relation of Sparrows to Agriculture. U. S. Dept. Agr. Biol. Surv. Bull., 15:82-86.

92. JULL, M. A. 1924. The Relation of Antecedent Egg Production to the Sex Ratio of the Domestic Fowl. Jour. Agr. Research, 28 (3):199-224.

93. KENDEIGH, S. C. 1933. Abundance and Conservation of the Bob-white in Ohio. Ohio Jour. Science, 33:1-18.

94. 1934. The Rôle of Environment in the Life of Birds. Ecological Monographs, 4:299-417.

95. KENDEIGH, S. C., and S. P. BALDWIN. 1930. The Mechanical Recording of the Nesting Activities of Birds. Auk, 47:471-480.

96. KLEIBER, M., and J. E. DOUGHERTY. 1934. The Influence of Environmental Temperature on the Utilization of Food Energy in Baby Chicks. Jour. General Physiology, 17:701-726.

97. KLUIJVER, H. N. 1933. Bijdrage tot de Biologie en de Ecologie van den Spreeuw (Sturnus vulgaris L.) gedurende zijn Voortplantingstijd. Wageningen, Veeman and Zonen. 145 p.

98. 1935. Waarnemingen over de Levenswijze van den Spreeuw (Sturnus v. vulgaris L.) met Behulp van Geringde Individuen. Ardea, 24:133-166.

98a. KÜCHLER, W. 1935. Jahreszyklische Veränderungen im histologischen Bau der Vogelschilddrüse. Jour. für Ornith., 83:414-461.

99. LACK, D. 1933. Nesting Conditions as a Factor Controlling Breeding Time in Birds. Proc. Zool. Soc. London: 231-237.

99a. LAMBERT, H. 1932. Geschwisterehe der Schwanzmeise. 8. Jahresb. d. Zweigberingungsstelle Untermain: 31.

100. LASKEY, A. R. 1933. A Territory and Mating Study of Mockingbirds. The Migrant, 4:29-35.

100a. 1935. Mockingbird Life History Studies. Auk, 52:370-382.

101. LEBEURIER, E., and J. RAPINE. 1935. Ornithologie de la Basse-Bretagne. Anthus pratensis L. 1758. Le Pipit des Prés. L'Oiseau et la Rev. franç. d'Ornithologie, 5:462-480.

101a. 1936. Ornithologie de la Basse-Bretagne. (Suite.) Saxicola torquata hibernans (Hartert) 1910. Le Traquet patre britannique. L'Oiseau et la Rev. franç. d'Ornithologie, 6:86-103.

101b. LEOPOLD, A. 1933. Game Management. Scribners, N. Y. 481 p.

102. LEWIS, H. F. 1929. The Natural History of the Double-Crested Cormorant (*Phalacrocorax auritus auritus* (Lesson)). Ottawa, 94 p.

102a. 1930. Notes on Banding Operations on the North Shore of the Gulf of St. Lawrence in 1929. Bird-Banding, 1:95-103.

103. LINCOLN, F. C. 1931. Some Causes of Mortality among Birds. Auk, 48:538-546.

104. 1934. The Operation of Homing Instinct. Bird-Banding, 5:149-155.

104a. 1935. The Migration of North American Birds. U. S. Dept. Agri. Circ. 363. Washington, D. C. 72 p.

105. LINCOLN, F. C., and S. P. BALDWIN. 1929. Manual for Bird Banders. U. S. Dept. Agr. Misc. Pub., 58. 112 p.

106. LINSDALE, J. M. 1928. Variations in the Fox Sparrow (*Passerella iliaca*) with Reference to Natural History and Osteology. Univ. California Pub. Zool., 30:251-392.

107. 1933. The Nesting Season in Doniphan County, Kansas. Condor, 35:155-160.

108. LINSDALE, J. M., and E. L. SUMNER, SR. 1934. Variability in Weight in the Golden-crowned Sparrow. Univ. California Pub. Zool., 40 (5):309-320.

109. 1934. Winter Weights of Golden-crowned and Fox Sparrows. Condor, 36:107-112.

110. LOCKLEY, R. M. 1935. A Census over Seven Years on Skokholm, Pembrokeshire. Jour. Animal Ecology, 4:52-57.

111. LOFBERG, L. M. 1928. Bird Banding at Florence Lake, 7,340 Feet Altitude. Condor, 30:308-314.

112. LORENZ, K. 1935. Der Kumpan in der Umwelt des Vogels. (Schluss.) Jour. f. Ornithologie, 83:289-413.

113. LOW, S. H. 1933. Further Notes on the Nesting of the Tree Swallows. Bird-Banding, 4:76-87.

113a. 1933. Notes on the Nesting of Bluebirds. Bird-Banding, 4:109-111.

114. 1934. Nest Distribution and Survival Ratio of Tree Swallows. Bird-Banding, 5:24-30.

115. v. LUCANUS, F. 1923. Die Rätsel des Vogelzuges. II. Aufl. Beyer & Söhne, Langensalza.

116. LYON, W. I. 1935. "Homing" Instinct of Cowbirds. Inland Bird Banding News, 7 (1):7.

117. MAGEE, M. J. 1928. How Long do Purple Finches Live? Bull. Northeastern Bird-Banding Ass., 4:132-136.

118. 1935. How Long do Purple Finches Live? Bird-Banding, 6:104-105.

118a. 1936. The Wing Molt in Purple Finches. Bird-Banding, 7:73-76.

119. MANWELL, R. D., and C. HERMAN. 1935. Blood-parasites of Birds and their Relation to Migratory and Other Habits of their Hosts. Bird-Banding, 6:130-133.

119a. 1935. The Occurrence of the Avian Malarias in Nature. Am. Jour. Tropical Medicine, 15:661-673.

120. MAY, J. B. 1931. Items of Interest. Mass. Dept. Agri. Div. Ornithology. September.

120a. McATEE, W. L. 1936. The Malthusian Principle in Nature. Scientific Monthly, 42:444-456.

121. MEISE, W. 1930. Revierbesitz im Vogelleben. Mitt. Vereins sächs. Ornithologen, 3:48-68.

122. MERRIAM, C. H. 1894. Laws of Temperature Control of the Geographic Distribution of Terrestrial Animals and Plants. Nat. Geog. Mag., 6:229-236.

123. MICHENER, H. and J. R. 1935. Mockingbirds, their Territories and Individualities. Condor, 37:97-140.

124. MIDDLETON, R. J. 1929. Notes from Norristown, Pennsylvania. Three Permanent Resident Song Sparrows. Bull. Northeastern Bird-Banding Ass., 5:62-65.

125. MILLER, A. H. 1931. Systematic Revision and Natural History of the American Shrikes (Lanius). Univ. California Pub. Zool., 38:11-242.

126. MOFFAT, C. B. 1903. The Spring Rivalry of Birds. Some Views on the Limit to Multiplication. Irish Naturalist, 12:152-166. Reprinted 1934 in The Irish Naturalists' Journal, 5:84-87, 115-120, 155-156.

126a. MOREAU, R. E. 1936. Breeding Seasons of Birds in East African Evergreen Forest. Proc. Zool. Soc. London, 1936:631-653.

127. MUSSELMAN, T. E. 1935. Three Years of Eastern Bluebird Banding and Study. Bird-Banding, 6:117-125.

127a. NICE, M. M. 1923. Nesting Records from 1920 to 1923 from Norman, Oklahoma. Proc. Oklahoma Acad. Science, 3:61-67.

128. 1930. Do Birds Usually Change Mates for the Second Brood? Bird-Banding, 1:70-72.

129. 1930. The Technique of Studying Nesting Song Sparrows. Bird-Banding, 1:177-181.

130. 1931. Survival and Reproduction in a Song Sparrow Population during One Season. Wilson Bulletin, 43:91-102.

131.   1931. Returns of Song Sparrows in 1931. Bird-Banding, 2:89-98.

132.   1932. The Song Sparrow Breeding Season of 1931. Bird-Banding, 3:45-50.

133.   1933. Migratory Behavior in Song Sparrows. Condor, 35:219-224.

134.   1933. Relations between the Sexes in Song Sparrows. Wilson Bulletin, 45:51-59.

135.   1933. Nesting Success during Three Seasons in a Song Sparrow Population. Bird-Banding, 4:119-131.

136.   1933. The Theory of Territorialism and its Development. Fifty Years' Progress of American Ornithology. Lancaster, Pa.: 89-100.

137.   1933-34. Zur Naturgeschichte des Singammers. Jour. f. Ornithologie, 81:552-595; 82:1-96.

138.   1934. Review of Dutch Studies on Nesting. Wilson Bulletin, 46:130-132.

139.   1934. Song Sparrows and Territory. Condor, 36:49-57.

140.   1934. Les Oiseaux et le "Cantonnement." Alauda, 6:275-297.

140a.   1934. Ten Year Old Passerines. Condor, 36:243.

141.   NICHOLSON, A. J. 1933. The Balance of Animal Populations. Jour. Animal Ecology, 2:132-178.

142.   NICHOLSON, E. M. 1929. How Birds Live. 2nd Ed. London. 150 p.

143.   1930. Birds. Encyclopedia Brittanica, 14th Ed., 3:634.

144.   OWEN, J. H. 1926. The Eggs of the Sparrow Hawk. British Birds, 20:114-120.

145.   PARTIN, J. L. 1933. A Year's Study of House Finch Weights. Condor, 35:60-68.

146.   PETERS, H. S. 1936. A List of External Parasites from Birds of the Eastern Part of the United States. Bird-Banding, 7:9-27.

147.   PICKWELL, G. B. 1931. The Prairie Horned Lark. Trans. Acad. Science of St. Louis, 27:1-153.

147a.   PITT, F. 1929. Notes on the Effect of Temperature upon the Breeding Behaviour of Birds, with Special Reference to the Northern Golden Plover (*Charadrius apricarius altifrons*), and the Fieldfare (*Turdus pilaris*). Ibis, Ser. 12, 5:53-71.

148.   POTTER, J. K. 1915. Eggs and Nestling Destruction. Cassinia, 19:30-32.

149.   PRAEGER, R. L. 1921. Birds' Nests and their Fate. Irish Naturalist, 30:25-26.

149a.   PRICE, J. B. 1936. The Family Relations of the Plain Titmouse. Condor, 38:23-28.

149b.   PUNNETT, R. C. 1933. Inheritance of Egg-colour in the Parasitic Cuckoos. Nature, 132:892-893.

150.   RIDDLE, O. 1911. On the Formation, Significance and Chemistry of the White and Yellow Yolk of Ova. Jour. Morph., 22:455-491.

151. 1921. Studies on the Physiology of Reproduction in Birds. X. Inadequate Egg Shells and the Early Death of Embryos in the Egg. Am. Jour. Physiology, 57:250-263.

152. 1928. Internal Secretions in Evolution and Reproduction. Scientific Monthly, 26:202-216.

153. RIDDLE, O., and A. A. SPOHN. 1919. Studies on the Physiology of Reproduction in Birds. IV. When a Gland Functions for the First Time is its Secretion the Equivalent of Subsequent Secretions? Am. Jour. Physiology, 41:419-422.

154. RIDDLE, O., and H. E. HONEYWELL. 1923. Studies on the Physiology of Reproduction in Birds. XVIII. Effects of the Onset of Cold Weather on Blood Sugar and Ovulation Rate in Pigeons. Am. Jour. Physiology, 67:337-345.

155. RIDDLE, O., and W. S. FISCHER. 1925. Seasonal Variation of Thyroid Size in Pigeons. Am. Jour. Physiology, 72:464-487.

156. RIDDLE, O., G. C. SMITH, and F. G. BENEDICT. 1932. The Basal Metabolism of the Mourning Dove and Some of its Hybrids. Am. Jour. Physiology, 101 (2):260-267.

157. 1934. Seasonal and Temperature Factors and their Determination in Pigeons of Percentage Metabolism Change per Degree of Temperature Change. Am. Jour. Physiology, 107:333-342.

158. RIDDLE, O., and P. F. B. BRAUCHER. 1934. Studies on the Physiology of Reproduction in Birds. XXXIII. Body Size Changes in Doves and Pigeons Incident to Stages of the Reproductive Cycle. Am. Jour. Physiology, 107:343-347.

159. RIDGWAY, R. 1874. The Lower Wabash Valley. Proc. Boston Soc. Nat. Hist., 16:304-332.

160. 1901. Birds of North and Middle America. Bull. U. S. National Museum, 50. Part I:1-715.

161. ROBERTS, T. S. 1932. Birds of Minnesota. 2 Vols. Minneapolis.

162. ROWAN, W. 1929. Experiments in Bird Migration. I. Manipulation of the Reproductive Cycle: Seasonal Histological Changes in the Gonads. Proc. Boston Soc. Nat. Hist., 39 (5):151-208.

163. 1931. The Riddle of Migration. Baltimore. Williams and Wilkins. 151 p.

163a. RUTHVEN, A. G. 1908. Variations and Genetic Relationships of the Garter Snakes. U. S. Nat. Mus. Bull. 61.

164. RYVES, B. H. 1930. The Breeding-season of 1929 in North Cornwall. Ann. and Mag. Nat. Hist., 5 (29):564-567.

165. RYVES, COL., and MRS. B. H. 1934. The Breeding-habits of the Corn-Bunting as Observed in North Cornwall: with special Reference to its Polygamous Habit. British Birds, 28:2-26.

236

166. 1934. Supplementary Notes on the Breeding Habits of the Corn-Bunting as Observed in North Cornwall in 1934. British Birds, 28:154-164.

167. VON SANDEN, W. 1935. Beobachtungen an dem Schwanenbestand des Nordenburgersees in Ostpreussen seit seiner Besiedlung mit *Cygnus olor.* Orn. Monatsber., 43:82-85.

168. SCHENK, J. 1923/24. Bericht über die ungarischen Vogelberingungen im Jahre 1923. Aquila, 30/31.

169. 1931/34. Die Vogelberingungen des Kgl. Ungarischen Ornithologischen Institutes in den Jahren 1931-1932. Aquila, 38-41:91-114.

169a. SCHIFFERLI, A. 1933. 8. Bericht der schweizerischen Vogelwarte Sempach (1931). Der Ornithologische Beobachter, 26:1-10.

170. SCHILDMACHER, H. 1929. Ueber den Wärmehaushalt kleiner Körnerfresser. Orn. Monatsber., 37:102-106.

171. SCHJELDERUP-EBBE, T. 1924. Zur Sozialpsychologie der Vögel. Ztschr. f. Psych. u. Phys., 88:225-252.

171a. 1935. Social Behavior of Birds. In C. Murchison's "Handbook of Social Psychology," Clark Univ. Press: 947-972.

172. SCHNEIDER, W. 1927. Erfahrungen bei der Starenberingung. Mitt. Vereins sächs. Ornithologen, 2:72-80.

173. SCHÖNWETTER, M. 1924. Relatives Schalengewicht inbesondere bei Spar-und Doppeleiern. Beitr. z. Fortpflb. d. Vögel, 1:49-52.

174. 1932. The Mathematical Side of Oology, as Applied to the Study of Cuckoo's Eggs. Oologists' Record, 12:83-86.

175. SEMPLE, J. B., and G. M. SUTTON. 1932. Nesting of Harris's Sparrow (*Zonotrichia querula*) at Churchill, Manitoba. Auk, 49:166-183.

75a. SEVERTZOFF, S. A. 1934. On the Dynamics of Populations of Vertebrates. Quarterly Review of Biology, 9:409-437.

175b. 1934. Vom Massenwechsel bei den Wildtieren. Biol. Zent., 54:337-364.

176. SHAW, T. 1935. Variation in the Body Weight of the Tree Sparrow, *Passer montanus saturatus* Stejneger. Bull. Fan Mem. Inst. Biol. Peiping, 6:65-69.

177. SHELFORD, V. E. 1930. Phenology and One of its Modern Descendants. Quarterly Review of Biology, 5:207-216.

178. SHELLEY, L. 1932. Inbreeding Downy Woodpeckers. Bird-Banding, 3:69-70.

179. SHERMAN, A. R. 1924. "Animal Aggregations." A Reply. Condor, 26:85-88.

179a. STADIE, R. 1935. Vom Zug der pommerschen Lachmöwen. Ber. Ver. Schles. Ornith., 19:1-29.

180. STEVENSON, J. 1933. Experiments on the Digestion of Food by Birds. Wilson Bulletin, 45:155-167.

181. STIEVE, H. 1918. Die Entwicklung des Eierstockeies der Dohle (*Coloeus monedula*). Arch. mikr. Anat., 92, Ab. II :137-288.

182. STODDARD, H. L. 1931. The Bobwhite Quail. N. Y. Scribners.

183. STONER, D. 1926. Observations and Banding Notes on the Bank Swallow. II. Auk, 43 :196-213.

183a. 1928. Op. cit. III. Auk, 45 :41-45.

184. STRESEMANN, E. 1927-1934. Aves. In : Kükenthal-Krumbach, Handb. Zool., 7. Bd., 2. Hälfte. 899 p.

184a. SUMNER, E. L., Jr. 1935. A Life History of the California Quail. Part I. California Fish and Game, 21 (3) :167-266.

185. SUMNER, E. L., Sr. 1933. Seasonal Behavior of Some Banded Golden-crowned Sparrows. Condor, 35 :180-182.

185a. SUNKEL, W. 1933. Uferschwalben-Forschung. Vogelring, 5, 2/3 :9-41.

186. THIENEMANN, J. 1922. XX. Jahresbericht (1920) der Vogelwarte Rossitten der Deutschen Ornithologischen Gesellschaft. Jour. f. Ornithologie, 70 :61-89.

187. THOMAS, E. S. 1934. A Study of Starlings Banded at Columbus, Ohio. Bird-Banding, 5 :118-128.

188. 1936. Additional Records of 'Protocalliphora. Bird-Banding, 7 :46-47.

189. THOMAS, J. F. 1933. Some Results of Ringing and Trapping Swallows in Carmarthenshire. British Birds, 26 :253-255.

189a. 1925. Some Results and Methods of Marking Wheatears. British Birds, 19 :98.

190. THOMSON, A. L. 1926. Problems of Bird Migration. London, 350 p.

191. 1929. The Migrations of British and Irish Woodcock. British Birds, 23 :74-92.

191a. TOLENAAR, D. 1922. Legperioden en Eierproductie bij eenige wilde Vogelsoorten, vergeleken met die bij Hoenderrassen. Meded. Landbouwhoogeschool. Wageningen. 23 (2) :1-46.

192. UCHIDA, S. 1932. Studies of Swallows by the Banding Method. Bird-Banding, 3 :1-11.

192a. VÄLIKANGAS, I. 1933. Finnische Zugvögel aus englischen Vogeleiern. Vogelzug, 4 :159-166.

193. VERWEY, J. 1930. Die Paarungsbiologie des Fischreihers. Zoolog. Jahrbücher, 48 :1-120.

194. 1931. Eierzahl der Feldlerche und einiger anderer Vogelarten. Beitr. z. Fortpflb. d. Vögel, 7 :66-67.

195. WACHS, H. 1926. Die Wanderungen der Vögel. Ergebnisse der Biologie, 1 :476-637.

195a. WALKINSHAW, L. H. 1936. Notes on the Field Sparrow in Michigan. Wilson Bulletin, 48:94-101.

195b. WEEKS, E. C. 1932. An Old Song Sparrow. Bird-Banding, 3:119.

196. WEIGOLD, H. 1924. VII. Bericht der Vogelwarte der Staatl. Biologischen Anstalt auf Helgoland. Jour. f. Ornithologie, 72:17-68.

196a. WETHERBEE, MRS. H. B. 1933. Some Complicated Bluebird Family History. Bird-Banding, 4:114-115.

197. 1934. Some Measurements and Weights of Live Birds. Bird-Banding, 5:55-64.

198. 1935. A Singing Female Song Sparrow. Bird-Banding, 6:32-33.

198a. WETMORE, A. 1936. The Number of Contour Feathers in Passeriform and Related Birds. Auk, 53:159-169.

199. WHARTON, W. P. 1929. Notes on Banding at Groton, Massachusetts, 1922-1928. Bull. Northeastern Bird-Banding Ass., 5:98-105.

200. 1931. New Returning Species. Bird-Banding, 2:186.

201. 1933. Banding at Groton, Massachusetts, 1929-1931. Bird-Banding, 4:100-109.

202. WHITTLE, C. L. 1926. The Bearing of a Knowledge of Nest-Spacing among Birds on the Work of the Bird-Bander. Bull. Northeastern Bird-Banding Ass., 2:78-81.

203. 1929. Recent Song Sparrow Weighings. Bull. Northeastern Bird-Banding Ass., 5:152-154.

204. 1930. Additional Live Bird Weights. Bird-Banding, 1:192-193.

205. 1932. Are Nesting Territories Always Available for Returning Juvenile Song Sparrows? Bird-Banding, 3:106-108.

206. WHITTLE, C. L. and H. G. 1926. Return Ratios in their Relation to Annual Mortality among Birds. Bull. Northeastern Bird-Banding Ass., 2:48-50.

207. WILLIAMS, H. S. 1934. Nest Building—New Style. Natural History, 34:431-446.

208. WING, L. W. 1935. Wildlife Cycles in Relation to the Sun. Trans. 21st American Game Conf. New York City: 345-363.

209. WINTERBOTTOM, J. M. 1935. Periodism in Tropical Birds. Ostrich, 6:34-38.

209a. VON WISSEL, C. 1927. Fasanenzucht. Neudamm.

210. WITHERBY, H. F. 1926. The Duration of Life of Birds. British Birds, 20:71-73.

211. 1930. Recovery of Marked Birds. British Birds, 24:182-183.

211a. WITSCHI, E. 1935. Seasonal Sex Characters in Birds and their Hormonal Control. Wilson Bull., 42:177-256.

212. WOLDA, G. 1923. Akklimatisierung und Deklimatisierung. Genetica, 5: 497-526.

213. 1926. Verslag van het ornithologisch Onderzoek 1925. Plantenziekenkundige Dienst, Wageningen. 24 p.

214. 1929. Verslag van de ornithologische Afdeeling over het Jaar 1928. Plantenziekenkundige Dienst. 27 p.

214a. 1932. Studies over Vogels en hun Omgeving. Vers. Med. Plantenziektenkundigen Dienst te Wageningen, 65:1-63.

215. WYNNE-EDWARDS, V. C. 1933. Inheritance of Egg-Colour in the "Parasitic" Cuckoos. Nature, 132:822.

216. ZEDLITZ, O. 1926. Vogelgewichte als Hilfsmittel für biologische Forschung. Jour. f. Ornithologie, 74:296-308.

217. ZIMMERMANN, R. 1932. Ueber quantitative Bestandsaufnahmen in der Vogelwelt. Mitt. Vereins sächs. Ornithologen, 3:253-267.

INDEX OF SUBJECTS

INDEX OF SPECIES

CATALOG OF DOVER BOOKS

Books Explaining Science and Mathematics

WHAT IS SCIENCE?, N. Campbell. The role of experiment and measurement, the function of mathematics, the nature of scientific laws, the difference between laws and theories, the limitations of science, and many similarly provocative topics are treated clearly and without technicalities by an eminent scientist. "Still an excellent introduction to scientific philosophy," H. Margenau in PHYSICS TODAY. "A first-rate primer . . . deserves a wide audience," SCIENTIFIC AMERICAN. 192pp. 5⅜ x 8.   S43 Paperbound **$1.25**

THE NATURE OF PHYSICAL THEORY, P. W. Bridgman. A Nobel Laureate's clear, non-technical lectures on difficulties and paradoxes connected with frontier research on the physical sciences. Concerned with such central concepts as thought, logic, mathematics, relativity, probability, wave mechanics, etc. he analyzes the contributions of such men as Newton, Einstein, Bohr, Heisenberg, and many others. "Lucid and entertaining . . . recommended to anyone who wants to get some insight into current philosophies of science," THE NEW PHILOSOPHY. Index. xi + 138pp. 5⅜ x 8.   S33 Paperbound **$1.25**

EXPERIMENT AND THEORY IN PHYSICS, Max Born. A Nobel Laureate examines the nature of experiment and theory in theoretical physics and analyzes the advances made by the great physicists of our day: Heisenberg, Einstein, Bohr, Planck, Dirac, and others. The actual process of creation is detailed step-by-step by one who participated. A fine examination of the scientific method at work. 44pp. 5⅜ x 8.   S308 Paperbound **75¢**

THE PSYCHOLOGY OF INVENTION IN THE MATHEMATICAL FIELD, J. Hadamard. The reports of such men as Descartes, Pascal, Einstein, Poincaré, and others are considered in this investigation of the method of idea-creation in mathematics and other sciences and the thinking process in general. How do ideas originate? What is the role of the unconscious? What is Poincaré's forgetting hypothesis? are some of the fascinating questions treated. A penetrating analysis of Einstein's thought processes concludes the book. xiii + 145pp. 5⅜ x 8.   T107 Paperbound **$1.25**

THE NATURE OF LIGHT AND COLOUR IN THE OPEN AIR, M. Minnaert. Why are shadows sometimes blue, sometimes green, or other colors depending on the light and surroundings? What causes mirages? Why do multiple suns and moons appear in the sky? Professor Minnaert explains these unusual phenomena and hundreds of others in simple, easy-to-understand terms based on optical laws and the properties of light and color. No mathematics is required but artists, scientists, students, and everyone fascinated by these "tricks" of nature will find thousands of useful and amazing pieces of information. Hundreds of observational experiments are suggested which require no special equipment. 200 illustrations; 42 photos. xvi + 362pp. 5⅜ x 8.   T196 Paperbound **$1.95**

THE UNIVERSE OF LIGHT, W. Bragg. Sir William Bragg, Nobel Laureate and great modern physicist, is also well known for his powers of clear exposition. Here he analyzes all aspects of light for the layman: lenses, reflection, refraction, the optics of vision, x-rays, the photoelectric effect, etc. He tells you what causes the color of spectra, rainbows, and soap bubbles, how magic mirrors work, and much more. Dozens of simple experiments are described. Preface. Index. 199 line drawings and photographs, including 2 full-page color plates. x + 283pp. 5⅜ x 8.   T538 Paperbound **$1.85**

SOAP-BUBBLES: THEIR COLOURS AND THE FORCES THAT MOULD THEM, C. V. Boys. For continuing popularity and validity as scientific primer, few books can match this volume of easily-followed experiments, explanations. Lucid exposition of complexities of liquid films, surface tension and related phenomena, bubbles' reaction to heat, motion, music, magnetic fields. Experiments with capillary attraction, soap bubbles on frames, composite bubbles, liquid cylinders and jets, bubbles other than soap, etc. Wonderful introduction to scientific method, natural laws that have many ramifications in areas of modern physics. Only complete edition in print. New Introduction by S. Z. Lewin, New York University. 83 illustrations; 1 full-page color plate. xii + 190pp. 5⅜ x 8½.   T542 Paperbound **95¢**

CATALOGUE OF DOVER BOOKS

THE STORY OF X-RAYS FROM RONTGEN TO ISOTOPES, A. R. Bleich, M.D. This book, by a member of the American College of Radiology, gives the scientific explanation of x-rays, their applications in medicine, industry and art, and their danger (and that of atmospheric radiation) to the individual and the species. You learn how radiation therapy is applied against cancer, how x-rays diagnose heart disease and other ailments, how they are used to examine mummies for information on diseases of early societies, and industrial materials for hidden weaknesses. 54 illustrations show x-rays of flowers, bones, stomach, gears with flaws, etc. 1st publication. Index. xix + 186pp. 5⅜ x 8. **T622 Paperbound $1.35**

SPINNING TOPS AND GYROSCOPIC MOTION, John Perry. A classic elementary text of the dynamics of rotation — the behavior and use of rotating bodies such as gyroscopes and tops. In simple, everyday English you are shown how quasi-rigidity is induced in discs of paper, smoke rings, chains, etc., by rapid motions; why a gyrostat falls and why a top rises; precession; how the earth's motion affects climate; and many other phenomena. Appendix on practical use of gyroscopes. 62 figures. 128pp. 5⅜ x 8. **T416 Paperbound $1.00**

SNOW CRYSTALS, W. A. Bentley, M. J. Humphreys. For almost 50 years W. A. Bentley photographed snow flakes in his laboratory in Jericho, Vermont; in 1931 the American Meteorological Society gathered together the best of his work, some 2400 photographs of snow flakes, plus a few ice flowers, windowpane frosts, dew, frozen rain, and other ice formations. Pictures were selected for beauty and scientific value. A very valuable work to anyone in meteorology, cryology; most interesting to layman; extremely useful for artist who wants beautiful, crystalline designs. All copyright free. Unabridged reprint of 1931 edition. 2453 illustrations. 227pp. 8 x 10½. **T287 Paperbound $2.95**

A DOVER SCIENCE SAMPLER, edited by George Barkin. A collection of brief, non-technical passages from 44 Dover Books Explaining Science for the enjoyment of the science-minded browser. Includes work of Bertrand Russell, Poincaré, Laplace, Max Born, Galileo, Newton; material on physics, mathematics, metallurgy, anatomy, astronomy, chemistry, etc. You will be fascinated by Martin Gardner's analysis of the sincere pseudo-scientist, Moritz's account of Newton's absentmindedness, Bernard's examples of human vivisection, etc. Illustrations from the Diderot Pictorial Encyclopedia and De Re Metallica. 64 pages. **FREE**

THE STORY OF ATOMIC THEORY AND ATOMIC ENERGY, J. G. Feinberg. A broader approach to subject of nuclear energy and its cultural implications than any other similar source. Very readable, informal, completely non-technical text. Begins with first atomic theory, 600 B.C. and carries you through the work of Mendelejeff, Röntgen, Madame Curie, to Einstein's equation and the A-bomb. New chapter goes through thermonuclear fission, binding energy, other events up to 1959. Radioactive decay and radiation hazards, future benefits, work of Bohr, moderns, hundreds more topics. "Deserves special mention . . . not only authoritative but thoroughly popular in the best sense of the word," Saturday Review. Formerly, "The Atom Story." Expanded with new chapter. Three appendixes. Index. 34 illustrations. vii + 243pp. 5⅜ x 8. **T625 Paperbound $1.45**

THE STRANGE STORY OF THE QUANTUM, AN ACCOUNT FOR THE GENERAL READER OF THE GROWTH OF IDEAS UNDERLYING OUR PRESENT ATOMIC KNOWLEDGE, B. Hoffmann. Presents lucidly and expertly, with barest amount of mathematics, the problems and theories which led to modern quantum physics. Dr. Hoffmann begins with the closing years of the 19th century, when certain trifling discrepancies were noticed, and with illuminating analogies and examples takes you through the brilliant concepts of Planck, Einstein, Pauli, Broglie, Bohr, Schroedinger, Heisenberg, Dirac, Sommerfeld, Feynman, etc. This edition includes a new, long postscript carrying the story through 1958. "Of the books attempting an account of the history and contents of our modern atomic physics which have come to my attention, this is the best," H. Margenau, Yale University, in "American Journal of Physics." 32 tables and line illustrations. Index. 275pp. 5⅜ x 8. **T518 Paperbound $1.45**

SPACE AND TIME, E. Borel. Written by a versatile mathematician of world renown with his customary lucidity and precision, this introduction to relativity for the layman presents scores of examples, analogies, and illustrations that open up new ways of thinking about space and time. It covers abstract geometry and geographical maps, continuity and topology, the propagation of light, the special theory of relativity, the general theory of relativity, theoretical researches, and much more. Mathematical notes. 2 Indexes. 4 Appendices. 15 figures. xvi + 243pp. 5⅜ x 8. **T592 Paperbound $1.45**

FROM EUCLID TO EDDINGTON: A STUDY OF THE CONCEPTIONS OF THE EXTERNAL WORLD, Sir Edmund Whittaker. A foremost British scientist traces the development of theories of natural philosophy from the western rediscovery of Euclid to Eddington, Einstein, Dirac, etc. The inadequacy of classical physics is contrasted with present day attempts to understand the physical world through relativity, non-Euclidean geometry, space curvature, wave mechanics, etc. 5 major divisions of examination: Space; Time and Movement; the Concepts of Classical Physics; the Concepts of Quantum Mechanics; the Eddington Universe. 212pp. 5⅜ x 8. **T491 Paperbound $1.35**

Nature, Biology

NATURE RECREATION: Group Guidance for the Out-of-doors, William Gould Vinal. Intended for both the uninitiated nature instructor and the education student on the college level, this complete "how-to" program surveys the entire area of nature education for the young. Philosophy of nature recreation; requirements, responsibilities, important information for group leaders; nature games; suggested group projects; conducting meetings and getting discussions started; etc. Scores of immediately applicable teaching aids, plus completely updated sources of information, pamphlets, field guides, recordings, etc. Bibliography. 74 photographs. + 310pp. 5⅜ x 8½.   **T1015 Paperbound $1.75**

HOW TO KNOW THE WILD FLOWERS, Mrs. William Starr Dana. Classic nature book that has introduced thousands to wonders of American wild flowers. Color-season principle of organization is easy to use, even by those with no botanical training, and the genial, refreshing discussions of history, folklore, uses of over 1,000 native and escape flowers, foliage plants are informative as well as fun to read. Over 170 full-page plates, collected from several editions, may be colored in to make permanent records of finds. Revised to conform with 1950 edition of Gray's Manual of Botany. xlii + 438pp. 5⅜ x 8½.   **T332 Paperbound $1.85**

HOW TO KNOW THE FERNS, F. T. Parsons. Ferns, among our most lovely native plants, are all too little known. This classic of nature lore will enable the layman to identify almost any American fern he may come across. After an introduction on the structure and life of ferns, the 57 most important ferns are fully pictured and described (arranged upon a simple identification key). Index of Latin and English names. 61 illustrations and 42 full-page plates. xiv + 215pp. 5⅜ x 8.   **T740 Paperbound $1.25**

MANUAL OF THE TREES OF NORTH AMERICA, Charles Sprague Sargent. Still unsurpassed as most comprehensive, reliable study of North American tree characteristics, precise locations and distribution. By dean of American dendrologists. Every tree native to U.S., Canada, Alaska, 185 genera, 717 species, described in detail—leaves, flowers, fruit, winterbuds, bark, wood, growth habits etc. plus discussion of varieties and local variants, immaturity variations. Over 100 keys, including unusual 11-page analytical key to genera, aid in identification. 783 clear illustrations of flowers, fruit, leaves. An unmatched permanent reference work for all nature lovers. Second enlarged (1926) edition. Synopsis of families. Analytical key to genera. Glossary of technical terms. Index. 783 illustrations, 1 map. Two volumes. Total of 982pp. 5⅜ x 8.   **T277 Vol. I Paperbound $2.00**
                                                             T278 Vol. II Paperbound $2.00
                                                             The set $4.00

TREES OF THE EASTERN AND CENTRAL UNITED STATES AND CANADA, W. M. Harlow. A revised edition of a standard middle-level guide to native trees and important escapes. More than 140 trees are described in detail, and illustrated with more than 600 drawings and photographs. Supplementary keys will enable the careful reader to identify almost any tree he might encounter. xiii + 288pp. 5⅜ x 8.   **T395 Paperbound $1.35**

GUIDE TO SOUTHERN TREES, Ellwood S. Harrar and J. George Harrar. All the essential information about trees indigenous to the South, in an extremely handy format. Introductory essay on methods of tree classification and study, nomenclature, chief divisions of Southern trees, etc. Approximately 100 keys and synopses allow for swift, accurate identification of trees. Numerous excellent illustrations, non-technical text make this a useful book for teachers of biology or natural science, nature lovers, amateur naturalists. Revised 1962 edition. Index. Bibliography. Glossary of technical terms. 920 illustrations; 201 full-page plates. ix + 709pp. 4⅝ x 6⅜.   **T945 Paperbound $2.25**

FRUIT KEY AND TWIG KEY TO TREES AND SHRUBS, W. M. Harlow. Bound together in one volume for the first time, these handy and accurate keys to fruit and twig identification are the only guides of their sort with photographs (up to 3 times natural size). "Fruit Key": Key to over 120 different deciduous and evergreen fruits. 139 photographs and 11 line drawings. Synoptic summary of fruit types. Bibliography. 2 Indexes (common and scientific names). "Twig Key": Key to over 160 different twigs and buds. 173 photographs. Glossary of technical terms. Bibliography. 2 Indexes (common and scientific names). Two volumes bound as one. Total of xvii + 126pp. 5⅝ x 8⅜.   **T511 Paperbound $1.25**

INSECT LIFE AND INSECT NATURAL HISTORY, S. W. Frost. A work emphasizing habits, social life, and ecological relations of insects, rather than more academic aspects of classification and morphology. Prof. Frost's enthusiasm and knowledge are everywhere evident as he discusses insect associations and specialized habits like leaf-rolling, leaf-mining, and case-making, the gall insects, the boring insects, aquatic insects, etc. He examines all sorts of matters not usually covered in general works, such as: insects as human food, insect music and musicians, insect response to electric and radio waves, use of insects in art and literature. The admirably executed purpose of this book, which covers the middle ground between elementary treatment and scholarly monographs, is to excite the reader to observe for himself. Over 700 illustrations. Extensive bibliography. x + 524pp. 5⅜ x 8.   **T517 Paperbound $2.45**

CATALOGUE OF DOVER BOOKS

COMMON SPIDERS OF THE UNITED STATES, J. H. Emerton. Here is a nature hobby you can pursue right in your own cellar! Only non-technical, but thorough, reliable guide to spiders for the layman. Over 200 spiders from all parts of the country, arranged by scientific classification, are identified by shape and color, number of eyes, habitat and range, habits, etc. Full text, 501 line drawings and photographs, and valuable introduction explain webs, poisons, threads, capturing and preserving spiders, etc. Index. New synoptic key by S. W. Frost. xxiv + 225pp. 5⅜ x 8. T223 Paperbound **$1.35**

THE LIFE STORY OF THE FISH: HIS MANNERS AND MORALS, Brian Curtis. A comprehensive, non-technical survey of just about everything worth knowing about fish. Written for the aquarist, the angler, and the layman with an inquisitive mind, the text covers such topics as evolution, external covering and protective coloration, physics and physiology of vision, maintenance of equilibrium, function of the lateral line canal for auditory and temperature senses, nervous system, function of the air bladder, reproductive system and methods—courtship, mating, spawning, care of young—and many more. Also sections on game fish, the problems of conservation and a fascinating chapter on fish curiosities. "Clear, simple language . . . excellent judgment in choice of subjects . . . delightful sense of humor," New York Times. Revised (1949) edition. Index. Bibliography of 72 items. 6 full-page photographic plates. xii + 284pp. 5⅜ x 8. T929 Paperbound **$1.50**

BATS, Glover Morrill Allen. The most comprehensive study of bats as a life-form by the world's foremost authority. A thorough summary of just about everything known about this fascinating and mysterious flying mammal, including its unique location sense, hibernation and cycles, its habitats and distribution, its wing structure and flying habits, and its relationship to man in the long history of folklore and superstition. Written on a middle-level, the book can be profitably studied by a trained zoologist and thoroughly enjoyed by the layman. "An absorbing text with excellent illustrations. Bats should have more friends and fewer thoughtless detractors as a result of the publication of this volume," William Beebe, Books. Extensive bibliography. 57 photographs and illustrations. x + 368pp. 5⅜ x 8½. T984 Paperbound **$2.00**

BIRDS AND THEIR ATTRIBUTES, Glover Morrill Allen. A fine general introduction to birds as living organisms, especially valuable because of emphasis on structure, physiology, habits, behavior. Discusses relationship of bird to man, early attempts at scientific ornithology, feathers and coloration, skeletal structure including bills, legs and feet, wings. Also food habits, evolution and present distribution, feeding and nest-building, still unsolved questions of migrations and location sense, many more similar topics. Final chapter on classification, nomenclature. A good popular-level summary for the biologist; a first-rate introduction for the layman. Reprint of 1925 edition. References and index. 51 illustrations. viii + 338pp. 5⅜ x 8½. T957 Paperbound **$1.85**

LIFE HISTORIES OF NORTH AMERICAN BIRDS, Arthur Cleveland Bent. Bent's monumental series of books on North American birds, prepared and published under auspices of Smithsonian Institute, is the definitive coverage of the subject, the most-used single source of information. Now the entire set is to be made available by Dover in inexpensive editions. This encyclopedic collection of detailed, specific observations utilizes reports of hundreds of contemporary observers, writings of such naturalists as Audubon, Burroughs, William Brewster, as well as author's own extensive investigations. Contains literally everything known about life history of each bird considered: nesting, eggs, plumage, distribution and migration, voice, enemies, courtship, etc. These not over-technical works are musts for ornithologists, conservationists, amateur naturalists, anyone seriously interested in American birds.

BIRDS OF PREY. More than 100 subspecies of hawks, falcons, eagles, buzzards, condors and owls, from the common barn owl to the extinct caracara of Guadaloupe Island. 400 photographs. Two volume set. Index for each volume. Bibliographies of 403, 520 items. 197 full-page plates. Total of 907pp. 5⅜ x 8½. Vol. I T931 Paperbound **$2.35**
 Vol. II T932 Paperbound **$2.35**

WILD FOWL. Ducks, geese, swans, and tree ducks—73 different subspecies. Two volume set. Index for each volume. Bibliographies of 124, 144 items. 106 full-page plates. Total of 685pp. 5⅜ x 8½. Vol. I T285 Paperbound **$2.35**
 Vol. II T286 Paperbound **$2.35**

SHORE BIRDS. 81 varieties (sandpipers, woodcocks, plovers, snipes, phalaropes, curlews, oyster catchers, etc.). More than 200 photographs of eggs, nesting sites, adult and young of important species. Two volume set. Index for each volume. Bibliographies of 261, 188 items. 121 full-page plates. Total of 860pp. 5⅜ x 8½. Vol. I T933 Paperbound **$2.35**
 Vol. II T934 Paperbound **$2.35**

THE LIFE OF PASTEUR, R. Vallery-Radot. 13th edition of this definitive biography, cited in Encyclopaedia Britannica. Authoritative, scholarly, well-documented with contemporary quotes, observations; gives complete picture of Pasteur's personal life; especially thorough presentation of scientific activities with silkworms, fermentation, hydrophobia, inoculation, etc. Introduction by Sir William Osler. Index. 505pp. 5⅜ x 8. T632 Paperbound **$2.00**

Puzzles, Mathematical Recreations

SYMBOLIC LOGIC and THE GAME OF LOGIC, Lewis Carroll. "Symbolic Logic" is not concerned with modern symbolic logic, but is instead a collection of over 380 problems posed with charm and imagination, using the syllogism, and a fascinating diagrammatic method of drawing conclusions. In "The Game of Logic" Carroll's whimsical imagination devises a logical game played with 2 diagrams and counters (included) to manipulate hundreds of tricky syllogisms. The final section, "Hit or Miss" is a lagniappe of 101 additional puzzles in the delightful Carroll manner. Until this reprint edition, both of these books were rarities costing up to $15 each. Symbolic Logic: Index. xxxi + 199pp. The Game of Logic: 96pp. 2 vols. bound as one. 5⅜ x 8. T492 Paperbound **$1.50**

PILLOW PROBLEMS and A TANGLED TALE, Lewis Carroll. One of the rarest of all Carroll's works, "Pillow Problems" contains 72 original math puzzles, all typically ingenious. Particularly fascinating are Carroll's answers which remain exactly as he thought them out, reflecting his actual mental process. The problems in "A Tangled Tale" are in story form, originally appearing as a monthly magazine serial. Carroll not only gives the solutions, but uses answers sent in by readers to discuss wrong approaches and misleading paths, and grades them for insight. Both of these books were rarities until this edition. "Pillow Problems" costing up to $25, and "A Tangled Tale" $15. Pillow Problems: Preface and Introduction by Lewis Carroll. xx + 109pp. A Tangled Tale: 6 illustrations. 152pp. Two vols. bound as one. 5⅜ x 8. T493 Paperbound **$1.50**

AMUSEMENTS IN MATHEMATICS, Henry Ernest Dudeney. The foremost British originator of mathematical puzzles is always intriguing, witty, and paradoxical in this classic, one of the largest collections of mathematical amusements. More than 430 puzzles, problems, and paradoxes. Mazes and games, problems on number manipulation, unicursal and other route problems, puzzles on measuring, weighing, packing, age, kinship, chessboards, joiners', crossing river, plane figure dissection, and many others. Solutions. More than 450 illustrations. vii + 258pp. 5⅜ x 8. T473 Paperbound **$1.25**

THE CANTERBURY PUZZLES, Henry Dudeney. Chaucer's pilgrims set one another problems in story form. Also Adventures of the Puzzle Club, the Strange Escape of the King's Jester, the Monks of Riddlewell, the Squire's Christmas Puzzle Party, and others. All puzzles are original, based on dissecting plane figures, arithmetic, algebra, elementary calculus and other branches of mathematics, and purely logical ingenuity. "The limit of ingenuity and intricacy," The Observer. Over 110 puzzles. Full Solutions. 150 illustrations. vii + 225pp. 5⅜ x 8. T474 Paperbound **$1.25**

MATHEMATICAL EXCURSIONS, H. A. Merrill. Even if you hardly remember your high school math, you'll enjoy the 90 stimulating problems contained in this book and you will come to understand a great many mathematical principles with surprisingly little effort. Many useful shortcuts and diversions not generally known are included: division by inspection, Russian peasant multiplication, memory systems for pi, building odd and even magic squares, square roots by geometry, dyadic systems, and many more. Solutions to difficult problems. 50 illustrations. 145pp. 5⅜ x 8. T350 Paperbound **$1.00**

MAGIC SQUARES AND CUBES, W. S. Andrews. Only book-length treatment in English, a thorough non-technical description and analysis. Here are nasik, overlapping, pandiagonal, serrated squares; magic circles, cubes, spheres, rhombuses. Try your hand at 4-dimensional magical figures! Much unusual folklore and tradition included. High school algebra is sufficient. 754 diagrams and illustrations. viii + 419pp. 5⅜ x 8. T658 Paperbound **$1.85**

CALIBAN'S PROBLEM BOOK: MATHEMATICAL, INFERENTIAL AND CRYPTOGRAPHIC PUZZLES, H. Phillips (Caliban), S. T. Shovelton, G. S. Marshall. 105 ingenious problems by the greatest living creator of puzzles based on logic and inference. Rigorous, modern, piquant; reflecting their author's unusual personality, these intermediate and advanced puzzles all involve the ability to reason clearly through complex situations; some call for mathematical knowledge, ranging from algebra to number theory. Solutions. xi + 180pp. 5⅜ x 8.
T736 Paperbound **$1.25**

MATHEMATICAL PUZZLES FOR BEGINNERS AND ENTHUSIASTS, G. Mott-Smith. 188 mathematical puzzles based on algebra, dissection of plane figures, permutations, and probability, that will test and improve your powers of inference and interpretation. The Odic Force, The Spider's Cousin, Ellipse Drawing, theory and strategy of card and board games like tit-tat-toe, go moku, salvo, and many others. 100 pages of detailed mathematical explanations. Appendix of primes, square roots, etc. 135 illustrations. 2nd revised edition. 248pp. 5⅜ x 8.
T198 Paperbound **$1.00**

MATHEMAGIC, MAGIC PUZZLES, AND GAMES WITH NUMBERS, R. V. Heath. More than 60 new puzzles and stunts based on the properties of numbers. Easy techniques for multiplying large numbers mentally, revealing hidden numbers magically, finding the date of any day in any year, and dozens more. Over 30 pages devoted to magic squares, triangles, cubes, circles, etc. Edited by J. S. Meyer. 76 illustrations. 128pp. 5⅜ x 8. T110 Paperbound **$1.00**

THE BOOK OF MODERN PUZZLES, G. L. Kaufman. A completely new series of puzzles as fascinating as crossword and deduction puzzles but based upon different principles and techniques. Simple 2-minute teasers, word labyrinths, design and pattern puzzles, logic and observation puzzles — over 150 braincrackers. Answers to all problems. 116 illustrations. 192pp. 5⅜ x 8.
T143 Paperbound **$1.00**

NEW WORD PUZZLES, G. L. Kaufman. 100 ENTIRELY NEW puzzles based on words and their combinations that will delight crossword puzzle, Scrabble and Jotto fans. Chess words, based on the moves of the chess king; design-onyms, symmetrical designs made of synonyms; rhymed double-crostics; syllable sentences; addle letter anagrams; alphagrams; linkograms; and many others all brand new. Full solutions. Space to work problems. 196 figures. vi + 122pp. 5⅜ x 8.
T344 Paperbound **$1.00**

MAZES AND LABYRINTHS: A BOOK OF PUZZLES, W. Shepherd. Mazes, formerly associated with mystery and ritual, are still among the most intriguing of intellectual puzzles. This is a novel and different collection of 50 amusements that embody the principle of the maze: mazes in the classical tradition; 3-dimensional, ribbon, and Möbius-strip mazes; hidden messages; spatial arrangements; etc.—almost all built on amusing story situations. 84 illustrations. Essay on maze psychology. Solutions. xv + 122pp. 5⅜ x 8.
T731 Paperbound **$1.00**

MAGIC TRICKS & CARD TRICKS, W. Jonson. Two books bound as one. 52 tricks with cards, 37 tricks with coins, bills, eggs, smoke, ribbons, slates, etc. Details on presentation, misdirection, and routining will help you master such famous tricks as the Changing Card, Card in the Pocket, Four Aces, Coin Through the Hand, Bill in the Egg, Afghan Bands, and over 75 others. If you follow the lucid exposition and key diagrams carefully, you will finish these two books with an astonishing mastery of magic. 106 figures. 224pp. 5⅜ x 8. T909 Paperbound **$1.00**

PANORAMA OF MAGIC, Milbourne Christopher. A profusely illustrated history of stage magic, a unique selection of prints and engravings from the author's private collection of magic memorabilia, the largest of its kind. Apparatus, stage settings and costumes; ingenious ads distributed by the performers and satiric broadsides passed around in the streets ridiculing pompous showmen; programs; decorative souvenirs. The lively text, by one of America's foremost professional magicians, is full of anecdotes about almost legendary wizards: Dede, the Egyptian; Philadelphia, the wonder-worker; Robert-Houdin, "the father of modern magic;" Harry Houdini; scores more. Altogether a pleasure package for anyone interested in magic, stage setting and design, ethnology, psychology, or simply in unusual people. A Dover original. 295 illustrations; 8 in full color. Index. viii + 216pp. 8⅜ x 11¼.
T774 Paperbound **$2.25**

HOUDINI ON MAGIC, Harry Houdini. One of the greatest magicians of modern times explains his most prized secrets. How locks are picked, with illustrated picks and skeleton keys; how a girl is sawed into twins; how to walk through a brick wall — Houdini's explanations of 44 stage tricks with many diagrams. Also included is a fascinating discussion of great magicians of the past and the story of his fight against fraudulent mediums and spiritualists. Edited by W.B. Gibson and M.N. Young. Bibliography. 155 figures, photos. xv + 280pp. 5⅜ x 8.
T384 Paperbound **$1.25**

MATHEMATICS, MAGIC AND MYSTERY, Martin Gardner. Why do card tricks work? How do magicians perform astonishing mathematical feats? How is stage mind-reading possible? This is the first book length study explaining the application of probability, set theory, theory of numbers, topology, etc., to achieve many startling tricks. Non-technical, accurate, detailed! 115 sections discuss tricks with cards, dice, coins, knots, geometrical vanishing illusions, how a Curry square "demonstrates" that the sum of the parts may be greater than the whole, and dozens of others. No sleight of hand necessary! 135 illustrations. xii + 174pp. 5⅜ x 8.
T335 Paperbound **$1.00**

EASY-TO-DO ENTERTAINMENTS AND DIVERSIONS WITH COINS, CARDS, STRING, PAPER AND MATCHES, R. M. Abraham. Over 300 tricks, games and puzzles will provide young readers with absorbing fun. Sections on card games; paper-folding; tricks with coins, matches and pieces of string; games for the agile; toy-making from common household objects; mathematical recreations; and 50 miscellaneous pastimes. Anyone in charge of groups of youngsters, including hard-pressed parents, and in need of suggestions on how to keep children sensibly amused and quietly content will find this book indispensable. Clear, simple text, copious number of delightful line drawings and illustrative diagrams. Originally titled "Winter Nights Entertainments." Introduction by Lord Baden Powell. 329 illustrations. v + 186pp. 5⅜ x 8½.
T921 Paperbound **$1.00**

STRING FIGURES AND HOW TO MAKE THEM, Caroline Furness Jayne. 107 string figures plus variations selected from the best primitive and modern examples developed by Navajo, Apache, pygmies of Africa, Eskimo, in Europe, Australia, China, etc. The most readily understandable, easy-to-follow book in English on perennially popular recreation. Crystal-clear exposition; step-by-step diagrams. Everyone from kindergarten children to adults looking for unusual diversion will be endlessly amused. Index. Bibliography. Introduction by A. C. Haddon. 17 full-page plates. 960 illustrations. xxiii + 401pp. 5⅜ x 8½.
T152 Paperbound **$2.00**

Entertainments, Humor

ODDITIES AND CURIOSITIES OF WORDS AND LITERATURE, C. Bombaugh, edited by M. Gardner. The largest collection of idiosyncratic prose and poetry techniques in English, a legendary work in the curious and amusing bypaths of literary recreations and the play technique in literature—so important in modern works. Contains alphabetic poetry, acrostics, palindromes, scissors verse, centos, emblematic poetry, famous literary puns, hoaxes, notorious slips of the press, hilarious mistranslations, and much more. Revised and enlarged with modern material by Martin Gardner. 368pp. 5⅜ x 8. **T759 Paperbound $1.50**

A NONSENSE ANTHOLOGY, collected by Carolyn Wells. 245 of the best nonsense verses ever written, including nonsense puns, absurd arguments, mock epics and sagas, nonsense ballads, odes, "sick" verses, dog-Latin verses, French nonsense verses, songs. By Edward Lear, Lewis Carroll, Gelett Burgess, W. S. Gilbert, Hilaire Belloc, Peter Newell, Oliver Herford, etc., 83 writers in all plus over four score anonymous nonsense verses. A special section of limericks, plus famous nonsense such as Carroll's "Jabberwocky" and Lear's "The Jumblies" and much excellent verse virtually impossible to locate elsewhere. For 50 years considered the best anthology available. Index of first lines specially prepared for this edition. Introduction by Carolyn Wells. 3 indexes: Title, Author, First lines. xxxiii + 279pp. **T499 Paperbound $1.25**

THE BAD CHILD'S BOOK OF BEASTS, MORE BEASTS FOR WORSE CHILDREN, and A MORAL ALPHABET, H. Belloc. Hardly an anthology of humorous verse has appeared in the last 50 years without at least a couple of these famous nonsense verses. But one must see the entire volumes—with all the delightful original illustrations by Sir Basil Blackwood—to appreciate fully Belloc's charming and witty verses that play so subacidly on the platitudes of life and morals that beset his day—and ours. A great humor classic. Three books in one. Total of 157pp. 5⅜ x 8. **T749 Paperbound $1.00**

THE DEVIL'S DICTIONARY, Ambrose Bierce. Sardonic and irreverent barbs puncturing the pomposities and absurdities of American politics, business, religion, literature, and arts, by the country's greatest satirist in the classic tradition. Epigrammatic as Shaw, piercing as Swift, American as Mark Twain, Will Rogers, and Fred Allen, Bierce will always remain the favorite of a small coterie of enthusiasts, and of writers and speakers whom he supplies with "some of the most gorgeous witticisms of the English language" (H. L. Mencken). Over 1000 entries in alphabetical order. 144pp. 5⅜ x 8. **T487 Paperbound $1.00**

THE PURPLE COW AND OTHER NONSENSE, Gelett Burgess. The best of Burgess's early nonsense, selected from the first edition of the "Burgess Nonsense Book." Contains many of his most unusual and truly awe-inspiring pieces: 36 nonsense quatrains, the Poems of Patagonia, Alphabet of Famous Goops, and the other hilarious (and rare) adult nonsense that place him in the forefront of American humorists. All pieces are accompanied by the original Burgess illustrations. 123 illustrations. xiii + 113pp. 5⅜ x 8. **T772 Paperbound $1.00**

MY PIOUS FRIENDS AND DRUNKEN COMPANIONS and MORE PIOUS FRIENDS AND DRUNKEN COMPANIONS, Frank Shay. Folksingers, amateur and professional, and everyone who loves singing: here, available for the first time in 30 years, is this valued collection of 132 ballads, blues, vaudeville numbers, drinking songs, sea chanties, comedy songs. Songs of pre-Beatnik Bohemia; songs from all over America, England, France, Australia; the great songs of the Naughty Nineties and early twentieth-century America. Over a third with music. Woodcuts by John Held, Jr. convey perfectly the brash insouciance of an era of rollicking unabashed song. 12 illustrations by John Held, Jr. Two indexes (Titles and First lines and Choruses). Introductions by the author. Two volumes bound as one. Total of xvi + 235pp. 5⅜ x 8½. **T946 Paperbound $1.00**

HOW TO TELL THE BIRDS FROM THE FLOWERS, R. W. Wood. How not to confuse a carrot with a parrot, a grape with an ape, a puffin with nuffin. Delightful drawings, clever puns, absurd little poems point out far-fetched resemblances in nature. The author was a leading physicist. Introduction by Margaret Wood White. 106 illus. 60pp. 5⅜ x 8. **T523 Paperbound 75¢**

PECK'S BAD BOY AND HIS PA, George W. Peck. The complete edition, containing both volumes, of one of the most widely read American humor books. The endless ingenious pranks played by bad boy "Hennery" on his pa and the grocery man, the outraged pomposity of Pa, the perpetual ridiculing of middle class institutions, are as entertaining today as they were in 1883. No pale sophistications or subtleties, but rather humor vigorous, raw, earthy, imaginative, and, as folk humor often is, sadistic. This peculiarly fascinating book is also valuable to historians and students of American culture as a portrait of an age. 100 original illustrations by True Williams. Introduction by E. F. Bleiler. 347pp. 5⅜ x 8. **T497 Paperbound $1.35**

CATALOGUE OF DOVER BOOKS

THE HUMOROUS VERSE OF LEWIS CARROLL. Almost every poem Carroll ever wrote, the largest collection ever published, including much never published elsewhere: 150 parodies, burlesques, riddles, ballads, acrostics, etc., with 130 original illustrations by Tenniel, Carroll, and others. "Addicts will be grateful . . . there is nothing for the faithful to do but sit down and fall to the banquet," N. Y. Times. Index to first lines. xiv + 446pp. 5⅜ x 8.
T654 Paperbound **$1.85**

DIVERSIONS AND DIGRESSIONS OF LEWIS CARROLL. A major new treasure for Carroll fans! Rare privately published humor, fantasy, puzzles, and games by Carroll at his whimsical best, with a new vein of frank satire. Includes many new mathematical amusements and recreations, among them the fragmentary Part III of "Curiosa Mathematica." Contains "The Rectory Umbrella," "The New Belfry," "The Vision of the Three T's," and much more. New 32-page supplement of rare photographs taken by Carroll. x + 375pp. 5⅜ x 8.
T732 Paperbound **$1.65**

THE COMPLETE NONSENSE OF EDWARD LEAR. This is the only complete edition of this master of gentle madness available at a popular price. A BOOK OF NONSENSE, NONSENSE SONGS, MORE NONSENSE SONGS AND STORIES in their entirety with all the old favorites that have delighted children and adults for years. The Dong With A Luminous Nose, The Jumblies, The Owl and the Pussycat, and hundreds of other bits of wonderful nonsense. 214 limericks, 3 sets of Nonsense Botany, 5 Nonsense Alphabets, 546 drawings by Lear himself, and much more. 320pp. 5⅜ x 8.
T167 Paperbound **$1.00**

THE MELANCHOLY LUTE, The Humorous Verse of Franklin P. Adams ("FPA"). The author's own selection of light verse, drawn from thirty years of FPA's column, "The Conning Tower," syndicated all over the English-speaking world. Witty, perceptive, literate, these ninety-six poems range from parodies of other poets, Millay, Longfellow, Edgar Guest, Kipling, Masefield, etc., and free and hilarious translations of Horace and other Latin poets, to satiric comments on fabled American institutions—the New York Subways, preposterous ads, suburbanites, sensational journalism, etc. They reveal with vigor and clarity the humor, integrity and restraint of a wise and gentle American satirist. Introduction by Robert Hutchinson. vi + 122pp. 5⅜ x 8½.
T108 Paperbound **$1.00**

SINGULAR TRAVELS, CAMPAIGNS, AND ADVENTURES OF BARON MUNCHAUSEN, R. E. Raspe, with 90 illustrations by Gustave Doré. The first edition in over 150 years to reestablish the deeds of the Prince of Liars exactly as Raspe first recorded them in 1785—the genuine Baron Munchausen, one of the most popular personalities in English literature. Included also are the best of the many sequels, written by other hands. Introduction on Raspe by J. Carswell. Bibliography of early editions. xliv + 192pp. 5⅜ x 8.
T698 Paperbound **$1.00**

THE WIT AND HUMOR OF OSCAR WILDE, ed. by Alvin Redman. Wilde at his most brilliant, in 1000 epigrams exposing weaknesses and hypocrisies of "civilized" society. Divided into 49 categories—sin, wealth, women, America, etc.—to aid writers, speakers. Includes excerpts from his trials, books, plays, criticism. Formerly "The Epigrams of Oscar Wilde." Introduction by Vyvyan Holland, Wilde's only living son. Introductory essay by editor. 260pp. 5⅜ x 8.
T602 Paperbound **$1.00**

MAX AND MORITZ, Wilhelm Busch. Busch is one of the great humorists of all time, as well as the father of the modern comic strip. This volume, translated by H. A. Klein and other hands, contains the perennial favorite "Max and Moritz" (translated by C. T. Brooks), Plisch and Plum, Das Rabennest, Eispeter, and seven other whimsical, sardonic, jovial, diabolical cartoon and verse stories. Lively English translations parallel the original German. This work has delighted millions, since it first appeared in the 19th century, and is guaranteed to please almost anyone. Edited by H. A. Klein, with an afterword. x + 205pp. 5⅝ x 8½.
T181 Paperbound **$1.00**

HYPOCRITICAL HELENA, Wilhelm Busch. A companion volume to "Max and Moritz," with the title piece (Die Fromme Helena) and 10 other highly amusing cartoon and verse stories, all newly translated by H. A. Klein and M. C. Klein: Adventure on New Year's Eve (Abenteuer in der Neujahrsnacht), Hangover on the Morning after New Year's Eve (Der Katzenjammer am Neujahrsmorgen), etc. English and German in parallel columns. Hours of pleasure, also a fine language aid. x + 205pp. 5⅝ x 8½.
T184 Paperbound **$1.00**

THE BEAR THAT WASN'T, Frank Tashlin. What does it mean? Is it simply delightful wry humor, or a charming story of a bear who wakes up in the midst of a factory, or a satire on Big Business, or an existential cartoon-story of the human condition, or a symbolization of the struggle between conformity and the individual? New York Herald Tribune said of the first edition: ". . . a fable for grownups that will be fun for children. Sit down with the book and get your own bearings." Long an underground favorite with readers of all ages and opinions. v + 51pp. Illustrated. 5⅜ x 8½.
T939 Paperbound **75¢**

RUTHLESS RHYMES FOR HEARTLESS HOMES and MORE RUTHLESS RHYMES FOR HEARTLESS HOMES, Harry Graham ("Col. D. Streamer"). Two volumes of Little Willy and 48 other poetic disasters. A bright, new reprint of oft-quoted, never forgotten, devastating humor by a precursor of today's "sick" joke school. For connoisseurs of wicked, wacky humor and all who delight in the comedy of manners. Original drawings are a perfect complement. 61 illustrations. Index. vi + 69pp. Two vols. bound as one. 5⅜ x 8½.
T930 Paperbound **75¢**

CATALOGUE OF DOVER BOOKS

Say It language phrase books

These handy phrase books (128 to 196 pages each) make grammatical drills unnecessary for an elementary knowledge of a spoken foreign language. Covering most matters of travel and everyday life each volume contains:

Over 1000 phrases and sentences in immediately useful forms — foreign language plus English.

Modern usage designed for Americans. Specific phrases like, "Give me small change," and "Please call a taxi."

Simplified phonetic transcription you will be able to read at sight.

The only completely indexed phrase books on the market.

Covers scores of important situations: — Greetings, restaurants, sightseeing, useful expressions, etc.

These books are prepared by native linguists who are professors at Columbia, N.Y.U., Fordham and other great universities. Use them independently or with any other book or record course. They provide a supplementary living element that most other courses lack. Individual volumes in:

Russian 75¢	Italian 75¢	Spanish 75¢	German 75¢
Hebrew 75¢	Danish 75¢	Japanese 75¢	Swedish 75¢
Dutch 75¢	Esperanto 75¢	Modern Greek 75¢	Portuguese 75¢
Norwegian 75¢	Polish 75¢	French 75¢	Yiddish 75¢
Turkish 75¢			

English for Italian-speaking people 75¢

English for German-speaking people 75¢
English for Spanish-speaking people 75¢

Large clear type. 128-196 pages each. 3½ x 5¼. Sturdy paper binding.

Listen and Learn language records

LISTEN & LEARN is the only language record course designed especially to meet your travel and everyday needs. It is available in separate sets for FRENCH, SPANISH, GERMAN, JAPANESE, RUSSIAN, MODERN GREEK, PORTUGUESE, ITALIAN and HEBREW, and each set contains three 33⅓ rpm long-playing records—1½ hours of recorded speech by eminent native speakers who are professors at Columbia, New York University, Queens College.

Check the following special features found only in LISTEN & LEARN:

- **Dual-language recording. 812 selected phrases and sentences, over 3200 words,** spoken first in English, then in their foreign language equivalents. A suitable pause follows each foreign phrase, allowing you time to repeat the expression. You learn by unconscious assimilation.

- **128 to 206-page manual** contains everything on the records, plus a simple phonetic pronunciation guide.

- **Indexed for convenience. The only set on the market** that is completely indexed. No more puzzling over where to find the phrase you need. Just look in the rear of the manual.

- **Practical.** No time wasted on material you can find in any grammar. LISTEN & LEARN covers central core material with phrase approach. Ideal for the person with limited learning time.

- **Living, modern expressions,** not found in other courses. Hygienic products, modern equipment, shopping—expressions used every day, like "nylon" and "air-conditioned."

- **Limited objective.** Everything you learn, no matter where you stop, is immediately useful. You have to finish other courses, wade through grammar and vocabulary drill, before they help you.

- **High-fidelity recording.** LISTEN & LEARN records equal in clarity and surface-silence any record on the market costing up to $6.

"Excellent . . . the spoken records . . . impress me as being among the very best on the market," **Prof. Mario Pei,** Dept. of Romance Languages, Columbia University. "Inexpensive and well-done . . . it would make an ideal present," CHICAGO SUNDAY TRIBUNE. "More genuinely helpful than anything of its kind which I have previously encountered," **Sidney Clark,** well-known author of "ALL THE BEST" travel books.

UNCONDITIONAL GUARANTEE. Try LISTEN & LEARN, then return it within 10 days for full refund if you are not satisfied.

Each set contains three twelve-inch 33⅓ records, manual, and album.

SPANISH	the set $5.95	GERMAN	the set $5.95
FRENCH	the set $5.95	ITALIAN	the set $5.95
RUSSIAN	the set $5.95	JAPANESE	the set $5.95
PORTUGUESE	the set $5.95	MODERN GREEK	the set $5.95
MODERN HEBREW	the set $5.95		

Americana

THE EYES OF DISCOVERY, J. Bakeless. A vivid reconstruction of how unspoiled America appeared to the first white men. Authentic and enlightening accounts of Hudson's landing in New York, Coronado's trek through the Southwest; scores of explorers, settlers, trappers, soldiers. America's pristine flora, fauna, and Indians in every region and state in fresh and unusual new aspects. "A fascinating view of what the land was like before the first highway went through," Time. 68 contemporary illustrations, 39 newly added in this edition. Index. Bibliography. x + 500pp. 5⅜ x 8. **T761 Paperbound $2.00**

AUDUBON AND HIS JOURNALS, J. J. Audubon. A collection of fascinating accounts of Europe and America in the early 1800's through Audubon's own eyes. Includes the Missouri River Journals —an eventful trip through America's untouched heartland, the Labrador Journals, the European Journals, the famous "Episodes", and other rare Audubon material, including the descriptive chapters from the original letterpress edition of the "Ornithological Studies", omitted in all later editions. Indispensable for ornithologists, naturalists, and all lovers of Americana and adventure. 70-page biography by Audubon's granddaughter. 38 illustrations. Index. Total of 1106pp. 5⅜ x 8.
T675 Vol I Paperbound $2.00
T676 Vol II Paperbound $2.00
The set $4.00

TRAVELS OF WILLIAM BARTRAM, edited by Mark Van Doren. The first inexpensive illustrated edition of one of the 18th century's most delightful books is an excellent source of first-hand material on American geography, anthropology, and natural history. Many descriptions of early Indian tribes are our only source of information on them prior to the infiltration of the white man. "The mind of a scientist with the soul of a poet," John Livingston Lowes. 13 original illustrations and maps. Edited with an introduction by Mark Van Doren. 448pp. 5⅜ x 8.
T13 Paperbound $2.00

GARRETS AND PRETENDERS: A HISTORY OF BOHEMIANISM IN AMERICA, A. Parry. The colorful and fantastic history of American Bohemianism from Poe to Kerouac. This is the only complete record of hoboes, cranks, starving poets, and suicides. Here are Pfaff, Whitman, Crane, Bierce, Pound, and many others. New chapters by the author and by H. T. Moore bring this thorough and well-documented history down to the Beatniks. "An excellent account," N. Y. Times. Scores of cartoons, drawings, and caricatures. Bibliography. Index. xxviii + 421pp. 5⅝ x 8⅜.
T708 Paperbound $1.95

THE EXPLORATION OF THE COLORADO RIVER AND ITS CANYONS, J. W. Powell. The thrilling first-hand account of the expedition that filled in the last white space on the map of the United States. Rapids, famine, hostile Indians, and mutiny are among the perils encountered as the unknown Colorado Valley reveals its secrets. This is the only uncut version of Major Powell's classic of exploration that has been printed in the last 60 years. Includes later reflections and subsequent expedition. 250 illustrations, new map. 400pp. 5⅝ x 8⅜.
T94 Paperbound $2.00

THE JOURNAL OF HENRY D. THOREAU, Edited by Bradford Torrey and Francis H. Allen. Henry Thoreau is not only one of the most important figures in American literature and social thought; his voluminous journals (from which his books emerged as selections and crystallizations) constitute both the longest, most sensitive record of personal internal development and a most penetrating description of a historical moment in American culture. This present set, which was first issued in fourteen volumes, contains Thoreau's entire journals from 1837 to 1862, with the exception of the lost years which were found only recently. We are reissuing it, complete and unabridged, with a new introduction by Walter Harding, Secretary of the Thoreau Society. Fourteen volumes reissued in two volumes. Foreword by Henry Seidel Canby. Total of 1888pp. 8⅜ x 12¼. **T312-3 Two volume set, Clothbound $20.00**

GAMES AND SONGS OF AMERICAN CHILDREN, collected by William Wells Newell. A remarkable collection of 190 games with songs that accompany many of them; cross references to show similarities, differences among them; variations; musical notation for 38 songs. Textual discussions show relations with folk-drama and other aspects of folk tradition. Grouped into categories for ready comparative study: Love-games, histories, playing at work, human life, bird and beast, mythology, guessing-games, etc. New introduction covers relations of songs and dances to timeless heritage of folklore, biographical sketch of Newell, other pertinent data. A good source of inspiration for those in charge of groups of children and a valuable reference for anthropologists, sociologists, psychiatrists. Introduction by Carl Withers. New indexes of first lines, games. 5⅜ x 8½. xii + 242pp. **T354 Paperbound $1.65**

Art, History of Art, Antiques, Graphic Arts, Handcrafts

ART STUDENTS' ANATOMY, E. J. Farris. Outstanding art anatomy that uses chiefly living objects for its illustrations. 71 photos of undraped men, women, children are accompanied by carefully labeled matching sketches to illustrate the skeletal system, articulations and movements, bony landmarks, the muscular system, skin, fasciae, fat, etc. 9 x-ray photos show movement of joints. Undraped models are shown in such actions as serving in tennis, drawing a bow in archery, playing football, dancing, preparing to spring and to dive. Also discussed and illustrated are proportions, age and sex differences, the anatomy of the smile, etc. 8 plates by the great early 18th century anatomic illustrator Siegfried Albinus are also included. Glossary. 158 figures, 7 in color. x + 159pp. 5⅝ x 8⅜.   T744 Paperbound **$1.45**

AN ATLAS OF ANATOMY FOR ARTISTS, F Schider. A new 3rd edition of this standard text enlarged by 52 new illustrations of hands, anatomical studies by Cloquet, and expressive life studies of the body by Barcsay. 189 clear, detailed plates offer you precise information of impeccable accuracy. 29 plates show all aspects of the skeleton, with closeups of special areas, while 54 full-page plates, mostly in two colors, give human musculature as seen from four different points of view, with cutaways for important portions of the body. 14 full-page plates provide photographs of hand forms, eyelids, female breasts, and indicate the location of muscles upon models. 59 additional plates show how great artists of the past utilized human anatomy. They reproduce sketches and finished work by such artists as Michelangelo, Leonardo da Vinci, Goya, and 15 others. This is a lifetime reference work which will be one of the most important books in any artist's library. "The standard reference tool," AMERICAN LIBRARY ASSOCIATION. "Excellent," AMERICAN ARTIST. Third enlarged edition. 189 plates, 647 illustrations. xxvi + 192pp. 7⅞ x 10⅝.   T241 Clothbound **$6.00**

AN ATLAS OF ANIMAL ANATOMY FOR ARTISTS, W. Ellenberger, H. Baum, H. Dittrich. The largest, richest animal anatomy for artists available in English. 99 detailed anatomical plates of such animals as the horse, dog, cat, lion, deer, seal, kangaroo, flying squirrel, cow, bull, goat, monkey, hare, and bat. Surface features are clearly indicated, while progressive beneath-the-skin pictures show musculature, tendons, and bone structure. Rest and action are exhibited in terms of musculature and skeletal structure and detailed cross-sections are given for heads and important features. The animals chosen are representative of specific families so that a study of these anatomies will provide knowledge of hundreds of related species. "Highly recommended as one of the very few books on the subject worthy of being used as an authoritative guide," DESIGN. "Gives a fundamental knowledge," AMERICAN ARTIST. Second revised, enlarged edition with new plates from Cuvier, Stubbs, etc. 288 illustrations. 153pp. 11⅜ x 9.   T82 Clothbound **$6.00**

THE HUMAN FIGURE IN MOTION, Eadweard Muybridge. The largest selection in print of Muybridge's famous high-speed action photos of the human figure in motion. 4789 photographs illustrate 162 different actions: men, women, children—mostly undraped—are shown walking, running, carrying various objects, sitting, lying down, climbing, throwing, arising, and performing over 150 other actions. Some actions are shown in as many as 150 photographs each. All in all there are more than 500 action strips in this enormous volume, series shots taken at shutter speeds of as high as 1/6000th of a second! These are not posed shots, but true stopped motion. They show bone and muscle in situations that the human eye is not fast enough to capture. Earlier, smaller editions of these prints have brought $40 and more on the out-of-print market. "A must for artists," ART IN FOCUS. "An unparalleled dictionary of action for all artists," AMERICAN ARTIST. 390 full-page plates, with 4789 photographs. Printed on heavy glossy stock. Reinforced binding with headbands. xxi + 390pp. 7⅞ x 10⅝.
          T204 Clothbound **$10.00**

ANIMALS IN MOTION, Eadweard Muybridge. This is the largest collection of animal action photos in print. 34 different animals (horses, mules, oxen, goats, camels, pigs, cats, guanacos, lions, gnus, deer, monkeys, eagles—and 21 others) in 132 characteristic actions. The horse alone is shown in more than 40 different actions. All 3919 photographs are taken in series at speeds up to 1/6000th of a second. The secrets of leg motion, spinal patterns, head movements, strains and contortions shown nowhere else are captured. You will see exactly how a lion sets his foot down; how an elephant's knees are like a human's—and how they differ; the position of a kangaroo's legs in mid-leap; how an ostrich's head bobs; details of the flight of birds—and thousands of facets of motion only the fastest cameras can catch. Photographed from domestic animals and animals in the Philadelphia zoo, it contains neither semiposed artificial shots nor distorted telephoto shots taken under adverse conditions. Artists, biologists, decorators, cartoonists, will find this book indispensable for understanding animals in motion. "A really marvelous series of plates," NATURE (London). "The dry plate's most spectacular early use was by Eadweard Muybridge," LIFE. 3919 photographs; 380 full pages of plates. 440pp. Printed on heavy glossy paper. Deluxe binding with headbands. 7⅞ x 10⅝.   T203 Clothbound **$10.00**

CATALOGUE OF DOVER BOOKS

THE AUTOBIOGRAPHY OF AN IDEA, Louis Sullivan. The pioneer architect whom Frank Lloyd Wright called "the master" reveals an acute sensitivity to social forces and values in this passionately honest account. He records the crystallization of his opinions and theories, the growth of his organic theory of architecture that still influences American designers and architects, contemporary ideas, etc. This volume contains the first appearance of 34 full-page plates of his finest architecture. Unabridged reissue of 1924 edition. New introduction by R. M. Line. Index. xiv + 335pp. 5⅜ x 8. T281 Paperbound **$2.00**

THE DRAWINGS OF HEINRICH KLEY. The first uncut republication of both of Kley's devastating sketchbooks, which first appeared in pre-World War I Germany. One of the greatest cartoonists and social satirists of modern times, his exuberant and iconoclastic fantasy and his extraordinary technique place him in the great tradition of Bosch, Breughel, and Goya, while his subject matter has all the immediacy and tension of our century. 200 drawings. viii + 128pp. 7¾ x 10¾. T24 Paperbound **$1.85**

MORE DRAWINGS BY HEINRICH KLEY. All the sketches from Leut' Und Viecher (1912) and Sammel-Album (1923) not included in the previous Dover edition of Drawings. More of the bizarre, mercilessly iconoclastic sketches that shocked and amused on their original publication. Nothing was too sacred, no one too eminent for satirization by this imaginative, individual and accomplished master cartoonist. A total of 158 illustrations. Iv + 104pp. 7¾ x 10¾. T41 Paperbound **$1.85**

PINE FURNITURE OF EARLY NEW ENGLAND, R. H. Kettell. A rich understanding of one of America's most original folk arts that collectors of antiques, interior decorators, craftsmen, woodworkers, and everyone interested in American history and art will find fascinating and immensely useful. 413 illustrations of more than 300 chairs, benches, racks, beds, cupboards, mirrors, shelves, tables, and other furniture will show all the simple beauty and character of early New England furniture. 55 detailed drawings carefully analyze outstanding pieces. "With its rich store of illustrations, this book emphasizes the individuality and varied design of early American pine furniture. It should be welcomed," ANTIQUES. 413 illustrations and 55 working drawings. 475. 8 x 10¾. T145 Clothbound **$10.00**

THE HUMAN FIGURE, J. H. Vanderpoel. Every important artistic element of the human figure is pointed out in minutely detailed word descriptions in this classic text and illustrated as well in 430 pencil and charcoal drawings. Thus the text of this book directs your attention to all the characteristic features and subtle differences of the male and female (adults, children, and aged persons), as though a master artist were telling you what to look for at each stage. 2nd edition, revised and enlarged by George Bridgman. Foreword. 430 illustrations. 143pp. 6⅛ x 9¼. T432 Paperbound **$1.50**

LETTERING AND ALPHABETS, J. A. Cavanagh. This unabridged reissue of LETTERING offers a full discussion, analysis, illustration of 89 basic hand lettering styles — styles derived from Caslons, Bodonis, Garamonds, Gothic, Black Letter, Oriental, and many others. Upper and lower cases, numerals and common signs pictured. Hundreds of technical hints on make-up, construction, artistic validity, strokes, pens, brushes, white areas, etc. May be reproduced without permission! 89 complete alphabets; 72 lettered specimens. 121pp. 9¾ x 8. T53 Paperbound **$1.25**

STICKS AND STONES, Lewis Mumford. A survey of the forces that have conditioned American architecture and altered its forms. The author discusses the medieval tradition in early New England villages; the Renaissance influence which developed with the rise of the merchant class; the classical influence of Jefferson's time; the "Mechanicsvilles" of Poe's generation; the Brown Decades; the philosophy of the Imperial facade; and finally the modern machine age. "A truly remarkable book," SAT. REV. OF LITERATURE. 2nd revised edition. 21 illustrations. xvii + 228pp. 5⅜ x 8. T202 Paperbound **$1.60**

THE STANDARD BOOK OF QUILT MAKING AND COLLECTING, Marguerite Ickis. A complete easy-to-follow guide with all the information you need to make beautiful, useful quilts. How to plan, design, cut, sew, appliqué, avoid sewing problems, use rag bag, make borders, tuft, every other aspect. Over 100 traditional quilts shown, including over 40 full-size patterns. At-home hobby for fun, profit. Index. 483 illus. 1 color plate. 287pp. 6¾ x 9½. T582 Paperbound **$2.00**

THE BOOK OF SIGNS, Rudolf Koch. Formerly $20 to $25 on the out-of-print market, now only $1.00 in this unabridged new edition! 493 symbols from ancient manuscripts, medieval cathedrals, coins, catacombs, pottery, etc. Crosses, monograms of Roman emperors, astrological, chemical, botanical, runes, housemarks, and 7 other categories. Invaluable for handicraft workers, illustrators, scholars, etc., this material may be reproduced without permission. 493 illustrations by Fritz Kredel. 104pp. 6½ x 9¼. T162 Paperbound **$1.00**

PRIMITIVE ART, Franz Boas. This authoritative and exhaustive work by a great American anthropologist covers the entire gamut of primitive art. Pottery, leatherwork, metal work, stone work, wood, basketry, are treated in detail. Theories of primitive art, historical depth in art history, technical virtuosity, unconscious levels of patterning, symbolism, styles, literature, music, dance, etc. A must book for the interested layman, the anthropologist, artist, handicrafter (hundreds of unusual motifs), and the historian. Over 900 illustrations (50 ceramic vessels, 12 totem poles, etc.). 376pp. 5⅜ x 8. T25 Paperbound **$1.95**

Fiction

FLATLAND, E. A. Abbott. A science-fiction classic of life in a 2-dimensional world that is also a first-rate introduction to such aspects of modern science as relativity and hyperspace. Political, moral, satirical, and humorous overtones have made FLATLAND fascinating reading for thousands. 7th edition. New introduction by Banesh Hoffmann. 16 illustrations. 128pp. 5⅜ x 8.
T1 Paperbound **$1.00**

THE WONDERFUL WIZARD OF OZ, L. F. Baum. Only edition in print with all the original W. W. Denslow illustrations in full color—as much a part of "The Wizard" as Tenniel's drawings are of "Alice in Wonderland." "The Wizard" is still America's best-loved fairy tale, in which, as the author expresses it, "The wonderment and joy are retained and the heartaches and nightmares left out." Now today's young readers can enjoy every word and wonderful picture of the original book. New introduction by Martin Gardner. A Baum bibliography. 23 full-page color plates. viii + 268pp. 5⅜ x 8.
T691 Paperbound **$1.45**

THE MARVELOUS LAND OF OZ, L. F. Baum. This is the equally enchanting sequel to the "Wizard," continuing the adventures of the Scarecrow and the Tin Woodman. The hero this time is a little boy named Tip, and all the delightful Oz magic is still present. This is the Oz book with the Animated Saw-Horse, the Woggle-Bug, and Jack Pumpkinhead. All the original John R. Neill illustrations, 10 in full color. 287 pp. 5⅜ x 8.
T692 Paperbound **$1.45**

FIVE GREAT DOG NOVELS, edited by Blanche Cirker. The complete original texts of five classic dog novels that have delighted and thrilled millions of children and adults throughout the world with their stories of loyalty, adventure, and courage. Full texts of Jack London's "The Call of the Wild"; John Brown's "Rab and His Friends"; Alfred Ollivant's "Bob, Son of Battle"; Marshall Saunders's "Beautiful Joe"; and Ouida's "A Dog of Flanders." 21 Illustrations from the original editions. 495pp. 5⅜ x 8.
T777 Paperbound **$1.50**

TO THE SUN? and OFF ON A COMET!, Jules Verne. Complete texts of two of the most imaginative flights into fancy in world literature display the high adventure that have kept Verne's novels read for nearly a century. Only unabridged edition of the best translation, by Edward Roth. Large, easily readable type. 50 illustrations selected from first editions. 462pp. 5⅜ x 8.
T634 Paperbound **$1.75**

FROM THE EARTH TO THE MOON and ALL AROUND THE MOON, Jules Verne. Complete editions of 2 of Verne's most successful novels, in finest Edward Roth translations, now available after many years out of print. Verne's visions of submarines, airplanes, television, rockets, interplanetary travel; of scientific and not-so-scientific beliefs; of peculiarities of Americans; all delight and engross us today as much as when they first appeared. Large, easily readable type. 42 illus. from first French edition. 476pp. 5⅜ x 8.
T633 Paperbound **$1.75**

THE CRUISE OF THE CACHALOT, Frank T. Bullen. Out of the experiences of many years on the high-seas, First Mate Bullen created this novel of adventure aboard an American whaler, shipping out of New Bedford, Mass., when American whaling was at the height of its splendor. Originally published in 1899, the story of the round-the-world cruise of the "Cachalot" in pursuit of the sperm whale has thrilled generations of readers. A maritime classic that will fascinate anyone interested in reading about the sea or looking for a solid old-fashioned yarn, while the vivid recreation of a brief but important chapter of Americana and the British author's often biting commentary on nineteenth-century Yankee mores offer insights into the colorful era of America's coming of age. 8 plates. xiii + 271pp. 5⅜ x 8½.
T774 Paperbound **$1.00**

28 SCIENCE FICTION STORIES OF H. G. WELLS. Two full unabridged novels, MEN LIKE GODS and STAR BEGOTTEN, plus 26 short stories by the master science-fiction writer of all time! Stories of space, time, invention, exploration, future adventure—an indispensable part of the library of everyone interested in science and adventure. PARTIAL CONTENTS: Men Like Gods, The Country of the Blind, In the Abyss, The Crystal Egg, The Man Who Could Work Miracles, A Story of the Days to Come, The Valley of Spiders, and 21 more! 928pp. 5⅜ x 8.
T265 Clothbound **$3.95**

DAVID HARUM, E. N. Westcott. This novel of one of the most lovable, humorous characters in American literature is a prime example of regional humor. It continues to delight people who like their humor dry, their characters quaint, and their plots ingenuous. First book edition to contain complete novel plus chapter found after author's death. Illustrations from first illustrated edition. 192pp. 5⅜ x 8.
T580 Paperbound **$1.15**

GESTA ROMANORUM, trans. by Charles Swan, ed. by Wynnard Hooper. 181 tales of Greeks, Romans, Britons, Biblical characters, comprise one of greatest medieval story collections, source of plots for writers including Shakespeare, Chaucer, Gower, etc. Imaginative tales of wars, incest, thwarted love, magic, fantasy, allegory, humor, tell about kings, prostitutes, philosophers, fair damsels, knights, Noah, pirates, all walks, stations of life. Introduction. Notes. 500pp. 5⅜ x 8.
T535 Paperbound **$1.85**

Music

A GENERAL HISTORY OF MUSIC, Charles Burney. A detailed coverage of music from the Greeks up to 1789, with full information on all types of music: sacred and secular, vocal and instrumental, operatic and symphonic. Theory, notation, forms, instruments, innovators, composers, performers, typical and important works, and much more in an easy, entertaining style. Burney covered much of Europe and spoke with hundreds of authorities and composers so that this work is more than a compilation of records . . . it is a living work of careful and first-hand scholarship. Its account of thoroughbass (18th century) Italian music is probably still the best introduction on the subject. A recent NEW YORK TIMES review said, "Surprisingly few of Burney's statements have been invalidated by modern research . . . still of great value." Edited and corrected by Frank Mercer. 35 figures. Indices. 1915pp. 5⅜ x 8. 2 volumes. **T36 The Set, Clothbound $12.50**

A DICTIONARY OF HYMNOLOGY, John Julian. This exhaustive and scholarly work has become known as an invaluable source of hundreds of thousands of important and often difficult to obtain facts on the history and use of hymns in the western world. Everyone interested in hymns will be fascinated by the accounts of famous hymns and hymn writers and amazed by the amount of practical information he will find. More than 30,000 entries on individual hymns, giving authorship, date and circumstances of composition, publication, textual variations, translations, denominational and ritual usage, etc. Biographies of more than 9,000 hymn writers, and essays on important topics such as Christmas carols and children's hymns, and much other unusual and valuable information. A 200 page double-columned index of first lines — the largest in print. Total of 1786 pages in two reinforced clothbound volumes. 6¼ x 9¼. **The set, T333 Clothbound $15.00**

MUSIC IN MEDIEVAL BRITAIN, F. Ll. Harrison. The most thorough, up-to-date, and accurate treatment of the subject ever published, beautifully illustrated. Complete account of institutions and choirs; carols, masses, and motets; liturgy and plainsong; and polyphonic music from the Norman Conquest to the Reformation. Discusses the various schools of music and their reciprocal influences; the origin and development of new ritual forms; development and use of instruments; and new evidence on many problems of the period. Reproductions of scores, over 200 excerpts from medieval melodies. Rules of harmony and dissonance; influence of Continental styles; great composers (Dunstable, Cornysh, Fairfax, etc.); and much more. Register and index of more than 400 musicians. Index of titles. General Index. 225-item bibliography. 6 Appendices. xix + 491pp. 5⅝ x 8¾. **T705 Clothbound $10.00**

THE MUSIC OF SPAIN, Gilbert Chase. Only book in English to give concise, comprehensive account of Iberian music; new Chapter covers music since 1941. Victoria, Albéniz, Cabezón, Pedrell, Turina, hundreds of other composers; popular and folk music; the Gypsies; the guitar; dance, theatre, opera, with only extensive discussion in English of the Zarzuela; virtuosi such as Casals; much more. "Distinguished . . . readable," Saturday Review. 400-item bibliography. Index. 27 photos. 383pp. 5⅜ x 8. **T549 Paperbound $2.00**

ON STUDYING SINGING, Sergius Kagen. An intelligent method of voice-training, which leads you around pitfalls that waste your time, money, and effort. Exposes rigid, mechanical systems, baseless theories, deleterious exercises. "Logical, clear, convincing . . . dead right," Virgil Thomson, N.Y. Herald Tribune. "I recommend this volume highly," Maggie Teyte, Saturday Review. 119pp. 5⅜ x 8. **T622 Paperbound $1.25**

Dover publishes books on art, music, philosophy, literature, languages, history, social sciences, psychology, handcrafts, orientalia, puzzles and entertainments, chess, pets and gardens, books explaining science, intermediate and higher mathematics mathematical physics, engineering, biological sciences, earth sciences, classics of science, etc. Write to:

Dept. catrr.
Dover Publications, Inc.
180 Varick Street, N. Y. 14, N. Y.